8.00

518

ARMATURE WINDING
AND
MOTOR REPAIR

ARMATURE WINDING

AND

MOTOR REPAIR

Practical Information and Data Covering Winding and Reconnecting
Procedure for Direct and Alternating Current Machines, Compiled
for Electrical Men Responsible for the Operation and Repair
of Motors and Generators in Industrial Plants and for
Repairmen and Armature Winders in
Electrical Repair Shops

BY

DANIEL H. BRAYMER, A. B., E. E.

MEMBER AMERICAN INSTITUTE OF ELECTRICAL ENGINEERS—MANAGING EDITOR
OF ELECTRICAL WORLD—FORMERLY EDITOR OF ELECTRICAL
ENGINEERING AND OF ELECTRICAL RECORD

FIRST EDITION
TWENTY-THIRD IMPRESSION

McGRAW-HILL BOOK COMPANY, INC.

NEW YORK AND LONDON

THE MAPLE PRESS · YORK PA

PREFACE

In this book no attempt has been made to discuss the subject of armature winding from theoretical or design standpoints. On the contrary, it is a compilation of practical methods that are used by repairmen and armature winders. In selecting the material a special effort has been made to include as far as possible details of those methods which have been found by actual experience to represent best practice in a repair shop of average size. In this work the writer has drawn from his own experience in repair work, from the experiences of repairmen and armature winders in large and small repair shops and manufacturing plants which have been visited, from descriptions of practical methods and the procedure followed in the solution of special problems as presented by practical men in technical journals.

The title of repairman as used throughout this book is one that a good engineer can bear with pride when he measures up to all its qualifications. Such an engineer is one who in in the majority of cases not only knows what to do in the case of an electrical trouble but just how to proceed to do that particular thing and who seldom guesses without a good percentage of the probabilities of being right in his favor. The main difference between the designer and the repairman is that the former must know *what* to do while the latter must know *how* to do it. A capable repairman combines both qualifications through years of experience.

When called upon to locate troubles in motors and generators, electricians and repairmen whose experience in this kind of work has been limited often find themselves wondering just what to do first. It is from just this viewpoint that the information on winding procedure and the hunting and correcting of troubles has been presented. That is, instead of discussing the fundamentals involved in any method of working out a repair problem, the actual problem or job as the case may be is discussed from the "how-to-do-it" standpoint. Then for each individual operation or procedure the applications of fundamental laws and rules are worked out. Considerable repetition of some details of similar methods will therefore be discovered in connection with information covering such procedure as the rewinding of machines of the same class but of different types. This has been considered advisable since a repairman should not be required to study a complete volume when details and information are desired at any one time on the procedure for a particular type of winding for a particular design of machine.

Liberal use has been made of practical data and practices in repair shops so as to combine the good features of a book of methods with handbook information covering these methods. If this book shall help young repairmen to absorb information that can be secured otherwise only through years of experience in handling one job after another, and if the older and more experienced repairmen find it a handy source of reference as a supplement to their own stock of information, then the aim of the author will be accomplished.

When material has been taken from the experiences of engineers and their recommendations on repair methods as published in the technical journals, it has been the aim to give credit to both the author and the journal in the paragraph, or section where the material is used. Special acknowledgment is made to A. H. McIntire, editor of the *Electric Journal,* for permission to make liberal use of information contained in several articles compiled at his suggestion and published in the *Journal.* This material has been incorporated in Chapters 3, 8, 9 and 11. To A. M. Dudley, engineer of the industrial division, Westinghouse Electric & Manufacturing Company, the author is also especially grateful for suggestions and for permission to use details of methods which he has developed for reconnecting and testing induction motor windings. This information appears in Chapters 9 and 11. The diagrams at the end of Chapter 11 have been selected from a series of eighty-one devised by Mr. Dudley and shortly to be published in a valuable treatise on "Connecting Induction Motors."

The author also desires to acknowledge the assistance rendered by H. S. Rich and Alex R. Knapp in the form of data and information compiled from their own experiences in solving a variety of motor troubles met with in industrial plants and in making repairs.   To Henry Scheril, formerly a member of the engineering department of the Crocker-Wheeler Company, acknowledgment is made for helpful suggestions in arranging the material and for assistance in checking and reading the proof.   Credit is also due and is hereby accorded to the electrical manufacturers who furnished the photographs from which many of the halftone illustrations were made.

DANIEL H. BRAYMER.

NEW YORK CITY,
December, 1919.

INTRODUCTION

Through the courtesy of the author of this book the writer has had the privilege of reading the proofs. I have found, with great delight, that the treatment of the subjects discussed is not only clear and easily understood but always from the practical man's standpoint. While the book will appeal strongly to practical men engaged in repair shop work, power station work and the maintenance of motors in industrial plants, it will also appeal, in the opinion of the writer, to students of electricity. Since the material presented in this book, which I dare say is unique in its field, has been obtained from actual practical experiences and outlines the practical remedies that have been applied by repairmen in the solving of puzzling problems, it will be of decided assistance to men who are in need of such practical help.

It is an "electrical book of knowledge," for in its pages readers will find answers to practically all armature winding questions and solutions of many of the repair problems that they will meet in practical work. The diagrams are clear and easily followed by the shop man and run in synchronism with the text. Theory with mathematical considerations have been resorted to only in a very few cases so that the reader of the book can make use of the information and understand the discussions of all phases of armature winding even though he may have only a limited knowledge of mathematics.

A book of this kind, in spite of the errors that are bound to creep in, is a very valuable asset to any practical man who desires to enlarge his own stock of knowledge by learning how other men in similar positions have solved the many electrical problems that come to the repairman.

HENRY SCHERIL.

NEW YORK CITY,
December, 1919.

ix

CONTENTS

CHAPTER III

CHAPTER VIII

CONTENTS

CHAPTER IX

CHAPTER X

CHAPTER XI

CHAPTER XII

COMMUTATOR REPAIRS

CHAPTER XIII

CHAPTER XIV

CHAPTER XV

CHAPTER XVI

CHAPTER XVII

MACHINE EQUIPMENT AND TOOLS NEEDED IN A REPAIR SHOP

ARMATURE WINDING
AND
MOTOR REPAIR

CHAPTER I

DIRECT-CURRENT WINDINGS

The essential physical differences between a complete direct-current and a complete alternating-current armature winding is that the former is wound on the rotating member of the machine while the latter is wound on the stationary member and that the direct-current winding requires a commutator while the alternating-current winding does not. However, since the practical make-up and construction of windings will be discussed later for particular types of direct and alternating-current machines, the general theory of armature windings will likewise be taken up first for direct-current and then for alternating-current machines (see Chapter II).

Action of a Commutator.—The emf and current produced in each armature conductor of a direct-current generator is alternating in character. It is the function of the commutator to deliver from the armature winding an electromotive force and current that is unidirectional, that is, such that one terminal will be always of positive polarity and the other of negative polarity. The commutator and its brushes accomplish this by being connected in series between the generator leads and the armature windings so as to reverse (in effect) the connections of the armature coils (connected to the commutator bars) with respect to the machine leads every time the emf and current induced in these coils reverse upon moving out of the influence of one pole into the field of the next adjacent

1

pole. The alternating emf and current generated in the armature winding is thus rectified or commutated into a unidirectional emf and current.

In the case of an alternating-current generator no such rectifying of induced emf and current is necessary so that the coils or elements making up the armature winding can be connected directly together with the resulting terminals of the winding becoming the terminals of the machine.

Types of D.-C. Armature Windings.—In general, armature windings are either of the open circuit or the closed circuit type. The latter is used in all modern direct-current machines, while alternating-current machines may have either open or closed windings. In the closed circuit winding of the direct-current machine the end joins up with the beginning or re-enters itself with the commutator tapped to the winding at equally distant points. In the case of open circuit winding of an alternating-current generator wound on the revolving member, the ends terminate in collector rings and the winding is thus open until closed by the brushes of the external circuit. When the winding is on the stator of an alternating-current machine the ends are joined through the load circuit. The following classification of closed circuit or direct-current windings may be made:

Direct-current windings (closed circuit).

1. Lap—multiple or parallel.
   (*a*) Single lap.
   (*b*) Multiplex lap.

2. Wave—series or two-circuit.
   (*a*) Single wave.
   (*b*) Multiplex wave or series-parallel windings.

Winding Parts and Terms.—In formulas for armature windings and in laying out a repair job, certain terms are used which refer to parts of the armature winding, the armature core and details of the arrangement of the former in the slots on the surface of the latter. In what follows these terms are explained. In most cases they are used alike both in windings for direct-current and for alternating-current machines.

Armature Conductor or Inductor.—That part of a wire which lies in an armature slot and cuts the magnetic lines of force or field flux as the armature rotates, is called an armature conductor or an inductor.

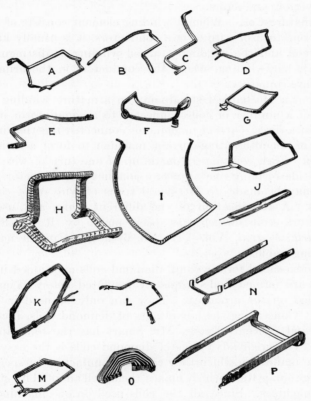

Fig. 1.—Different types of coils used in armature windings.

(A) One-piece series diamond strap coil. Leads at end of straight part. (B) One-piece series diamond coil. Leads at end of straight part. (C) Two-piece series diamond coil. (D) One-piece multiple diamond coil. Leads at point of diamond. (E) Two-piece multiple diamond coil. (F) Concentric coil bent down at both ends. (G) Concentric coil, straight. (H) One-piece wire wound involute coil. Leads at point of involute. I) Two-piece involute coil. Leads at point of involute. (J) Threaded-in type diamond coil. Leads at point of diamond before and after pulling. (K) Basket coil. (L) Same as B of threaded-in type. (M) Same as D of threaded-in type. (N) Bar and involute end connector. (O) Group of concentric end connectors. (P) Concentric shoved through type coil bent down on one end.

Winding Element or Section.—That part of an armature winding which is connected between two commutator bars is called a winding element. In its simplest form a winding element consists of a coil of one turn of wire or two conductors. An element therefore must have at least two conductors but may consist of more than one turn of wire or even number of conductors.

Armature Coil.—When a winding element consists of more than one turn of wire or two conductors, it is usually known as a coil and the winding is a coil winding as distinguished from a bar winding, where the conductors in the armature slots are copper bars.

From a mechanical standpoint an armature winding consists of a number of coils connected to a commutator in the case of a direct-current machine or connected together in the case of an alternating-current machine to form a series or group. Each coil may be made up of one turn of wire with each side forming one armature conductor or inductor, or a coil may be made up of several turns of wire or of copper strips. A classification of the different types and uses of armature coils which has been made by R. A. Smart (*Electric Journal*, Vol. VII, No. 6) is given in the accompanying table.

The so-called form-wound, diamond coils mentioned in the table are formed and completely insulated before being assembled on the armature. They can only be used in open slots Concerning the advantages of diamond coils, involute coils and concentric coils, Mr. Smart has the following to say: "The great advantage of diamond coils is the easy and simple manner in which they can be manufactured, especially in large quantities, which makes them well adapted for standard machines. Since all the coils used on one machine are of the same size and shape, only one winding mould over which to form them is necessary. Moreover, the number of spare parts which must be kept on hand for repairing is reduced and repairs can be made easily and quickly. From the electrical point of view, the diamond type of winding possesses the advantage of being absolutely symmetrical. Hence there is no tendency for unbalancing of voltages due to differences of self-induction; and in closed windings there is no tendency to produce internal circulating currents."

CLASSIFICATION OF ARMATURE COILS ACCORDING TO SLOTS IN WHICH
THEY ARE USED, THEIR FORM AND TRADE NAMES AS EMPLOYED
IN BOTH DIRECT- AND ALTERNATING-CURRENT-WINDINGS

Mould wound coil of insulated wire or ribbon	Open slots	Diamond		Leads at ends of straight part
				Leads at point of diamond
		Involute		Leads at ends of straight part
				Leads at point of involute
		Short type involute		Leads at point of involute
		Concentric		Straight
				Bent at both ends
	Partially closed slots	Shoved through concentric		Straight
				Bent at one end
				Bent at both ends
		Threaded	Diamond	Leads at end of straight part
				Leads at point of diamond
			Shuttle	Leads at ends of straight part
			Basket	Leads at point of diamond
		Hand-wound, pulled through concentric		Straight
				Bent at one end
				Bent at both ends
Form wound coil of bare wire or strap	Open slots	Diamond		Leads at end of straight part
				Leads at point of diamond
		Involute		Leads at end of straight part
				Leads at point of involute.
		Concentric		Straight
				Bent at both ends.
	Partially closed slots	Shoved through concentric.		Straight
				Bent at one end
		Threaded, diamond		Leads at ends of straight part
				Leads at point of diamond
Bars and connectors of bare strap	Partially closed slots	Involute end connectors		
		Concentric end connectors		

Involute Coils.—"Involute coils share the advantages of
the diamond coils in that all are of a standard size and shape.
They also require less space for end connection than any other
form of coil. They are, however, difficult to insulate properly
on account of the larger number of bends and are difficult to
assemble in position in the armature. For this reason their
use is restricted. The bar type of coil with involute end
connectors is easy to insulate and assemble and can be readily
repaired. Their principal use is for direct-current and industrial motors where end space must be reduced to a minimum."

Concentric Coils.—"Concentric coils can be used on any
kind of slot. They can be hand-wound, machine-wound, or
'shoved through' (a combination of the other two methods),
as best suited. The shape of coils is simple, hence they are

easy to wind either on a mould or by hand.   They can be adequately insulated, and can be securely braced with simple and
reliable coil support.   However, the coils belonging to the
same group are of different size, and the coils in different
groups, except on single-phase machines, are bent in at least
two and often in three different shapes.   This is a disadvantage
from the electrical point of view, since there will always be a
tendency toward unbalancing due to differences in self-
induction, and toward the production of circulating currents
in closed windings.   And it is also a disadvantage from the
mechanical point of view, since for one machine, a large
number of different moulds will be required and coils cannot
be interchanged.   Hence, the number of spare parts necessary
for repairs is greatly increased, and both the manufacturing
and repairing of the winding will require more time and be
more expensive."

Winding Pitch or Coil Pitch.—The distance between the
beginning of one winding element or coil side to the beginning

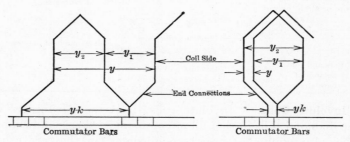

Figs. 2 and 3.—Comparison of wave and lap windings.

At the left a wave winding showing front pitch of coils as y_1; back pitch as y_2; total
pitch as y and commutator pitch as yk.   At right, a lap winding with the same notations
for the different pitches of coils.

of the next element or coil side connected to the first one is
called the total winding pitch.   This is shown as y for both lap
and wave windings in Figs. 2 and 3.   Winding pitch is measured in number of slots or by number of elements or coil
sides spanned by a single coil or by the number of commutator
bars between the connections to the commutator of the two
sides of a coil.   In the third instance the measurement is
known as *commutator pitch* and indicated as yk in Fig. 2

and Fig. 3. In this chapter unless otherwise stated coil pitch will be designated by the number of winding spaces or coil sides spanned. There are two winding spaces per slot in a double layer winding.

Front Pitch.—The distance between the two coil sides connected to the same commutator bar, measured in coil sides at the front or commutator end of the armature, is called the front pitch. It is indicated as y_1 in Figs. 2 and 3.

Back Pitch.—The distance between two sides of a coil, measured in coil sides, at the back end of the armature is known as the back pitch. It is shown as y_2 in Figs. 2 and 3. The total winding pitch y is equal to the algebraic sum

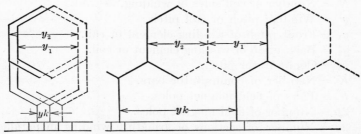

Fig. 4.—Lap and wave windings showing connections of formed coils to the commutator in double layer windings.

of the front and back pitches. That is, since in a lap winding the front and back pitches are of opposite sign, being laid off in opposite directions on the armature, the total pitch y will be the difference between them. In a wave winding where the front and back pitches are laid off in the same direction, the total pitch y will be their sum.

Full Pitch and Fractional Pitch Coils.—When a coil spans exactly the distance between the centers of adjacent field poles (known as *pole-pitch*) it is said to be a full-pitch coil. In cases where a coil is less than full pitch, it is said to have a *fractional pitch* or to be a *short-pitch* coil. Such a winding is often referred to as a *short-chord* winding.

Fractional pitch windings are much used because of the following advantages: (1) They make possible shorter end-connections and therefore call for less copper. (2) Armature reaction is reduced since the currents in the neutral zone flow partly in opposite directions and neutralize each other. (3) In alternating current generators a smoothing out of the wave of induced emf is produced so as to more nearly approach a sine form.

Symbols Used in Winding Formulas.—The symbols which are much used in winding formulas for the parts of windings defined in the preceding paragraphs are as follows:

Z = Total number of armature conductors, $(2gC)$ or $(2gK)$.

C = Number of winding elements or coils usually equal to K.

g = Number of turns per winding element or coil.

$2g$ = Number of conductors per winding element or coil.

N = Number of coil sides of winding.

y = Winding pitch or coil pitch.

y_1 = Front pitch of winding element or coil.

y_2 = Back pitch of winding element or coil.

y_k = Commutator pitch.

K = Number of commutator bars.

p = Pairs of field magnet poles.

$2p$ = Number of field magnet poles.

$2a$ = Number of sections of armature winding in parallel.

s = Number of slots on the armature.

Numbering of Coil Sides in Armature Slots.—Form wound coils are usually arranged in two layers with one side of each

FIG. 5.—Winding with two   FIG. 6.—Winding with four coil sides
coil sides per slot.   per slot. The coil pitch in this case is
                                        7 winding spaces or coil sides.

coil placed in the bottom of a slot and the other side in the top. For convenience in laying out windings, the coil sides forming the top layers in the slot are given odd numbers and those forming the bottom layers even numbers. This scheme of numbering is shown in Figs. 5 and 6. In those cases where the winding element consists of a coil of a number of turns of wire instead of two conductors or bars, numbers are assigned to the consecutive bundle of conductors or wires of which the coil is made instead of assigning numbers to the individual conductors or inductors as they are sometimes called. When such coils are used, the front and back pitches are determined by counting consecutive half coils between the the two coil sides of any coil beginning from one coil side and counting forward as the coil is laid off and considering the first side of the coil as one. That is, in case of a double layer lap winding, with one coil side in the bottom of slot 3, and the other side in the top of slot 7, the back pitch would be 7 counted as follows, there being two coil sides in each slot: First coil side 6, next coil sides spanned are 7, 8, 9, 10, 11 and 12. The number of slots spanned by the coil is called the *slot pitch* or *throw of the coil*. The throw of the coil, more often called coil throw, in the case mentioned, where one side of a coil is in slot 3 and the other in slot 7, is 4 slots. In the case of a four-pole machine and an armature having 16 slots, this coil throw is a full pole pitch, that is, from the center of one field pole to the center of the next, and the winding is a full pitch winding.

LAP—MULTIPLE OR PARALLEL WINDINGS

A lap winding is so called from the lapping back of the coils or winding elements as they are wound on the armature core. This is shown in Figs. 7 and 8. A better name is a multi-

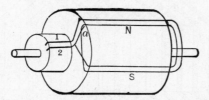

Fig. 7.—Lap winding showing the relative position of one winding element or coil of two turns on the armature of a 4-pole machine.

ple or parallel winding because of the fact that such a winding consists of as many circuits as there are field poles and these circuits are connected in parallel between the brushes. The number of brushes required therefore equals the number of armature sections in parallel and also equals the number of poles. That is $a = p$. A lap winding can be distinguished

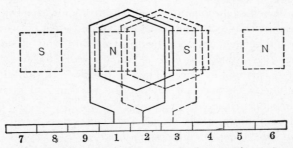

FIG. 8.—Winding diagram for the lap winding of Fig. 7 showing how the finish end of one winding element or coil of two turns is joined to the commutator and to the start end of the next coil under the same pair of poles.

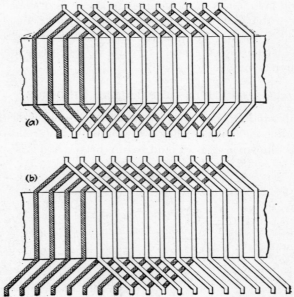

FIG. 9.—(a) Lap winding showing both end connections of each coil side bent toward center of the coil. (b) Wave winding showing end connections of each coil side bent in opposite directions.

from a so-called wave winding from the appearance of the end connections of coils. In the wave winding the front and rear ends of the coils lead in opposite directions while in the lap winding they continue in the same direction around the armature, as shown in Fig. 9.

Formulas for Lap Winding.—The following rules and restrictions govern the assembling and use of a lap winding:

1. The front and back pitches (in winding spaces or coil sides) must both be odd numbers and differ by two or some multiple thereof.
2. The front and back pitches are of opposite sign (one positive and the other negative) since they are laid off in opposite directions on the armature.
3. The winding pitch is equal to the algebraic sum of the front and back pitches. That is, in case the front pitch is + 9 and the back pitch − 7, the algebraic sum is (9 − 7) or 2.
4. The total number of armature conductors or inductors must be a multiple of the number of slots on the armature.
5. The number of armature slots may be odd or even.
6. The number of current collecting points or brushes on the commutator must equal the number of poles.
7. The maximum emf between two consecutive coil sides (top and bottom) in the same slot, is equal to or a little less than the terminal voltage.
8. The end of one coil is joined to the commutator and to the start of another coil (usually the next) under the same pair of poles.

The following formulas apply in lap windings:

$$\text{Front pitch} \quad = y_1 = \frac{N \pm b}{2p} \pm 2$$

$$\text{Back pitch} \quad = y_k = \frac{N \pm b}{2p}$$

Winding pitch $= y =$ algebraic sum of y_1 and $y_2 = \pm 2$
Commutator pitch $= y_k = \pm 1$

In the formulas for front and back pitches, N (as given on page 8) is the number of coil sides in the winding; p the number of pairs of poles and b any even number which will make both y_1 and y_2 odd whole numbers and about equal to the pole pitch. The value of b should be taken as large as allowable but not too large for then there is liability of the two sides of a coil coming under the influence of poles of the same polarity so that the induced emfs would oppose each other.   For $b = 0$, the back pitch y_2 becomes equal to the pole pitch.   When b is positive y_2 becomes greater than the pole pitch, while with b negative, y_2 becomes less than the pole pitch.   In most cases b is taken negative so that y_2 is equal to or less than the pole pitch.

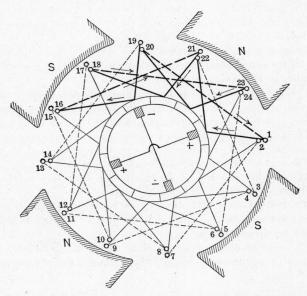

FIG. 10.—Lap winding for a 4-pole machine showing the direction of current flow in one of the four current paths for the brush positions as illustrated.

The current (i) which flows in each conductor of a lap winding is,

$$i = \frac{I}{2p}$$

Where I is the total armature current or that flowing in the external circuit.   The value of (i) should be considered when selecting the proper size of wire in making up or ordering coils.

The only practical lap winding from the standpoint of symmetry is the one in which the number of pairs of circuits (current paths) in parallel equals the number of pairs of poles or $a = p$.

A lap winding is symmetrical when $s \div a$ and $s \div p$ is a whole number. Here s equals the number of slots, a the pairs of circuits in parallel and p, the pairs of poles. With four-pole motors it is not always found that $s \div a$ and $s \div p$ are whole numbers, since manufacturers sometimes make the number of commutator bars and slots odd so as to make the armature suitable for a two-circuit wave winding as well as a lap winding.

In lap windings where the commutator pitch (y_k) equals one, when $a = p$, the common factor of the number of commutator bars, and y_k will always be unity and there will be a single winding.

In a double layer winding with two coil sides per slot, the number of slots equals the number of coils in the winding. When there are more than two coil sides in a slot, the number of coils, $C = sN_s \div 2$ with no idle coils; where s equals the number of slots and N_s equals the number of coil sides per slot. More than two coil sides per slot greatly reduces the number of slots required. Such a winding is symmetrical only when $s \div a$ is a whole number.

For a lap winding the potential pitch, $y_p = K \div p$, where K equals the number of commutator bars and p is the number of pairs of poles.

When equalized rings are needed with lap winding, it is good practice to use one ring for every 6 or 12 commutator bars.

Multiplex, Single, Double and Triple Windings.—In cases where it is necessary that the armature shall carry a very heavy current more than one winding may be used on the armature with an equal number of commutator bars for each. Both lap and wave windings may be so made up with one, two or three entirely separate windings. In the case of a double lap winding, the sides of a winding element or coil of one winding are sandwiched between the coil sides of the other and likewise the commutator bars of one winding are sandwiched between those of the other. Each brush must be thick enough to always touch two commutator bars so that both windings will always be connected to the brushes and both deliver or receive current evenly. Three windings so sandwiched make up a triple winding.

A single lap winding always has the same number of current paths between brush sets as there are field poles while a double lap winding has twice the number of current paths as there are field poles. The triple lap winding has three times the number of current paths as there are field poles. A single wave winding always has two current paths between brush sets while the double wave winding has four current paths between brush sets and the triple wave winding has six such paths between brush sets.

An armature has one winding (single) when the number of commutator bars K and commutator pitch y_k have no common factor; it is double when their common factor is two, and it is triple when their common factor is three.

Meaning of the Term Reentrant.—A winding is often said to be single or double reentrant. In the case of a single winding, this means that the winding closes on itself or returns to the beginning point after being traced through all the coils upon passing once around the armature core. A winding is doubly reentrant if it only re-enters itself after making two passages around the coils of the armature. A single winding may be either single reentrant or doubly reentrant.

In the case of double and triple windings, the term reentrant is sometimes used in an improper sense. For this reason it is advisable to specify types of armature windings by the number of separate windings, used. Thus a single winding as a single-closed; two windings as double-closed and three windings as triple-closed etc. A winding made up of two single windings, each of which re-enters itself, will therefore be a double-closed winding not a "double-reentrant" one.

Multiplex Lap Windings.—As explained under the heading of "Multiplex Windings," a lap winding may be made up of one, two or three separate windings in order to handle heavy armature currents. In the case of a double lap winding, two similar windings insulated from each other are placed in the armature slots with the even numbered commutator bars connected to one winding and the odd numbered bars connected to the other winding. In the same way for a triple lap winding one-third of the commutator bars provided would be connected to each winding.

The formulas which apply in multiplex lap windings are as follows:

Front pitch $= y_1 = \dfrac{N \pm b}{2p} \pm 2m$

Back pitch $= y_2 = \dfrac{N \pm b}{2p}$

Winding pitch $= y = y_2 - y_1 = \pm 2m$

Commutator pitch $= y_k = \dfrac{y_2 - y_1}{2} = \pm m$

In these formulas m is 2 for a double winding and 3 for a triple winding, etc. When the number of commutator bars is exactly divisible by m, the windings will be entirely separate from each other.

A double lap winding will have $2 \times (2p)$ current paths between brushes, where $2p$ is the *number of poles*. That is, each winding for a 4-pole machine will have four current paths so that a double lap winding on a 4-pole machine will have eight current paths between brushes.

In order that the two sides of a winding element or a coil may move simultaneously under field poles of opposite polarity, the total number of coil sides that make up the complete winding divided by the number of the field poles, that is $N \div 2p$, is the approximate value for both the front and back pitches as in the case of the single lap winding. Under such conditions the electromotive force induced in the two sides of a winding element add up. The smallest front or back pitch to satisfy this condition, is the distance across a single pole face and the largest front or back pitch is the distance from one pole tip to the nearest pole tip of the same polarity. If the front and back pitches are much less than $N \div 2p$, then a chorded winding results.

Since y_1 and y_2 must be odd numbers and approximately equal to $N \div 2p$, where $2p$ is the *number* of field poles, this value will help in determining the value of b to be used in the formula for front pitch (y_1) and back pitch (y_2).

The multiplex lap winding is largely confined to windings for small and medium sized machines carrying large currents and using coils made up of wire rather than copper strips or bars. This is for the reason that in such a winding for a large multipolar machine the bars would be too thin and a mechanical construction result which would make another type of winding advisable, probably a series-parallel design.

WAVE—SERIES OR TWO-CIRCUIT WINDING

The wave winding is so called from the zig zag or wave path that the winding takes through the slots of the armature, as shown in Figs. 11 and 12. This type of winding is more

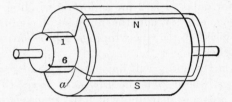

FIG. 11.—Wave winding showing relative position of one winding element or coil of two turns on the armature of a 4-pole machine.

definitely described as a series or two-circuit winding because of the fact that half of the armature coils or sections are connected in series and the two halves are connected in parallel. This winding therefore has only two current paths in parallel

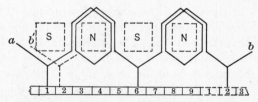

FIG. 12.—Winding diagram for wave winding of Fig. 11 showing how the finish end of one coil is joined to the commutator and connected to the start of the next coil under the next pair of poles. *b'* is a continuation of *b*.

between brushes regardless of the number of poles. Only two sets of brushes are required for a machine of any number of poles but improved commutation is brought about when the number of brushes equals the number of field poles. The wave winding is used in small and medium sized machines where it is desired to keep the number of coils as small as possible.

Formulas for Wave Winding.—The following rules and restrictions govern the assembling and use of a wave winding:

1. The front and back pitches (in winding spaces or coil sides) must both be odd.
2. The front and back pitches may be equal or may differ by two or some multiple thereof. The former condition is usually the case.
3. The front and back pitches are of the same sign since they are laid off in the same direction.
4. The winding pitch is equal to the sum of the front and back pitches.
5. The commutator pitch and number of commutator bars must not have a common factor.
6. The number of current collecting points or brushes on the commutator is always two for any number of poles but the number of sets of brushes may equal the number of poles.
7. The maximum emf between two consecutive coil sides (top and bottom) in the same slot, is equal or nearly equal to the terminal voltage of the machine.
8. The finish of one coil is joined to a commutator bar and to the start of another coil which lies under the next pair of poles.

The following formulas apply in wave winding:

Winding pitch $= y = y_1 + y_2 = \dfrac{N \pm 2}{p}$

Front pitch $= y_1$

Back pitch $= y_2$

Number pairs of poles $= p$

Commutator pitch $= y_k = \dfrac{y_1 + y_2}{2} = \dfrac{K \pm 1}{p}$

Number commutator bars $= K = \dfrac{N}{2} = p \times y_k \pm 1.$

The number of coil sides (N) must be such that $\dfrac{N \pm 2}{p}$ will be an even number with y_1 and y_2 both odd numbers. y_1 and y_2 are usually taken equal. Under these conditions the back pitch (y_2) is nearly equal to the pole pitch and the sum of the front and back pitches is nearly equal to double the pole pitch. If y_2 is reduced then y_1 must be increased so that $y_1 + y_2$ will be constant. This is what happens in a chorded or fractional pitch winding.

?

The current (i) which flows in each conductor of a wave winding is always one-half the total armature current. $i = I \div 2$. This value of (i) should be considered when selecting the proper size of conductors for coils of wave windings.

The closed winding formula for a wave winding is $y_k = (K \pm a) \div p$. Where y_k is the commutator pitch, K the num-

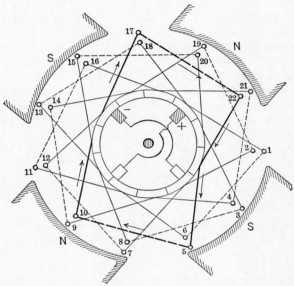

Fig. 13.—Wave winding for a 4-pole machine showing the direction of current flow in one of the two current paths for the brush position as illustrated.

ber of commutator bars, a the pairs of parallel circuits in the winding and p the number of pairs of poles. When $a = 1$, it is only possible to make a single winding. The highest common factor of y_k and K gives the type of winding, whether single, double, etc. The number of coil sides in a wave winding equals twice the number of commutator bars.

The number of slots without idle coils must satisfy the formula, $s = (2K) \div N_s$. Where K is the number commutator bars and N_s the number of coil sides per slot.

A wave winding is symmetrical when $K \div a$, $s \div a$ and $p \div a$, are whole numbers. Where K is the number of commutator bars, a, the number of pairs of parallel circuits in the winding, s the number of slots, and p the number of pairs of poles.

When equalizer rings are needed with a wave winding, the use of one ring to every 15 to 20 commutator bars is good practice.

Multiplex Wave or Series-Parallel Winding.—In a single wave or series winding the number of armature circuits in parallel is always equal to two, while in a lap or multiple winding the number of circuits in parallel is equal to the number of field poles. The series-parallel winding is a design of wave winding in which the number of armature circuits in parallel may be larger than two and yet smaller than the number of field poles. It is especially suitable for large multipolar armatures which use winding elements made up of copper bars.

Formulas for Series-Parallel Winding.—The following rules govern the assembling and use of this winding:

1. The front and back pitches (in winding spaces or coil sides) must be odd numbers. They may be equal to or different from each other although they are usually equal.
2. The winding should be symmetrical as shown by the number of field poles divided by the number of armature circuits in parallel being a whole number. If this is not the case the final winding should be made up of a sufficient number of independent windings to make the number of field poles divided by the number of armature circuits in parallel a whole number for each of the independent windings.
3. It is necessary that the number of commutator bars divided by one-half the number of armature circuits in parallel shall be a whole number. If the conditions of (2) are fulfilled, the condition named here is likewise satisfied at the same time.
4. If the number of commutator bars and the commutator pitch have no common factor, the winding is a single one; if the common factor is 2, the winding is double or if it is equal to m, the winding is multiplex of m separate windings. The common factor must, however, be smaller than half the number of circuits. An illustration will bring out these conditions. In the case of an 8-pole machine with 27 slots, 54 commutator bars, 4 conductors per slot, and a commutator pitch of 13, the two series windings are singly closed forming one winding, since 54 and 13

have no common factor.   For a machine of 4-poles, with 20 slots, 40 commutator bars, 4 conductors per slot, commutator pitch of 18, the winding may be made up of two series windings, the values 40, 18 and 4 have a common factor of 2.   This makes the winding doubly closed and consists of two series windings with each in turn consisting of two other series windings, each of the latter forming one continuous winding.

5. For large machines using series-parallel windings, it has been found advisable in most cases to use equipotential connections and connect about every fourth or eighth commutator section.   (See heading "Equipotential Connectors" on page 21.)

6. The number of current collecting points or brushes on the commutator is equal to the number of armature sections in parallel.

The following formulas apply in the case of a series-parallel winding:

Front pitch $= y_1$

Back pitch $= y_2$

Winding pitch $= y = y_1 + y_2 = \dfrac{N \pm 2a}{p}$

Commutator pitch $= y_k = \dfrac{K \pm a}{p}$

Number commutator bars $= K = \dfrac{N}{2}$

Where p is number of *pairs of poles* and N is the number of coil sides in the winding. N must be such a value that $\dfrac{N \pm 2a}{p}$ is a whole number.

Symmetrical Windings.—All armature windings should be made symmetrical if possible.   A winding is symmetrical when the total number of slots divided by one-half the number of armature sections in parallel is a whole number.   If this is not the case the emfs induced in different circuits will produce circulating currents.   A winding is also symmetrical if the number of field poles divided by the number of armature sections in parallel is a whole number or the number of commutator bars is divisible by one-half the number of armature sections in parallel.   To be sure that any winding is symmetrical all three of these conditions should be fulfilled.

Possible Symmetrical Windings for D.-C. Machines of Different Number of Poles.—In a discussion on armature windings, Stanley Parker Smith (*London Electrician*, June 16, 1916) has selected the following as the most suitable windings for machines of different number of poles:

1. For a two-pole machine either a two-circuit lap or wave winding can be used. The former is usually preferred.
2. For a four-pole machine either a two-circuit wave or a four-circuit lap winding can be used.
3. For a six-pole machine we are limited to the two-circuit wave and six-circuit lap windings, since the four-circuit wave winding ($a = 2$, $p = 3$) is unsymmetrical. This is probably the most objectionable restriction of all, because so many cases arise where four circuits are desirable in a six-pole machine.
4. For an eight-pole machine wave windings with two or four circuits and an eight-circuit lap winding can be used. This is the first instance of a symmetrical wave winding with $a > 1 < p$, and can be used with great advantage in many cases.
5. For a 10-pole machine there are again only two symmetrical windings—the two-circuit wave and 10-circuit lap windings.
6. For a 12-pole machine the possibilities are much greater, for wave windings with two, four or six circuits and a lap winding with 12 circuits can be used.
7. The list can be continued further, if desired, but it is plainly seen that certain very important advantages are open to the designer by making use of wave windings with more than two circuits in 8, 12 and 16-pole machines. It is necessary, however, to observe the other conditions of symmetry, namely s/a must be a whole number and idle coils must be avoided.

Equipotential Connectors (Equalizing Rings and Phase Tappings).—In a symmetrical winding, that is, a winding with identical K/a phase systems, there are always a coils at the same potential, and these can be joined together if desired. If no dissymmetry whatever were present, however, there would be little object in making such connections, unless they are needed as phase tappings to obtain an alternating pressure. Actually there are many cases of dissymmetry in a machine, apart from those due to the arrangement of the winding already mentioned. Thus, the magnetic material may not be uniform, the pole-shoes may not be properly spaced, the gap may not be uniform, and so on. In general, perfect symmetry must be regarded as an unattainable ideal in practice according to Mr. Smith, who calls attention to the following conditions:

Owing to these dissymmetries, the pressure induced in the several armature circuits varies, and causes equalizing currents to flow through the brushes. These equalizing currents, if of sufficient strength, produce sparking and in any case, load the brushes in an undesirable manner. It is interesting to note that, even when no equalizing rings are present, the positive and negative collecting rings act as equalizers, and the tendency of these equalizing currents is to neutralize the inequalities in the magnetic field to which they are due. When equalizing rings are used, however, large equalizing currents will flow along these and strongly damp out any inequalities in the field, and so reduce the difference of potential between corresponding points in the winding. Consequently the brushes are relieved, and are so much better able to perform their proper function of collecting the current.

Equalizing rings must not be regarded as in any way essential, and many machines work quite well without them. Nevertheless, they add a certain factor of safety which the manufacturer is often glad to purchase at so small a cost, for he is not only surer of his machine passing the test satisfactorily but also knows that after-effects, like wear of the bearings, cannot give rise to such serious trouble as when equalizers are absent. Consequently, equalizers are seen on many large machines with lap-wound armatures, or with wave windings with more than two circuits. Equalizing rings should not have an extremely low resistance. Such practice requires not only an excessive amount of copper, but leads to considerable loss and heating in the winding. All that is really necessary is to provide an alternative path of negligible resistance compared with that of the brushes, and for this purpose it is usually sufficient to make the section of the rings about half that of the conductors.

Regarding the number of equalizing rings, much depends on the opinion of the designer. With lap windings, one ring for every 6 to 12 segments is common practice, but this is scarcely feasible when $p > a$, for here the potential pitch,[1] $y_p = K/a$, may be fairly large and the number of rings becomes prohibitive. In such cases (wave windings with more than two circuits), one ring for every 15 to 20 segments may suffice. There is no need to make the pitch between all the rings the same, but designers generally prefer to split up y_p into a whole number of parts. In this case the tappings form a symmetrical polyphase system of pressures.

Best D.-C. Windings for a Repair Shop to Use.—To secure good commutation and eliminate heating troubles, all windings should be made symmetrical. This among other things means that there must not be more armature circuits in parallel than there are field poles. Where the number of armature circuits equals the number of poles either the lap or the wave winding may be used. The lap winding is however mostly used in such a case. The wave winding then need only be considered in those cases where the number of armature circuits is to be less than the number of field poles. A single winding is more simple and should be used in preference to a complicated one where conditions permit either a single winding or two or more separate windings except in those cases where a very heavy current is to be carried in the armature. In general then, where changes in armature windings are necessary that call for a choice of types of windings, it is advisable to employ either a lap winding with as many circuits as there are poles or a wave winding with two circuits. Usually a lap winding is possible if the number of coils is a common multiple of the number of poles and the number of slots. The number of coils is equal to the number of commutator bars.

Number of Armature Slots.—The open slot with parallel sides is most used for large armatures so that form wound coils can be easily assembled. These coils are held in place by wire bands or by wood or fiber wedges driven into grooves at the tips of the teeth as shown in Chapter III. The number of slots per pole is usually not less than 10. For multipolar armatures there are at least from three to four slots in the space

---

[1] The potential pitch is the number of commutator bars between successive equipotential points in the winding which can be joined together when equalizing rings are needed.

between pole tips. In the case of high speed machines having large pole pitch there may be from 14 to 18 slots per pole. For machines above say 5 hp. the area of the slot will approximate one square inch. A rough rule for the capacity of a slot of this area is about 1,000 amp. turns for machines under 500 volts.

Voltage between Commutator Segments.—For direct-current machines without interpoles, about 15 volts between segments of the commutator is the maximum allowed while double this value can be considered as the maximum for machines employing commutating interpoles. This value of voltage between segments can be obtained for an existing machine by measuring this voltage between plus and minus brushes and dividing by the number of commutator segments between these brushes. The voltage between a positive and negative brush will depend upon the number of inductors (wires making up one side of a coil) connected in series between the brushes. For calculating windings for machines, Prof. Still gives the following relationships between machine voltage and volts between commutator segments for good operation:

VOLTAGE BETWEEN SEGMENTS OF COMMUTATORS

Machine voltage	Volts between commutator segments
110	1 to 6
220	2.5 to 10
600	5 to 18
1200	9 to 25

Number of Commutator Bars.—The proper number of commutator bars for a particular winding depends on the voltage between commutator bars. The number of bars may be a multiple of the number of slots. For low voltage machine there may be one, two or three bars per slot while in higher voltage slow speed machines, there may be as many as four or five bars per slot. While improved commutation results from a large number of commutator bars the difficulty in repair and assembly from a mechanical standpoint offset their advantage over fewer bars for the same conditions of winding and machine operation.

Usual Speeds and Poles for Different Sizes of Generators.—
For direct current generators Prof. Still[1] gives the following
relationship between number of poles and speed for different
ratings of machines. This table represents usual practice
by designers.

NUMBER OF POLES AND USUAL SPEED LIMITS OF D.-C. GENERATORS

Output in kw.	Number of poles	Speed in rpm, maximum and minimum
0 to 10	2	2400 to 600
10 to 50	4	1300 to 350
50 to 100	4 or 6	1100 to 230
100 to 300	6 or 8	700 to 160
300 to 600	6 or 10	500 to 120
600 to 1000	8 or 12	400 to 100
1000 to 3000	10 or 20	200 to 70

Safe Armature Speeds.—The safe speed of an armature
varies with the armature construction. Direct-current machines are built with a peripheral speed of 2,500 to 3,500 feet
per minute. It is not advisable to exceed an armature peripheral speed of 6,000 feet per minute in machines which are
not designed to take care of the mechanical stresses incident
to the higher speeds.

[1] Principles of Electrical Design, page 81.

CHAPTER II

ALTERNATING-CURRENT WINDINGS

In the main, the windings for alternating-current motors and generators are alike. For this reason details of the windings that can be used for either machines will be given. It should be noted at this point that direct-current and alternating-current windings differ essentially by the former being of the closed-circuit type while most alternating-current windings are of the open-circuit type. Either open- or closed-circuit types of windings may however be employed in alternating-current machines, but the open type is in most common use. By a closed winding is meant one which has a continuous path through the armature and re-enters itself to form a closed circuit. Such a direct-current winding always has at least two current paths between brushes. In the case of an open-circuit alternating-circuit winding, there is a continuous path through the conductors of the coils of each phase of the winding, with the ends of this path forming two free ends. Such a winding does not close on itself.

In the closed-circuit windings of direct-current machines, the bars of the commutator are simply connected at equally distant points around the winding. In the open-circuit winding of an alternating-current generator with revolving armature, the terminals of the completed winding are connected to collector rings and the winding is open-circuited until closed by the connections between the brushes. Closed-circuit windings are only used for special alternating-current machines. The conditions which usually call for a closed-circuit winding are the following:

1. An alternating-current machine which must deliver a large current at low voltage. In such a case the winding usually consists of several similar paths connected in parallel to the

terminals of the armature, thus forming one or more closed circuits within the armature winding.

2. In designs of machines that must handle direct and alternating current, as in double current generators and in rotary converters.

In general it may be said that a direct-current winding may be changed so that the machine can be used as an alternator, but an alternating-current winding cannot be used for a direct current generator since it is not reentrant.

Types of A.-C. Windings.—With reference to the arrangements of coils used in an alternating-current armature, windings may be divided into two general classes as follows:

I. Distributed Windings.
    1. Spiral or chain.
    2. Lap.
    3. Wave.
II. Concentrated Windings.
    1. Lap.
    2. Wave.

Distributed Windings.—An armature winding which has its inductors of any one phase under a single pole placed in several slots, is said to be distributed. When these inductors are bunched together in one slot per pole, per phase, the winding is called concentrated. It is usual in a distributed winding to distribute the series inductors in any phase of the winding among two or more slots under each pole. This tends to diminish armature reactance and gives a better emf. wave, besides offering a better distribution of the heating due to armature copper loss than in concentrated windings.

Concentrated Windings.—The uni-slot or concentrated winding gives the largest possible emf from a given number of inductors in the winding. That is for a definite fixed speed and field strength in an alternator, the concentrated winding requires a less number of inductors than a distributed winding, but increases the number of turns per coil.

Spiral or Chain Winding.—In this winding as shown in Fig. 14 there is only one coil side in a slot. An odd or even number of inductors per slot may be used but several shapes of coils are required since the coils enclose each other and must

have special end shapes to clear each other. This arrangement, however, makes possible good insulation of end connections through adequate separating air spaces in high voltage machines. The number of coils required in this winding

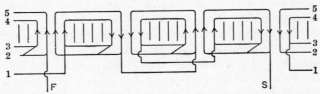

Fig. 14.—A spiral or chain winding for a 2-phase, 4-pole machine with
the coils of one phase in place and connected. The coils of the other phase
go in the slots shown by the full lines inside the coils.

is also small compared with other windings. This type of
winding is mainly used in alternating-current generators.

Lap and Wave Windings.—Both distributed and concentrated windings make use of lap and wave connections. These

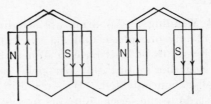

Fig. 15.—Single-phase lap winding for the same conditions as the wave
winding in Fig. 16.

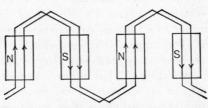

Fig. 16.—Single-phase distributed wave winding with two slots per pole per
phase and one coil side per slot.

arrangements are in principle the same as used in direct-current
windings.   (See Chapter I, pages 9 and 16.)   The diagrams of
Figs. 15 and 16 show single-phase distributed lap and wave

windings for a four-pole armature, having two slots per pole
with one inductor per slot.

In a double-layer lap or wave winding for an alternating-
current armature, the coils are usually of the same general
shape as used in direct-current windings. Instead of connecting the terminals of the coils to a commutator, they are
connected together in a definite order (see Chapter XI, page
288) for each phase. The phase windings are then connected
together in star or delta as shown in Fig. 22. In that diagram
a three-phase wave winding is shown for a four-pole machine.
In the double-layer winding, the number of conductors per

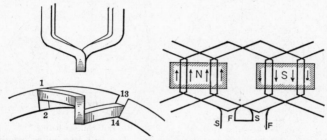

FIG. 17.—At the left is shown the appearance of one formed coil in a 2-
layer winding. One side of the coil lies in the top of the slot and the other
side in the bottom of the slot. The top side bears an odd number and the
bottom side an even number. The coil pitch in this case is 6 slots or 13
winding spaces. At the right the method of connecting coils for a 2-layer
winding using form coils is shown. The finish (*F*) of one coil is joined
to the start (*S*) of the next.

slot must be a multiple of two. It lends itself to a variety
of connections, particularly to a fractional pitch lap winding
where the two sides of a coil are not similarly placed in respect
to the center lines of the poles. The double-layer winding
is not, however, as well suited for high voltages as the single-
layer winding. For this reason many water-wheel types of
generators have been built with a single-layer winding, which
in its most common form, is known as the spiral or chain
winding.

When laying out or changing a double-layer winding, it
is usual to assign odd numbers to the sides of coils in the top
of the slots and even numbers to the sides in the bottom of
the slots. This is important when the pitch of the armature

coils is expressed in terms of coil sides (winding spaces) instead of slots.

Whole-coiled and Half-coiled Windings.—When the coils of an alternating current winding are connected so that there are as many coils per phase as there are poles, the winding is called "whole-coiled." When the coils are connected so that there is only one coil per phase per pair of poles, the winding is called "half-coiled." The main difference between these two connections is in the method of making the end connections

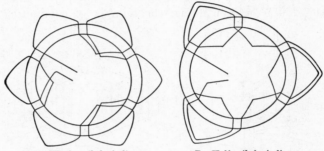

A—Whole-coiled winding   B—Half-coiled winding

Fig. 18.—A 6-pole stator with whole-coiled and half-coiled windings. The whole-coiled winding, *A*, has as many coils per phase as there are poles. The half-coiled winding *B* has only one coil per phase per pair of poles.

for the coils. In the "whole-coiled" winding each slot contains two coil sides. It is not, however, strictly a double-layer winding, as the coil sides are placed side by side and not one above the other. In the "half-coiled" winding, however, each coil may have twice the number of turns of a "whole-coiled" winding or the two coils under a north or south pole of the latter type may be connected in series and taped together to form one coil in case of a change in connections.

The "half-coiled" winding has the advantage that, when used with large generators the armature frame may be split into two sections for shipment or repair, without disturbing many of the end connections.

Single-phase and Polyphase Windings.—The winding of a single-phase motor or generator has only one group of inductors per pole, placed in one slot or several slots depending upon whether or not the winding is concentrated or distrib-

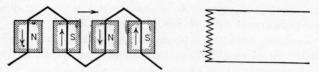

FIG. 19.—A simple single-phase winding.

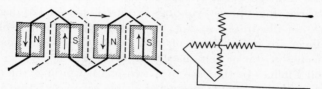

FIG. 20.—Simple 2-phase winding.

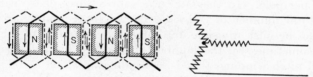

FIG. 21.—Simple 3-phase winding.

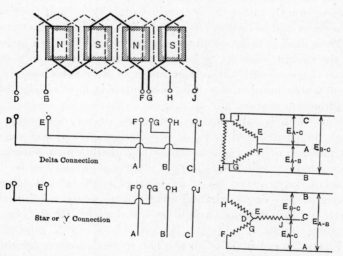

FIG. 22.—A 3-phase winding showing how it may be connected in delta or star.

uted. Such a single-phase concentrated wave winding for a four-pole armature is shown in Fig. 19.

Two-phase and three-phase windings may be considered as made up of single-phase windings properly placed on the same armature. For the two-phase windings two separate single-phase windings are used spaced 90 electrical degrees apart. This is shown in Fig. 20. For the three-phase winding, three single-phase windings are used, spaced 120 degrees apart, as illustrated in Fig. 21. Although the single-phase windings are independent of each other, their terminals are connected in star or delta as shown in Fig. 22.

Coil Pitch.—In the case of a two-phase winding, the total number of slots should be just divisible by two so that each phase will have the same number of winding elements or coils per pole. In the same way, for a three-phase winding the total number of coil sides or the total number of slots should be just divisible by three (the number of phases) and sometimes by the number of poles. This will result in a full pitch winding, that is, a winding in which a coil spans exactly the distance between the centers of adjacent poles. If the coil spans less than this distance, so that its two sides are not exactly under the centers of adjacent poles at the same time, it is said to have a fractional-pitch. When a fractional-pitch is used in alternators on account of the electrical factors of the design, such as to secure as nearly as possible a sine wave shape of emf, the total number of slots per phase must be a whole number. A fractional-pitch is also widely used in induction motors.

Coil pitch is expressed as a fraction of the pole pitch, in slots, in electrical degrees or in winding spaces (coil sides). In the case of a six-pole machine having 72 stator slots, and a double-layer winding, the pole pitch would be 12 slots. If the coil pitch were given as $\frac{2}{3}$, this would be 120 degrees or eight slots or 13 winding spaces (coil sides). A full coil pitch for this winding would be 180 degrees, 12 slots or 21 winding spaces.

Phase Spread of Windings.—The spread or space occupied by each single-phase winding is known as the phase spread of the winding. For a two-phase winding the phase spread is (180 ÷ 2) or 90 degrees. For a three-phase winding, it is (180 ÷ 3) or 60 degrees. In a single-phase winding, the phase spread is theoretically 180 degrees. Prof. Alfred Still points out, however, in his book on "Principles of Electrical Design," that nothing is gained by winding all the slots on the armature surface of a single-phase machine. After a certain width of winding has been reached the filling of additional slots merely increases the resistance and inductance of the winding without any appreciable gain in the developed voltage. In practice only about 75 per cent. of the available slot space is utilized making the phase spread for a single-phase winding about 135 electrical degrees.

The fact that, in polyphase machines, the whole of the armature surface is available for the winding, while only a portion is utilized in a single-phase alternator, accounts for the fact that the output of the latter is less than that of the polyphase machine using the same size of frame. In a three-phase machine it is only necessary to omit one of the phase windings entirely and connect the two remaining phases in series to obtain a single-phase generator. Such a modified generator will give about two-thirds of the output of the polyphase connection. A three-phase star connected induction motor can also be used as a single-phase motor by properly connecting two phases of it (see Chapter XI).

Two-phase from Four-phase Windings.—In many cases the two-phase induction motor is designed as a four-phase machine with the connections between conductors of the winding arranged so as to permit operation on a two-phase supply circuit. As shown in Fig. 23, a two-phase winding maybe secured from a four-phase grouping of coils by connecting the first and third groups in series and the second and fourth groups in series.

Three-phase from Six-phase Windings.—Few strictly three-phase induction motors are built. The design may be more properly called a six-phase winding with the three phases spaced 120 electrical degrees and the connections of coils such as to permit the motor to be operated on a three-phase circuit. As shown in Fig. 24 in a six-phase winding the coils of the six-phases are spaced 60 electrical degrees. For three-phase operation the coils of phases one and four, three and six, and five and two are connected in series. The terminals of phases two, four and six are connected to a common point.

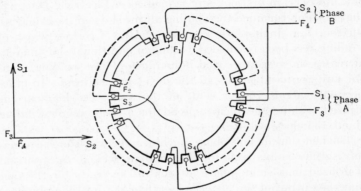

FIG. 23.—Connections for four windings spaced 90 electrical degrees apart to secure a 2-phase motor. There are really four phases shown, the first and third and the second and fourth are connected in series. The full lines are front connections of coils and dotted lines the back connections. S and F indicate the start and finish of the different groups of coils.

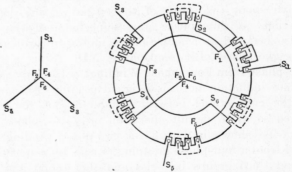

FIG. 24.—Connections for a 6-phase winding design so that a 3-phase winding is secured. The six windings are spaced 60 electrical degrees apart. In this diagram phases one and four, three and six, and five and two are connected in series and the terminals F_2, F_4 and F_6 jointed to a common point. The 3-phase leads are S_1, S_3, and S_5. The full lines indicate front connections and dotted lines back connections. S and F indicate the start and finish of the different groups of coils.

Wire, Strap and Bar Wound Coils.—For the coils used in small motors round insulated wire is most employed. These coils are either wound in the slots by hand or assembled by use of specially formed coils wound in forms and insulated before being placed in the slots. Such formed coils are usually used except in cases where the slots are closed or nearly closed. For further information on formed coils see page 4, Chapter I, and page 141, Chapter VI.

For large motors and generators where the amperes to be carried in each armature circuit is a large value, copper straps are frequently employed for making up the armature coils. In very large machines a copper bar is used instead of the copper straps. In such a case one bar serves as the inductor of a coil having one turn per slot. A two-layer bar winding made up of two bars per coil and four bars per slot is also used. The copper bars are connected to the end connections of the coils by brazing, welding or bolting. In all cases, whatever the construction of the coil used, the slots must be properly insulated with fullerboard, mica, fish paper or other suitable insulating material. For data on slot insulation see Chapter VII.

The current density in alternating-current windings is about 2500 amp. per square inch of armature conductor in small machines, 2000 amp. in medium sizes and 1500 amp. in high-voltage designs. Except in high-speed machines it is not safe to use the maximum limit owing to damage to windings from over heating.

METHODS FOR LAYING OUT AND CONNECTING ALTERNATING-CURRENT WINDINGS

In rewinding an alternating-current machine, the number of slots on the stator, the operating voltage, speed, phase and frequency of the supply circuit are points that must be considered in laying out a new winding or reconnecting an existing one. The fundamental requirements of windings and the ways in which they can be fulfilled as outlined by M. W. Bartmess (*Electric Journal*, Vol. VIII, No. 5) are given in what follows.

Group Windings.—Group winding may be defined as that class wherein the total winding is divided into separate parts, composed of adjacent coils or conductors. The grouping is, in the case of lap and wave windings, an arbitrary one, the coils being all similar and divided into groups solely by their connections. The number of coils per group may equal the number per pair of poles divided by the number of phases, or the number per pole divided by the number phases. The latter method of grouping is generally used on modern machines. In the case of a six-pole, three-phase winding of 36 slots, the number of coils per group is $36 \div (6 \times 3)$ or 2. When the number of slots is not evenly divisible by the product of poles

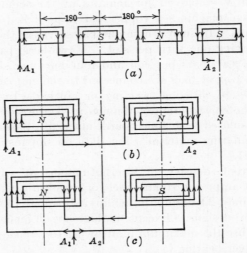

FIG. 25.—Methods of connecting pole-phase groups shown in (*a*), (*b*) and (*c*).

(*a*) Four-pole winding with alternately positive and negative pole-phase groups. (*b*) Four-pole winding of the consequent pole type. (*c*) Two-pole winding obtained from (*b*) by reconnecting the pole-phase groups alternately positive and negative.

and phases, dissimilar groups must be employed. In such cases it is advisable to arrange the grouping so that all the phases have an equal number of coils, and if possible the grouping should be arranged symmetrically with respect to the core itself. To prevent local currents, which may prove injurious, all circuits which are in parallel must have an equal number of coils and should be symmetrically arranged with respect to each other and to the other phases.

Although one turn coils only are shown in Figs. 27 to 29, the same connections are applicable to windings having any number of conductors per coil. These conductors may all be in series, in which case there is one lead at each end of the coil or the conductors may be divided into any number of equal parallels, in which case there are as many leads at the ends of the coils as there are parallel circuits. The leads at the beginning and end of the coils are connected in the same manner as indicated for the one turn per coil winding. For the sake of simplicity the number of coils per group and hence the total number of coils in the diagrams has been kept lower than is generally found in commercial machines.

Full and Fractional Pitch Windings.—The number of slots in the core, divided by the number of poles gives a value of the pole arc expressed in terms of the slots. A full pitch winding is one in which the effective span of the coils is equal to the pole arc, and a fractional pitch winding is one in which the effective span of the coils is not equal to the pole arc. For a two coil per slot, lap or wave winding, the effective span of the coil is equal to the actual span of the coil. In this case the full pitch winding is one where the coil throw is equal to $\left(\dfrac{\text{total number of slots}}{\text{number of poles}} \text{ plus } 1\right)$. For a one coil per slot lap winding the effective span of the coil may be greater or less than its actual span. In Fig. 26 (a) and (b) show two different coils, in each of which the effective span is the full pitch of 12 slots while the actual span in (a) is only 11 slots and that in (b) is 13 slots. Needless to say, (a) is more generally used on account of the saving in copper and space for end connections. A coil with a span either less or greater than that shown would result in a fractional pitch, as in (c) and (d).

Representative cases of concentric group windings are shown in Fig. 26, (e) and (f), (e) representing a three-bank winding, in which the number of coils per group equals the total number of coils per phase divided by the number of poles, while (f) represents a two-bank winding of the consequent pole type in which the number of coils per group equals the total number of coils per phase divided by the number of pairs of poles. Neither of these types can be conveniently wound with a fractional pitch, especially with formed coils. Where dissimilar groups are employed, that is where the number of slots is not evenly divisible by the product of phases and poles, the full pitch is frequently not a unit and hence a fractional pitch is necessary. In the case of a three-phase, four pole winding with 30 slots, 30 coils, two coils per slot, full pitch covers a span of 7.5 slots and the nearest lower even pitch gives a throw of 1–8.

In general, fractional pitch affects the performance of the apparatus similarly to a reduced number of turns in the wind-

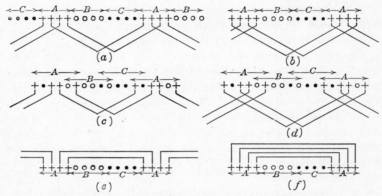

Fig. 26.—Possible pitch for one coil per slot windings.

(a) Full pitch, effective space 12, actual space 11, throw 1 to 12. (b) Full pitch, effective space 12, actual space 13, throw 1 to 14. (c) Fractional pitch, effective space 10, actual space 9, throw 1 to 10. (d) Fractional pitch, effective space 10, actual space 15, throw 1 to 16. (e) Concentric group, full pitch, effective space 12, actual space 9 and 11, throw 1 to 11. (f) Concentric group, full pitch, consequent poles, effective space 12, actual space 9, 11, 13, and 15, throw 1 to 13.

ing, but not in the same proportion. In a generator this reduces the voltage of the machine. In an induction motor, the maximum available torque is increased but the densities in the magnetic circuit are also increased with a resulting reduction of power-factor. For either motor or generator, considerable copper may thus be saved in the coil ends and a standard frame may frequently be used for special purposes.

Simple Winding Diagram.—It is evident that for all combinations the number of diagrams necessary would be unlimited. A simplified diagram may be employed which will not only reduce the required number of such diagrams but will also

minimize the labor in tracing out the connections. Thus it will
be seen that the diagram in Fig. 27, will satisfy many requirements for connections of groups. In addition to this it will
apply for any similarly connected three-phase, four-pole, series
star lap-winding, irrespective of the number of coils per
group (provided the groups are regular) or of the throw of the
coils, that is, whether the winding is full or fractional pitch.
This information for the throw of the coils and the number of
coils per group may be carried
on the same specification with
the remaining winding constants. The groups are formed
by connecting the required number of coils together, the end of
the first coil to the beginning of
the second, etc., the beginning
of the first coil and the end of
the last coil in the group forming
the beginning and end of the
group. Such diagrams may be
made for any number of phases,
poles or possible parallel circuits,
and for any desired method of
connection of the groups. In

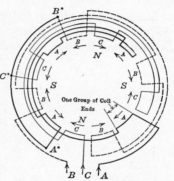

Fig. 27.—General winding diagram for a 3-phase, 4-pole motor
with pole-phase groups connected
in series star.

case the coils per group are irregular or unbalanced, it is advisable to have a special diagram giving the number of coils in each
group, their location and any other information necessary.

Reconnecting a Winding.—It is obvious that if a winding
gives satisfactory operation on a certain voltage, a similar
winding of one-half the number of series conductors, but of
double the current carrying capacity, will give satisfactory
operation on one-half the voltage. This latter condition may
be obtained by paralleling the groups, as in Figs. 28 and 29, or
where this is impossible by paralleling the series conductors in
the slots. For example, if the full voltage connection of a
14-pole motor corresponds to the parallel connection the only
method to change to half voltage would be to change the winding itself since 14 poles does not permit of a four-parallel
connection. Again an irregularity of coils per group will at

times prevent doubling the parallel circuits where otherwise this might be possible.

When it is desired to use one winding for either full or half voltage, the winding, if possible, is laid out for equally satisfactory operation on either connection, and for the minimum amount of labor required to connect from one to the other. This is exemplified by Figs. 28 and 29. It is evident that any eccentricity of the rotor with respect to the stator will affect equally the circuits which are in parallel.

Simple Method for Indicating Polarity of Coil Groups.— A simple method for obtaining the proper polarity of the groups is indicated in Figs. 27 and 28 for three-phase and Fig. 29

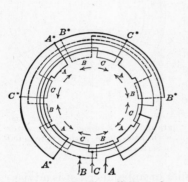

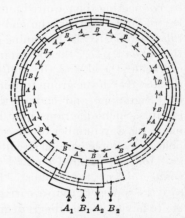

Fig. 28.—Winding diagram for a 3-phase, 4-pole motor with pole-phase groups connected in 2-parallel star. This is the winding of Fig. 27 connected in parallel.

Fig. 29.—Winding diagram for a 2-phase, 14-pole motor with pole-phase groups connected in 2 parallels.

for two-phase winding. In a three-phase star winding by traveling from each of the three leads to the star points, the direction of travel is reversed in adjacent groups. In a two-phase diagram the only necessary precaution in determining the proper polarity is to remember that adjacent groups of the same phase are reversed. By marking the groups A, B, C, etc., and indicating the direction of travel, it is a simple matter to connect them in the proper direction. Additional index marks may be given on the diagram to aid in connecting the winding, by marking those group ends which are joined by the same connector, with the same numeral. For further details in using this method see Chapter XI.

Changing Star to Delta Connection.—Any star diagram can be readily changed into a corresponding delta diagram by opening up the star points and connecting the inner end of phase *A* to the outer end of phase *B* or *C*, the inner end of phase *B* to the outer end of phase *C* or *A*, and the inner end of phase *C* to the outer end of phase *A* or *B*. If the star diagram is not symmetrical with respect to the three phases it is never advisable to change over to delta.

A.-C. Wave Windings.—In a wave winding, correspondingly placed conductors under adjacent poles are connected in series, the circuit proceeding from pole to pole one or more times around the core, and not forward and back upon itself as in a lap winding. The circuits are then interconnected in such a manner as to give the requisite phase relations. The total number of these circuits must be a multiple of the number of phases and is ordinarily twice the number of phases. Due to certain limitations, this type of winding is not used to as great an extent as the lap or the concentric windings. Its use on small motors is limited to phase-wound secondaries. Since a two-phase secondary would require four collector rings, or if connected for a three-wire system, would overload one of the rings, while a three-phase winding requires but three rings, the latter only is general for such applications.

Progressive and Retrogressive A.-C. Wave Windings.—The number of slots for a wave winding (plus or minus one) is so chosen as to be divisible by the number of pairs of poles or preferably by the number of poles. If plus one, it is said to be a *progressive winding*, since after traveling once around the circuit it returns to the starting slot plus one. If minus one, it is said to be *retrogressive* since the circuit returns the winding to the starting slot minus one. With this arrangement it is impossible to balance the phases exactly, but the effective unbalancing is small with a large number of slots. Since an unbalanced three-phase winding is less objectionable than a two-phase winding, the scheme is used chiefly for the former. Again, since an unbalanced winding is less detrimental in a secondary circuit than in a primary, the principal application of this type of winding has been in secondary circuits.

The diagram of Fig. 30 represents a two conductor per slot winding, such as a bar and end conductor type but is equally applicable to strap or wire wound coils of two or more series turns per coil, in which case the connector on the rear end of the coil takes care of itself and the front end is connected in a manner similar to the sketch. There are several methods of connecting up the three-phases depending on the desired voltage. The principal connection is indicated in Fig. 30. By connecting the end of each series circuit to the beginning of the next and taking off leads to the point of connection of series 1–2, 3–4, 5–6, instead of the connections between the series shown in Fig. 30, a connection is obtained for one-half voltage. An 86 per cent. voltage tap in terms of the connections shown in Fig. 30 is secured by connecting the end of series 2 to the beginning of series 3, the end of series 4 to the beginning of series 5, the end of series 6 to the beginning of series 1. To connect in star join the ends of series 1, series 3, and series 5, and take off leads at the beginning series 6, series 2, and series 4. Since this connection reduces the voltage without increasing the cross section of the copper the winding will be less efficient on account of higher copper loss for the same output. This is also true of the 50 per cent. voltage connection, since for the output the current density in the windings is 15 per cent. greater than for the full voltage connection.

It is possible, by choosing a number of slots which is divisible

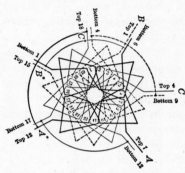

FIG. 30.—Wave winding for a 3-phase, 4-pole motor, having 19 slots, 19 coils, two coils per slot, throw 1 to 6, with unbalanced phases connected in series star.

First series begins in bottom slot 6, ends in top slot 12. Second series begins bottom slot 17, ends top slot 4. Third series begins bottom slot 9, ends top slot 15, Fourth series begins bottom slot 1, ends top slot 7. Fifth series begins bottom slot 12, ends top slot 18. Sixth series begins bottom slot 4, ends top slot 1.

by the product of the number of phases by the number of poles, to lay out a winding which is balanced. For such a winding the circuit after passing once around the armature, returns to the starting slot. It is then only necessary to supply a special connector to join it to the conductor in the starting slot plus or minus one. This winding thus embodies the best features of both types as, for example, an electrical balance, and a minimum number of special connections, which means a very compact and easily assembled winding. The number of special connections is comparatively small with respect to the number of coils, and this feature is more pronounced as the number of poles is increased. Hence for a winding for a large number of poles, 12 to 40, the number of special connections becomes insignificant.

Connections for Coils of Polyphase Windings.[1]—A two-phase winding for a four-pole alternator is shown in the simplest possible form, as a radial diagram, in Fig. 31. It is a concentrated wave winding, having one slot per pole per phase, full pitch. Each phase has one element of winding, or one slot, under each pole, and the elements of phase *B* are distant from the corresponding elements of phase *A* by exactly 90 electrical degrees. The whole winding is thus divided into two exactly similar halves, electrically distinct from each other, just like

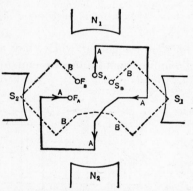

FIG. 31.—Radial diagram of a 2-phase winding for a 4-pole machine.

two single phases, their positions being relatively fixed so that S_a passes under middle N_1 just one-quarter period after (or before, depending on direction of rotation) S_b passes the same point. They are thus tied

[1] The following descriptions and illustrations of windings, pages 43 to 51, have been taken by permission from Alternating-Current Electricity by W. H. Timble and H. H. Higbie (John Wiley & Sons, Inc., New York, N. Y.).

together in phase relation through the magnetic field and
the mechanical distribution of the winding. The slip rings
of phase A would be connected to S_a and F_a, and the rings
of phase B to S_b and F_b.

A three-phase winding for a four-pole machine is shown in

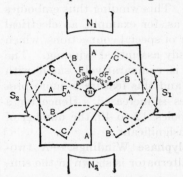

Figs. 32 to 34. The winding
is the simplest practicable one
to make, occupying only one
slot per pole per phase. This
winding is laid out as follows:
First, make sure that the total
number of slots is divisible by
3 (phases) and 4 (poles). Then,
holding the rotor stationary,
mark one element (or slot)
under the middle of each pole
as belonging to phase A, and
connect them properly to-
gether in series so that their

FIG. 32.—Radial diagram of a
3-phase winding for a 4-pole machine, star-connected.

emfs add together when they are in the position where the
maximum instantaneous emf for the whole group is induced
(as shown in Fig. 32). Mark one end of this series S_a as in

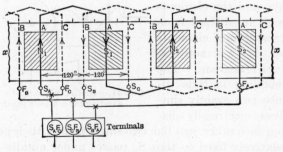

FIG. 33.—Developed diagram of the 3-phase winding of Fig. 32, delta-
connected.

Fig. 32, and the other end F_a. With the rotor still fixed in
the same position and starting from S_a, proceed to count the
slots or coils in one direction around the armature until two-
thirds of those which lie between the middle of adjacent

poles have been passed. Since the distance between the middle of adjacent poles is 180 electrical degrees, the distance passed over is 120 electrical degrees. Label this slot, element or coil S_b and locate the other three B elements or coils with respect to each other, exactly as the A elements are related to each other. Connect the B group in additive series exactly as the A group was connected, and mark F_b on the finishing end of the B series. Now from S_b continue to count slots or coils around in the same direction until you have passed as far ahead of S_b as S_b is ahead of S_a. This will be 120 electrical degrees from S_b or 240 electrical degrees from S_a. Mark this slot or coil S_c, and locate the other C slots or coils in similar positions with respect to all other poles. Connect the C slots together in additive series just as the A slots were connected, and put the F_c label on the finishing end of the series. If the emf. in phase A is at its maximum value from S_a to F_a at the position shown in Figs. 32 and 33, it is apparent that the emf S_a to F_a must pass through one-third cycle or 120 electrical degrees before the emf. from S_b to F_b reaches its maximum value (or is brought into the same position in the magnetic field by a counter-clockwise rotation of the rotor). Also, the emf from S_a to F_a must pass through $\frac{2}{3}$ cycle or 240 electrical degrees before the emf from S_c to F_c reaches its maximum value. Since these three emfs reach their maximum value in a direction away from S just 120 electrical degrees apart, consecutively, the S ends must be connected together to neutral, to get a star-connection. The terminals of the three-phase armature thus connected in star are F_a, F_b, F_c, as shown in Fig. 32.

A developed view of this same winding (three-phase, four-pole, one slot per pole per phase) is shown in Fig. 33, connected in delta or mesh. Notice that if only that end of each phase is marked which is separated by 120 electrical degrees from the similar end of the preceding phase, the connection becomes very simple, because we merely connect the finishing end of one phase to the starting end of the next phase 120 degrees ahead, and so on. Thus connect F_a to S_b, F_b to S_c and F_c to S_a. These junction points are then the terminals of the delta winding. The equal emfs $(S_a$ to $F_a)$, $(S_b$ to $F_b)$,

(S_c to F_c) are 120 electrical degrees apart successively in the same direction through the closed mesh or series. This relation gives a resultant emf of zero volts around the mesh.

If the winding is to occupy two slots per pole per phase, requiring $3 \times 4 \times 2 = 24$ slots altogether, the connections for a two-layer lap winding are shown in Fig. 34. There are as many coils as slots, and all coils are exactly alike. Each slot contains two coil-sides (Fig. 35). The one at the bottom is the right-hand side of a coil lying to the left of the slot, and the one at the top is the left-hand side of a coil lying to the right of the slot. The elements at the bottom of the slot are shown in dotted lines.

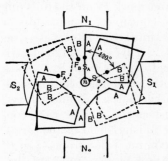

Fig. 34.—Three-phase winding having two slots per pole per phase. Two phases only are shown.

Such an arrangement of coils is typical of all lap-wound direct-current machines, and synchronous converters; but it may be used for any sort of an alternating-current winding, closed or open. If the similar end of every coil at its starting end is labeled S, and the other end F (as it is wound up on a form, for instance), then a closed winding is obtained by simply soldering the F of one coil to the S of the one lying in the next slot, and so on all around the armature until the last F is soldered to the first S. This closed winding could be tapped at equidistant points, depending on the number of poles. Or this closed winding could be opened up at two or more points and the parts connected in series as an open winding for any number of phases. The winding of Fig. 35 may be recognized for a four-pole stator, because each coil spans one-quarter of the circumference. To get the greater emf in a coil, its opposite sides should both come as nearly as possible simultaneously under the middle of adjacent poles. There are 24 coils altogether, for three phases and four poles, which allows two coils per pole per phase. These two will, of course, be adjacent coils, in order that their emfs shall be as nearly as possible in phase with each other so as to get the greatest possible resultant emf. from the series.

Double-layer Winding, Lap Connected.—In connecting a winding such as shown in Fig. 35, choose a coil located exactly under the middle of N_1 and S_1, and label it A_1. Mark its starting end S_a. Connect the finish end of coil A_1 to the starting end of coil A_2 which is adjacent to coil A_1. Now

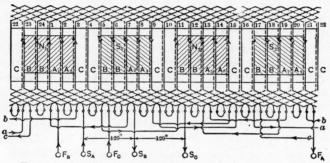

FIG. 35.—Two layer winding for a 3-phase, 4-pole machine.

FIG. 36.—Winding of Fig. 35, delta-connected.

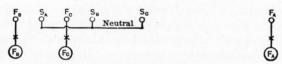

FIG. 37.—Winding of Fig. 35, star-connected.

locate coils A_3 and A_4, also belonging properly to phase A, because they are located with relation to pole S_1 and N_2 just exactly as coils A_1 and A_2 are located with relation to pole N_1 and S_1. Similarly, locate A_5 and A_6 under poles N_2 and S_2, and A_7 and A_8 under poles S_2 and N_1. Then group A_3 and A_4 in additive series by soldering the finish of A_3 to the start of A_4. Similarly, connect A_5 and A_6 together, and A_7 and A_8 together. Now, since the emf is clockwise around coils A_1 and A_2, counter-clockwise around coils A_3 and A_4, clockwise around A_5 and A_6, and counter-clockwise around A_7 and A_8, it will be seen, that in order to get these groups of coils together into additive series A_1, A_2, A_5 and A_6 must be connected together similarly but A_3, A_4, A_7 and A_8 oppositely. If the series of coils composing phase A are carefully traced starting at S_a and going right through to F_a, it will be seen that the instantaneous emfs are all in the same direction at about the same time when the emfs induced in the coils of phase A are greatest (which is about the position shown in the diagram).

Phase B has been started at one end, S_b (similar to the end S_a), of a coil located 120 electrical degrees from coil A_1, and from this point through to F_b the connections and arrangement of coils are an exact duplicate of phase A, except as to actual position in the magnetic field.   Likewise phase C is a duplicate of phase A_1, but S_c is located 120 degrees further along in the same direction from S_b, or 240 degrees from S_a.   This gives the six terminals of the three phases all properly labeled.   In Fig. 36 are shown the proper connections between these six terminals to give a three-phase delta.   In Fig. 37 are shown the connections between the same six terminals to give a three-phase star.

Connecting a Chain Winding.—The chain winding has been sometimes used by makers for alternating-current generators, in addition to the two-layer windings.   Fig. 38 represents a three-phase four-pole chain winding, using two slots per pole per phase on the same 24-slot armature which we have been using throughout for illustration.   In order not to confuse the diagram, phases A, B and C have been drawn out separately, in Figs. 38, 39 and 40.   Notice that they are exactly alike, except as to relative position on the armature.   Phase B is 120 electrical degrees from phase A, and phase C is 120 electrical degrees further in the same direction, from phase B, or 240 electrical degrees from phase A, the positive direction of emf in each phase being from the S end to the F end. When the three phases are assembled altogether as in Fig. 41, it is seen that there must be a different shape or length of coil for each phase in order that the ends of the coils shall not interfere with each other.   This is expressed usually by saying that the end-bends of the coils are in three ranges. This is due to the fact that the winding is a single-layer winding (the

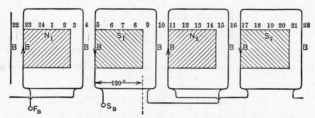

Fig. 38.—Phase A of a 3-phase chain winding. Two slots per pole per phase.

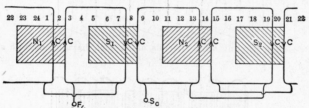

Fig. 39.—Phase B of the 3-phase chain winding of Fig. 38.

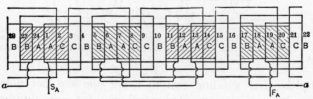

Fig. 40.—Phase C of the 3-phase chain winding of Fig. 38.

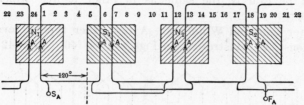

Fig. 41.—Three-phase chain winding for which the separate phases are shown in Figs. 38, 39 and 40. End connections of phase A only are shown. Three forms of coils are necessary.

coils of a two-layer winding are all exactly alike), and also because all coils in each phase have been made the same shape.

4

In Fig. 41 the end-connections between coils are shown only for phase A, to avoid confusion. The system of connections would be exactly the same as in other figures which are complete

Other Common Windings.—A few other typical forms of windings are illustrated in Figs. 42 to 46. Fig. 42 is a

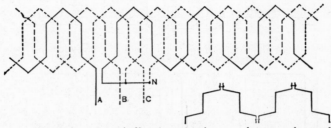

Fig. 42.—Three-phase bar winding (wave) using one slot per pole per phase, star-connected.

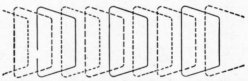

Fig. 43.—Skew winding with all coils alike, each having one side shorter than the other.

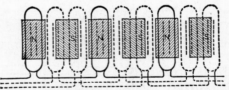

Fig. 44.—Short-coil winding with each coil only two-thirds of the pole pitch. The emf's of the two sides do not add to such good advantage as in other types.

three-phase bar winding (wave) using one slot per pole per phase. It may be extended as shown for any number of pairs of poles and is drawn star-connected. Fig. 43 is known as a "skew-coil" winding; although there is only one coil-side in each slot, all coils are of the same shape for all phases. Conflicts of the coil-ends are avoided by making one side of each coil longer than the other side. Fig. 44 illustrates what is called a "short-coil winding" for a three-phase machine using two slots per pole per phase. By making the breadth of each coil only $\frac{2}{3}$ of the pole pitch, overlapping of coils is altogether avoided, and all coils in the entire winding are exactly alike. The series emfs composing each phase are not added to as good advantage as in other types of winding using coils nearer full-pitch, and, therefore, more copper would

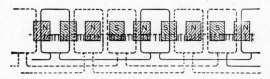

FIG. 45.—Creeping winding in which coils have a fractional pitch. Three coils cover four poles. The small dash lines represent slots left vacant for clearness.

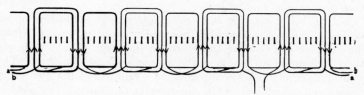

FIG. 46.—Single-phase, whole-coiled winding for 8 poles using 3 slots per pole. Armature has 64 slots.

be needed for the same capacity. The wave-form is also likely to be more peaked. Fig. 45 shows a "creeping winding" in which the coils are of fractional pitch and the series of coils in each phase are arranged so as to gain or lose one or more poles around the armature. In Fig. 45 three adjacent coils each spanning 240 electrical degrees, together cover 720 degrees or four poles. Fig. 46 shows a single-phase whole-coiled winding for eight poles, using three slots per pole, for an armature having altogether 64 slots.

Easily Remembered Rules for Arrangement of Coils in an Induction Motor.—The following are rules that can be easily remembered and cover conditions frequently encountered in laying out alternating-current windings.

1. Number of coils per pole-phase-group = No. slots ÷ (No. poles × No. phases).

2. When the number of slots is not evenly divisible by the number of poles times the number of phases, dissimilar groups must be employed. These groups should be arranged so that all the phases have an equal number of coils. The grouping should also be symmetrical, with respect to the core.

3. A full pitch winding is one in which the span of a coil equals the number of slots divided by the number of poles. That is in a 36 slot, six-pole, three-phase winding, $36 \div 6 = 6$ slots or the arc of the stator covered by one pole. A coil with a span of 6 slots makes the winding a full pitch winding. When the coil span is less than this, the winding is known as a fractional pitch winding.

4. If a particular winding has given satisfaction on any particular voltage, a similar winding of one-half the number of series conductors but of double the current-carrying capacity will also give satisfaction on one-half the voltage. This latter condition can usually be obtained by paralleling the groups of coils. Or when a machine has two windings connected in series, say for 440 volts, they can be connected in parallel for 220 volts.

5. In a wave winding, correspondingly placed conductors under adjacent poles are connected in series, and the circuit proceeds from pole to pole one or more times around the core. The circuits are then interconnected to give the requisite phase relations. The total number of these circuits must be a multiple of the number of phases and is ordinarily twice the number of phases. The number of slots for this winding (plus or minus one) should be divisible by the number of pairs of poles or preferably by the number of poles. If plus one, the winding is progressive, since after traveling once around the circuit it return to the starting slot plus one. If minus one, it is said to be retrogressive since the circuit returns the winding to the starting slot minus one. To have a balanced wave winding, the number of slots must be divisible by the product of the number of poles and phases. This winding returns to the starting slot after going once around the core and special connectors must be used to connect the finish end to the conductor in the starting slot plus or minus one.

Simple Rule for Checking Proper Phase Relationship in a Two- or Three-phase Winding.—A fundamental consideration when checking the instantaneous flow of current in a three-phase circuit, is to imagine that when the current flows in the same direction in two legs of the circuit, it flows in the opposite direction in the third leg. This principle can be applied to both motors and generators. When this scheme is applied to an alternating-current winding in checking the connections of the coils a great deal of experience is required

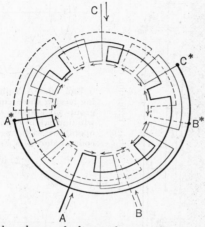

Fig. 47.—Simple scheme of alternately reversing arrows of pole-phase groups to check correct phase polarity of a 3-phase winding. It is supposed in this case that current flows in the three leads toward the star points of the winding which are indicated thus (*).

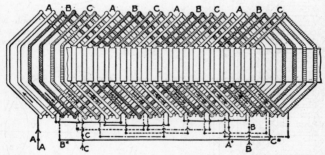

Fig. 48.—Developed winding diagram for a 4-pole induction motor showing series-star connected end connections.

This winding shows the groups of phase coils marked *A*, *B*, *C* with arrows pointing in opposite directions on adjacent pole-phase groups. It is another way of showing the connections illustrated in Fig. 47.

in order to make sure that the leads of the three-phases of the motor are brought out at an electrical angle of 120 degrees apart. This is usually a separation of two poles.

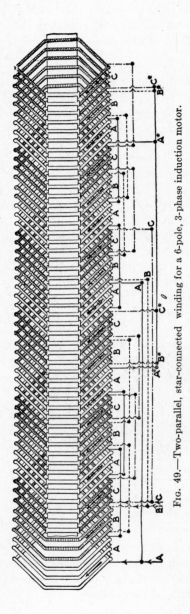

FIG. 49.—Two-parallel, star-connected winding for a 6-pole, 3-phase induction motor.

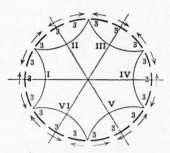

FIG. 50.—A 3-phase, 6-pole winding having three coils per pole-phase group on a stator of 54 slots. This winding can be connected for 2-phase operation with an odd grouping of coils as shown in Fig. 51.

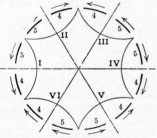

FIG. 51.—A 2-phase, 6-pole winding on a stator of 54 slots. The 3-phase, 6-pole winding is shown in Fig. 50.

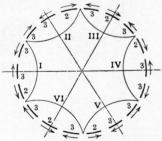

FIG. 52.—A 3-phase, 6-pole winding showing the arrangement of odd groups of coils. The groups of two coils are located diagonally opposite each other. The small arcs numbered I to VI each span one pole containing 8 coils. The stator in this case has 48 slots.

A simple and more reliable method for the repairman to use is shown in Fig. 47. In this scheme it must be supposed that current flows in all three leads of the star connection toward the point of the star connection. And that in the case of a delta connection the current flows around the three sides of the delta in the same direction. Then in either case for a three-phase winding, the polarity of each of the pole-phase-groups will alternate regularly around the winding and can be indicated by arrows as in Fig. 47. As shown, for a three-phase winding there will be three times as many pole-phase-groups as there are poles. By the use of this scheme there is no chance for a reversal of a phase to be passed by not noticed when checking the winding.

In adopting this scheme for a two-phase winding it need only be remembered that both groups of coils in each phase must reverse alternately, that is, they should be so indicated on the diagram by arrows, as shown in Fig. 29, page 40.

By marking each of the pole-phase groups on a diagram, *A, B, C*, to indicate a complete phase-group, and placing the arrows on each single group as shown in Fig. 47, the armature winder will have little trouble in understanding the diagram and making the proper connections. To make it still easier, the group ends that are to be joined by the same connector can be marked on the diagram with the same number.

The use of this method for regrouping coils of a three-phase winding for operation on a two-phase circuit and for any odd grouping of coils is shown in Figs. 50 to 52.

CHAPTER III

REPAIR SHOP METHODS FOR REWINDING DIRECT-CURRENT ARMATURES

Dismantling a D.-C. Armature.—When an armature is to be entirely rewound, it must be stripped and reinsulated throughout. First remove the wedges in the slots when banding wires are not used. If there are banding wires, remove them by filing in two parts. When using a hammer and chisel in cutting banding wires be careful not to mash the armature teeth out of shape. Now look over the connections to the commutator and the end connections of the coils to determine whether a lap or a wave winding was used. In a lap winding with formed coils, the start and finish terminals are connected to adjacent commutator bars while in the wave winding the terminals of any coil are a considerable distance apart around the commutator. This distance is approximately equal to the number of commutator bars divided by one-half the number of poles. Also in a lap winding the end connections of the coils at both ends of the armature bend toward the center of the coil or in the same direction, while in a wave winding they bend in opposite directions.

The wave winding usually has either two or four sets of brushes. Two sets of brushes only are needed regardless of the number of poles in the machine since there are only two current paths in parallel through the armature winding (see Fig. 13). In the lap winding there are as many paths for the current as there are poles in the machine (see Fig. 10) and there are usually as many sets of brushes as there are poles. Simply because there are only two brush holders on a multi-polar machine, however, does not always mean that a wave winding is used. The commutators of some few lap-wound machines have internal cross-connections so that the commutator bars of the same potential are joined together.

56

This permits the use of only two sets of brushes. In such a case an extra long commutator is used which will serve as an indication of such connections.

Winding Data Needed for the Dismantled Armature.— After having made an inspection of the winding, enter the following data in a note book:

1. Number of armature slots.
2. Number of coil sides per slot.
3. Number of commutator bars—when there are two coil sides per slot, the number of bars will equal the number of armature slots in both lap and wave windings.
4. Coil throw in slots.
5. Commutator pitch.
6. Number of turns per coil and size of wire used.

A convenient chart and diagram for recording these data are shown in Figs. 53 and 54 as used by a large manufacturer. In case new coils must be ordered, this is the information that the manufacturer needs. It is a good plan to have a note book with duplicate printed pages so that the record made on the first page can be transferred to the next by a piece of typewriter carbon paper. The first sheet can then be given to the armature winder and the copy kept in the book as an office record for use in case the winder destroys his copy, for use in making up a bill for the job and for reference in case further repairs should be later needed on the same machine. Such a record of repairs often helps in the location of new trouble in a repaired machine.

Removing the Old Coils.—The next operation is to unsolder the leads from the commutator, and proceed to remove the coils. This can be done usually by raising the top sides of the coils for a distance of the coil throw, when the bottom side of a coil can be reached and the others taken out one after the other. In removing the coils, try and preserve one in its original shape, to use as a guide for winding new ones. Enter in the note book the number of turns per coil, and with a wire gauge determine the size of wire. Also note whether the wire is single or double cotton covered. If the commutator contains twice as many bars as there are slots on the armature, then each armature coil will contain two coils taped together. Some armatures, especially those designed for low speed, may contain three or even four times as many bars as slots. By

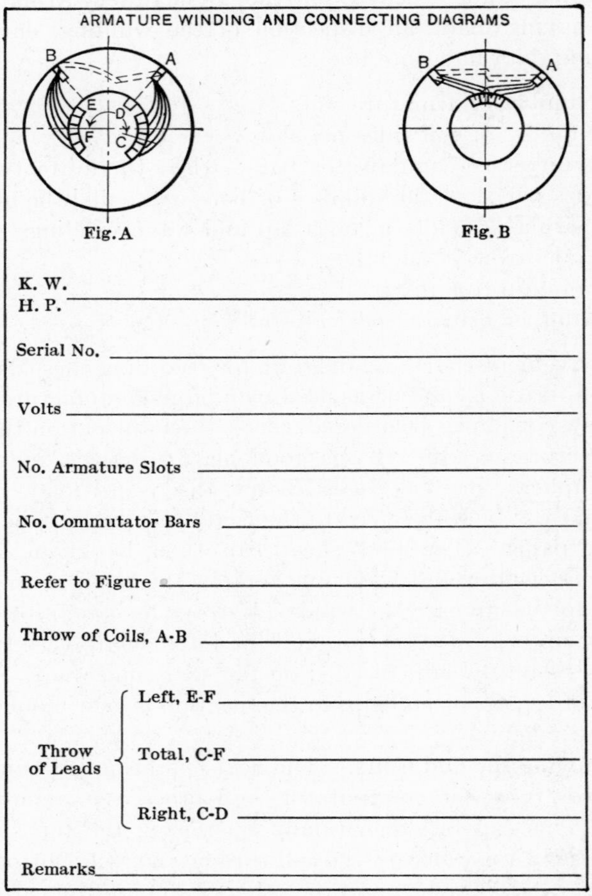
ARMATURE WINDING AND CONNECTING DIAGRAMS

K. W.
H. P. ______

Serial No. ______

Volts ______

No. Armature Slots ______

No. Commutator Bars ______

Refer to Figure ______

Throw of Coils, A-B ______

Throw of Leads:
- Left, E-F ______
- Total, C-F ______
- Right, C-D ______

Remarks ______

FIG. 53.—Convenient form for use in recording winding data when new coils must be ordered from the manufacturer.

this construction, the inductance and the current per coil is kept low, and the voltage between bars reduced.

When the armature has been stripped, all old insulation should be removed from the slots by scraping and burning with

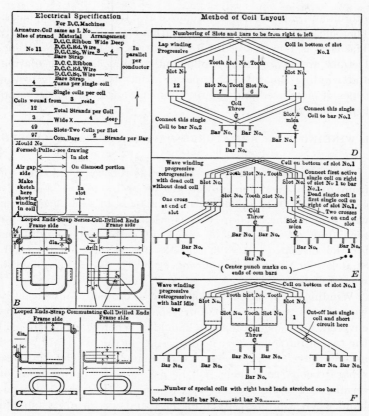

Fig. 54.—Diagrams for recording coil throw and commutator throw when stripping an armature or when ordering new coils.

These diagrams are useful for checking up a wave winding that must duplicate the original one. In this case center punch marks are made on the commutator bars and slots to indicate the coil throw and commutator connections of one of the orignal coils as indicated in section (*E*) of the illustration. Here two punch marks indicate terminal for coil side in bottom of slot and one punch mark for the terminal of the coil side in the top of the slot. Two crosses ($\times\times$) indicates the slot in which the coil side is at the bottom and one cross ($\times$) the slot in which it is at the top. When the center line of the coil is marked on the drawing to show whether it falls on a commutator bar or a mica, the commutator can be removed and replaced to line up with the original markings. For other details of determining the commutator throw, especially with dead coils, see "Practical Method for Locating First Connection to Commutator for a Wave Winding" on page 105. Section (D) of the above illustration shows the use of the diagram for marking the coil throw of a lap winding. Section (A) is filled out to indicate its use in specifying new coils for a wave winding.

a torch and each slot filed to remove any burrs or rough places. Then clean the core thoroughly with a blast of compressed air. The core is now ready for its insulation and a new winding. Details are given in the following paragraphs for insulating and winding the different types of armatures according to the types of slots used and the requirements of different sizes and types of machines.

I. WINDING D.-C. ARMATURES HAVING PARTIALLY CLOSED SLOTS

Direct-current motors of the industrial type in sizes of from one to five horsepower are often built with partially closed slots. When winding the armature of such a motor, a wire-wound, threaded-in coil is used. Practical details for rewinding an armature of this kind with recommendations for the insulation of slots and testing as outlined by G. I. Stadeker in the *Electric Journal*, Vol. VII, No. 7, are given in what follows:

Winding a Threaded-in Coil.—Each complete coil is usually wound with from one to four separate wires double cotton covered, on a special form or mould. When winding the coil the two or more wires are held together in the hand and wound as one wire. Such a coil is then made up of two or more separate coils, and there will be as many beginning ends or terminals and finish ends to the coil as there are wires-in-hand when winding. Each of these ends or terminals should be provided with an extra insulation in the form of woven cotton sleeves. As an aid when connecting the terminals to the commutator, sleeves of different colors should be used. For a coil wound with three wires, black, white and red sleeves can be used. The same color of sleeve must be used on the start and finish ends of each of the wires used in winding the coil. To make sure of this, two sleeves of the same color should be slipped over each wire before beginning to wind the coil. When starting to wind the coil, one set of the cotton sleeves should be slipped down to the end of each wire and adjusted to reach about three-quarters of an inch along the body or slot side of the coil. The other set of cotton sleeves can be slipped back along the wires as the coil is being wound.

Then fasten the ends of the wires on the form or mould. As the spindle on which the winding form is mounted is revolved slowly, the winder can guide the wires into the mould, placing strips of tape under them at the corners when the first turn is applied. The wires should be kept under some tension to make them conform closely to the shape of the mould or form. On the last turn another sleeve should be slipped down each wire and allowed to extend along the body of the coil a sufficient distance to be bound in place with the tape which was previously inserted. The leads can then be cut off to the proper length.

In case a coil of a large number of turns is to be wound and the cotton sleeves used do not slip easily over the wires, it may be quicker to use a test lamp to find the correct finish end on which to use the proper color of sleeve. In such a case one of the start ends of the coil can be placed on one terminal of the test lamp and each of the other finish ends tried until the lamp will light. On the two ends thus located the same color of sleeve should be used. The second pair of ends can be located in the same way.

Insulating Lining for Slots.—The slots should be insulated with an outer protective layer of fish paper (for thickness see pages 163 to 172, on "Insulation for Slots") about three-quarters of an inch longer than the slot and two inner cells of treated cloth. One of these cells should enclose the lower and the other the upper coil as shown in Fig. 55. For machines having a terminal voltage of 500 volts or over it is good practice to use a third cell of treated cloth placed next to the fish paper cell and enclosing both of the coils. This provides a better insulation of the winding from the core. These cells should be cut so that they will project about an inch beyond the slot opening to serve as a guide when the strands of the coil are being inserted in the slot.

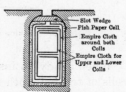

Fig. 55.—Slot insulation for a double layer winding in partially closed slots.

Inserting Coils in the Slots.—Since the slots are partially closed, all the bottom sides of the coils can be inserted in the slots before the top sides are inserted. In each case the individual strands may be forced into the slot with a flat fiber drift. As each coil is put in place the lower leads should be inserted into the slits of the proper commutator bars, care being taken that the different colored leads are connected always in the same order. (For details of connections for lap and wave windings, see Chapter "Making Connections to the Commutator," page 101).

After all the coils are in position in the bottoms of the slots, the protecting edges of the inner cell enclosing the lower coil side should be drawn up as far as the coil side will allow, then cut off close to the slot and folded in. With a fiber drift and mallet force the wires and cell into proper position in the lower half of the slot in order to make room for the upper coil side. The unprotected wires of the coil which cross the end of the core should now be taped up with cotton tape for about two-thirds of their length, starting up close to the core and enclosing the ends of the lower cells, which project from the slot.

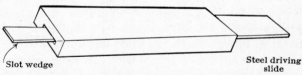

Slot wedge   Steel driving
                                                slide

FIG. 56.—Device for driving wood and fiber wedges in slots.

When ready to insert the top sides of the coils, the upper cells of treated cloth should be inserted in the slots preferably one at a time. Now face the commutator and count the throw already calculated for the winding in a counter-clockwise direction from the first slot prepared with its insulating cell, in order to determine which coil should go into this slot. The proper coil should then be bent into shape, its strands waxed and inserted into the slot. The edges of the projecting cell can now be clipped and folded in and hammered tightly into place with the mallet and drift. Then drive in a fiber wedge over the coil by using a wedge driver such as shown in Fig. 56. This consists of a hollow rectangular piece of steel fitted with a sliding steel strip about the same size as the wedge. The wedge is inserted into the driver, its end beveled and forced into the slot by tapping on the steel strip of the driver with a mallet.

Insulating Overlapping End Connections of Coils.—After the wedge has been driven in, take a piece of cotton tape and wrap firmly around the coil and the projecting tip of the wedge close up against the core and continue to tape up the end connection of the coil to the point where it was insulated from the bottom upward when the other side was placed in the bottom of the slot. Glue the ends of the tape where they meet.

When two or three of the top sides of coils have been placed in position, insert one or more strips of treated duck between the end connections of the upper and lower coils where they cross each other at each end of the armature. As the remaining upper sides of the coils are placed in the slots, these strips should be wound around the armature so that they finally form a complete band of insulation between the upper and lower coils. Each coil as it is finally placed should be shaped at its ends with a mallet and fiber drift so that one coil fits snugly against the other and there is a rigid construction when the armature is completed.

Connecting Finish Ends of Coils to Commutator.—The ends of the upper sides of the coils can now be connected to the commutator using a test lamp. Connect the colored leads in proper order as explained on page 101 under "Making Connections to the Commutator." Before soldering the coil ends, the entire winding must be tested for grounds with proper voltage and for short circuits and open circuits. (See page 122 under the heading of "Testing Armature Windings.") If no faults are discovered the ends of the coils can be soldered to the commutator and the latter turned and finished with sandpaper. The armature is now ready for banding.

Loop Windings for Small Motors.—Small direct-current armatures for fan motors and general utility use, are often wound by hand using what is sometimes called a loop winding. In the case of a 2-pole armature having 15 slots and 15 commutator bars, such a winding might be made up as follows: Wind slots Nos. 1 and 8 half full, using double cotton-covered wire, leaving the ends a little longer then needed to connect to

FIG. 57.—Winding the first coil in the slots of a small direct-current motor.

FIG. 58.—The operator is here shown completing the last turn of the winding.

FIG. 59.—In this illustration the operator is driving down the coils before inserting fiber wedges in the slots of the completely wound armature.

In Figs. 57 to 59 three steps are shown in winding a small direct-current armature. Before starting to wind the coils, the cores are insulated on the ends as shown in the lower right-hand corner of Fig. 57.   The armature illustrated is for a 32-volt motor and has 19 slots with a coil pitch of 1 to 8 slots.   Ten turns of No. 11 wire per coil are used with two coils per slot.   There are a total of 38 coils and 38 commutator bars (*Robbins & Myers Company*).

the commutator and without cutting the wire wind a similar coil in slots 2 and 9 and bring out a second loop. Proceed in this way throughout all the pairs of nearly opposite slots until on the second round the slots are completely filled when the beginning and the end of the wire can be twisted together for the 15th loop. Cotton sleeves can now be inserted over the loops and connections made to the commutator. Figs. 57 to 59 show an armature being wound by this method. In the illustrations the necessary insulation on the shaft close to the core and on the core at the ends of the slots is shown. The slots should be insulated in this case with heavy fish paper about 10 mils thick.

Banding a Small D.-C. Armature.—When applying the banding wire, the armature should be inserted in a lathe.

Fig. 60.—Dissembled view of a small direct-current motor showing banded armature (*Fidelity Electric Company*).

The first operation is to hammer down the ends of the coils until their diameter at the armature ends is no greater than that of the core. Extreme care must be taken not to injure the insulation with the mallet. As a base for the banding wires, two bands of cotton tape separated by a band of varnished paper should be wound over the end connections near the core and the whole tied down with several layers of twine. Short strips of tinned copper about 0.02 by 0.25 inch in cross-

5

section should be slipped under the temporary banding twine at intervals of two or three inches with two extra ones used where the banding wire is started and ended.   For the banding wire of small armatures No. 14 to No. 17 B. & S. gauge tinned steel wire can be used.   The start should be fastened to a peg slipped into an air duct or fastened to the end of the banding twine and the first layer guided so that it crosses itself to relieve the strain on the end fastening.   After two or three revolutions of the band wire the temporary banding twine can be cut off and the banding wire wound on tightly across the protecting tape.   After the required width has been wound, the copper strips at the start end should be turned up and clipped off so that about one-quarter inch projects from under the banding wire.   Then bend the strips over to hold the banding wire in position.

Without cutting the banding wire, it should be guided across the core to the opposite end of the armature and wound in the same manner as before to within about a quarter of an inch of the edges of the end connections.   The clips at beginning and end can now be bent over and soldered.   The banding wires on both ends of the armature should now be driven up close together, all the clips bent over and the wires soldered together.   In the soldering of band wires no acid should be used.   A solution of rosin in alcohol is recommended.   After the soldering operation is completed the surplus turns and crossovers of the banding wire can be cut off.   The armature is now completed except for the balancing.   (See page 150 under the heading of "Balancing an Armature.")

II. WINDING D.-C. ARMATURES HAVING OPEN SLOTS

Motors in sizes above five horsepower that nave armature cores with open slots may be wound with coils made up of wire or of copper strap.   The coils may be of the form wound or pull in types but are fully insulated before being inserted into the slots.   In general two types of open slots are found, one with wedge grooves in the top of the slot in which wedges can be driven to hold the coils in position; while the other is a slot with smooth sides requiring banding wire to hold the coils in place. Grooves are usually provided on the armature for bands in addition to those over the end connections. Very often the same armature core with open slots is used for different types and sizes of machines. The coils may therefore be smaller in some cases than the original ones and do not fill the slots. In these cases fillers must be used to fill out the sides and below the coils in the slot so that the wedges or band wire

Fig. 61.—Direct-current armature showing duck or canvas pad held by cordage on ring which supports coils

This insulation is used to prevent coils from rubbing on the frame and gives a larger margin of safety against grounds. Slot insulation made of treated pressboard is shown in place. Separators between coils in each slot are made of the same material but a little thicker (*Roth Brothers & Company*).

will press firmly on the top of the coils and prevent any possible motion of the coils in the slots that will result in chafing and damage to the insulation. Fillers most used consist of strips of treated fullerboard or treated wood. If a coil is only slightly loose it is better to add insulation to it.

Winding and Insulating Coils.—In case coils must be wound for a particular job proceed as outlined under the heading of "Forms for Winding Coils," on page 141. In rewinding a bar wound armature, it will seldom be necessary to form new coils, because each coil consists of a single turn of heavy copper strip, which is not as easily damaged as are wire wound coils. In this case, all that will generally be necessary is to reinsulate the coils and the armature core. When all the coils have been wound, they should be covered with cotton tape about three-

Fig. 62.—Armature shown in Fig. 61 with a partial lap winding in place.

The insulation on ends of coils and method of interlacing coils so that they occupy a minimum amount of space are shown. Coil ends are later to be fastened to supporting spider ring with treated canvas or duck and cordage. Band wires are wound on core with stripes or pads of thin canvas underneath, after winding is completed (*Roth Brothers & Company*).

quarter inch in width. The end of the tape winding can be made fast with a piece of thread, care being taken to have the taped end on a part of the coil that does not go into the slots, as the thickness of the thread on each side may be sufficient to cause the coil to stick while being placed in position on the core. The finished coils should go into the insulated slots without undue driving. The coils should now be given a coat of moisture repelling varnish and allowed to dry.   When thoroughly dry the armature can be rewound.

Insulating Open Slots.—When the armature is not too large it can be wound in a lathe or bench stand.   For large armatures a suitable floor stand can be easily made.   Place the armature in the lathe or on the stand with the commutator at the winder's right.   Before inserting the insulation for the slots, they should be thoroughly cleaned and all burrs and sharp edges removed with a file.   The same arrangement of slot insulation described for partially closed slots on page 61 can be employed. However, for low-voltage machines (not over 250 volts) to be used in dry places a satisfactory slot insulation consists of two layers of fish paper each 0.005 inch thick between which is placed a layer of empire cloth 0.010 inch thick.   This insulation should be cut so that it will extend about $\frac{1}{2}$ inch past the end of the slot and project about one inch above the entrance to the slots.   This will form a mechanical protection for the coils and serve as guides through which the coils can be slid into place.   The corners of the projecting edges should be clipped to keep them from interfering with the insertion of the coils.   If end-ring insulation is to be used, hold it in place by winding thread over the ends of the core through the slots.

Inserting Coils in Open Slots.—After the slots have been insulated, place one side of a coil in a slot and force it to the bottom with a fiber drift a little narrower than the width of the slot.   The other half of the coil (or top side) should be left out of the armature for the present.   Insert the bottom half of coil No. 2 in the next slot turning the armature in a counterclockwise direction (looking toward the commutator end). Proceed in this manner until the top side of one coil is to be placed into the slot containing the bottom side of the first coil placed on the armature.   This will be the first coil in which the top side can be placed in a slot over the bottom side of coil No. 1.   Before doing this, reference should be made to the note book data in case an armature is being rewound exactly as before, in order to make sure that the proper number of slots have been spanned.

To make this method of winding clear, refer to Fig. 63. Here the coils span five slots, that is, the top side of coil No. 1

is removed five slots from the bottom side of the same coil. The top half of coils Nos. 1, 2, 3, 4, and 5 (called the throw coils because they cover a part of the armature equal to the throw of a coil) are left out of the slots as shown, as the bottom half of other coils will have to be placed in these slots before these top halves can be put in. When the bottom half of coil No. 6 is placed in slot 11, its top side may be placed in slot 6, because the bottom side of coil 1 is located in this slot. Continue to place the coils on the core, traveling in the direction indicated by the arrow. The bottom half of coil No. 7 is

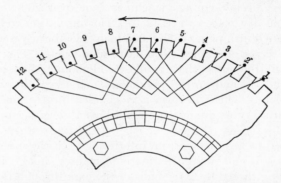

FIG. 63.—Method of placing throw coils on the armature of a lap winding.

placed in slot 12, and the top half in slot 7. Before inserting the coils in the slots it is a good plan to rub the sides with paraffin wax. This helps in inserting the coils and prevents damaging the insulation.

As the armature is being wound, a strip of heavy pressboard (about 0.050 inch thick) should be placed in the slots between coils to thoroughly insulate them from each other. When all the coils have been inserted, the top sides of coils Nos. 1, 2, 3, 4, and 5 can be placed in the slots. As each coil is put in position, the end connections should be carefully shaped to the core.

Shaping End Connections.—The end connections are shaped by means of a winding drift. This consists of a steel bar about 12 inches long, one inch wide and tapered in thickness from one-half to one-eighth inch, having all the corners rounded and smooth. The tip of this drift should be placed against the inner side of the end connection of the coil and tapped with a mallet, forcing the upper part of the end connection out from the armature and away from the lower half. Each coil as it

Fig. 64.—Rear and commutator ends of a wave-wound armature using strap coils. Note the insulation of slots and the insulated support of rear end connections (*General Electric Company*).

is put in place can be similarly shaped so that when the armature is completely wound a circular air chamber is formed between the upper and lower halves of the end connections at both front and rear. This process should be continued until the first slot is again reached.

Six Steps in Winding a Small Direct-current Armature

No. 1

Fig. 65.—This illustration and those of Figs. 66 to 71 show successive steps in winding a small direct-current armature (*Crocker-Wheeler Company*). The slot and shaft insulation and first two coils are shown in place here.

No. 2

Fig. 66.—Appearance of the winding before the last three coils are inserted in bottoms of the slots.

No. 3

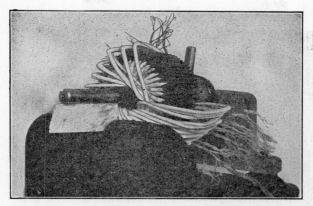

FIG. 67.—All bottom sides of coils in place and strips of insulation inserted between bottom and top coil sides ready for the top layer of the winding.

No. 4

FIG. 68.—Inserting the last few top sides of coils.   Note the shaping of the end connections of this winding alternately in and out to give the compact appearance shown in Fig. 71.

No. 5

FIG. 69.—Connecting the first two leads of bottom coil sides to the commutator.

No. 6

FIG. 70.—Connecting the leads of top coil sides to the commutator. Note the tape insulation between coil terminals.

FIG. 71.—Completed armature banded and treated with insulating compound. Note winding insulation over coil terminals at commutator end.

FIG. 72.—Portable floor stand for winding small direct-current armatures. The operator is shown shaping the end connections with a fiber drift.

Truing Up the Heads of the Winding.—When the winding is completed, bend the leads back over the surface of the core so as to expose the head of the winding. This must be trued by revolving the armature and marking the high places with chalk. These high spots can be driven down with a rawhide mallet, and the low places raised even with the others. The back head should also be carefully trued up so as to present a good appearance when running. Trim off the projecting slot insulation even with the surface of the armature if banding wires are to be used. In case the coils are to be held in place by wood or fiber retaining wedges, lap this insulation down over the coils and drive in the wedges. If the armature leads are not covered with tape, they must be protected in some manner and for this cotton sleeving can be used.

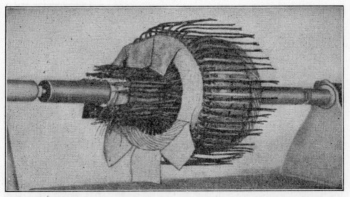

FIG. 73.—Insulation of end connections showing friction cloth blanket in place at the commutator end as a protection for the leads.

Insulation Between Commutator End Connections.—A friction cloth blanket should be placed over the end connections on the commutator end, as shown in Fig. 73, as a protection for the terminals of the coils. It is good practice to shape the ends or terminals of the side of the coils in the bottoms of the slots as shown in this illustration and to bend back over the core the terminals of the top sides of the coils. This helps in arranging the connections from the coils in the bottoms of the slots, which can now be made.

Now wrap several thicknesses of treated cloth in a belt over the bottom leads and bind with thread. The top lead, located by a lamp tester of magneto can now be connected to the commutator. In the same manner connect the remaining leads. Cut off the ends of the leads that project past the neck of the commutator, and if there is space after the lead have been driven down, these pieces can be used as "dummies" to fill such spaces. When this stage of the winding process has been reached, a short-circuit and open-circuit test must be made. (See page 122 under heading of "Testing D.-C. Armature Windings.") If the armature tests clear, the leads can be soldered in.

When the wedges are not used to hold the coils in place some means must be provided to prevent them from becoming loosened from the slots, during the subsequent operations before banding. To accomplish this a single band of wire can be tightly fastened around the coils at each end of the armature.

After these operations the commutator can be turned and polished and the armature banded if this is required. When balanced and painted with insulating varnish, the armature is ready for use.

III. WINDING LARGE D.-C. ARMATURES

In contrast with the winding of small armatures, the winding of large direct-current armatures is not a particularly complicated operation. Although the insulation throughout must be moisture and oil proof, no such elaborate precautions as in the case of industrial motors is necessary in the larger sizes of machines for they are in most cases installed in dry clean places. The centrifugal strains, however, may be higher in the larger machines and the windings must also be braced against the magnetic strains produced by heavy short circuits which may occur on account of the very low resistance of circuits using wire of large cross-section. The following recommendations are given for the winding of large armatures by a writer in the *Electric Journal*, Vol. VII, No. 11.

Coils for Large D.-C. Armatures.—For the large sizes of direct-current machines the armature coils are usually

formed of bare copper strap. They are usually of the one
piece or two piece, one turn, diamond type with the number
of coils equal to the number of commutator bars. To secure
best possible space factor, and for other mechanical reasons,
single coils are often bound together into a larger coil, each
single coil being insulated from the other and electrically
separated. In such a case the number of slots is only a
fraction of the number of commutator bars.

Fig. 74.—Lap-wound armature using two-part strap coils. Note the
four layers of insulation between end connections at commutator end (*General
Electric Company*).

The method of insulating this type of coil depends upon
the size, voltage and operating conditions of the machine and
on the number of single coils composing a complete coil.
When there are less than four single coils per complete coil,
the ends of each single coil are taped with one layer of cotton
tape, half overlapped. This taping extends a sufficient distance along the straight part to assure that the joint between
it and the rest of the insulation will be well protected. The
straight parts are then wrapped with a fish paper and mica
wrapper, interwoven between the straps in such a manner as to
furnish insulation between the single coils, and then wrapped
several times around the complete coil, the exact number of

turns depending on the size, voltage and operating conditions of the machine. (See "Coil Insulation," pages 163 to 172.)

When there are four or more single coils per complete coil, alternate single coils should be wrapped with one turn of fish paper and mica, held in place by a non-overlapping layer of cotton tape. The single coils are then assembled and a cell of fish paper and mica wrapped over the whole. The coil should then be taped with a layer of cotton tape, non-overlapping over the wrapper and half lapped over the ends. Then brush with or dip in a black finishing varnish and air dry. After this dip twice in insulating varnish and dry in an oven for twelve hours after each immersion. Before the coil is used in the armature, the leads should be cleaned of insulation and varnished and thoroughly tinned.

Lap and Wave Windings for Large Armatures.—In the main the same conditions outlined on page 112 under the heading "Wave Lap vs. Direct-current Windings" apply in the case of large armatures. The wave winding has the decided advantage, however, that no cross-connections are required. It has, therefore, a wide use in machines where the size of coil required does not become excessive nor the voltage between commutator segments too great to permit of good commutation. Under ordinary conditions this consideration limits the wave winding to four- or six-pole machines. Where the number of poles is greater the lap winding seems to suit the conditions of good operation best. With this winding the voltage between segments is kept down and high conductivity through the armature is made possible without using coils of large cross-sections. For both lap and wave windings, one-piece coils can be used, but a two piece or half coil has some advantages in that less skill is needed to wind the armature and the coils are easily repaired if the damage is only to the top half. The half coil however calls for a soldered joint at the rear of the armature which must be made with great care.

Insulating the Core.—Before starting the winding operation the core should be thoroughly cleaned with an air blast, thus removing any iron filings or other foreign matter from the slots. The commutator necks must then be carefully ex-

amined to see that all are straight and that the openings at
the top are wide enough to admit the coil leads easily.   Test
the commutator for breakdown to ground, and for short-
circuit between segments, with the standard test voltage for
the machine.   (See Chapter V, also page 175.)   All parts of
the spider which come in contact with the coils, such as coil
supports, etc., should be carefully insulated with either tape,

Fig. 75.—Medium-sized heavy duty armature showing use of strap coils
for a wave winding (*Westinghouse Electric & Mfg. Company*).

fullerboard channels, or two or three thicknesses of fish paper
strips.   When tape is used it is wrapped in overlapping layers
over the entire support.   At the point where the spurs which
hold the coil support in position prevent winding on the tape,
the iron should be covered with insulating cloth, and held in
place by the tape on each side.   Each layer of the tape should
be shellaced as it is wound.   When fullerboard strips are
used, the first layer is frequently screwed to the iron to prevent lateral motion.   Other layers are shellaced over this,

and the whole is usually bound with twine. Special care should be taken to stagger all joints.

Inserting the Coils.—The assembly of the different types of coils is essentially similar. Mark two slots with chalk to receive the first coil, and count off and mark the commutator necks into which its leads will be connected. Fish paper cells can then be inserted into the slots, and the coils driven into position one after another with a mallet and a fiber drift. If a two-piece coil is used, the lower half coils should be inserted first all the way around the armature and then the upper half

Fig. 76.—Wave-wound armature partly completed showing insulation used between end connections of coils.

coils. If one piece coils are used the coils should be inserted in regular succession, the bottom half of the coil being driven into the bottom of its slot first. The other half is driven into close contact with the coil which is already in the bottom of the slot. If there is no coil in the bottom of the slot, as happens with the throw coils, this top half is inserted only temporarily until the winding has been carried entirely around the armature. Then the throw coils must be removed so that the coil sides can be placed in the bottom of the slots.

When a one-piece coil is used in a wave winding, the throw coils span so large a part of the armature that it is not usually advisable to insert the upper part of the coils and then remove them but allow them to hang free as shown in Fig. 76 until all the coils have one side in place in the slots. The upper sides can then be driven into place in regular order. As in the smaller windings, the upper and lower coil ends or terminals should be separated with bands of oiled duck or drilling. With one piece coils, this should be threaded into place as the coils are inserted in the upper part of the slots. With two-piece coils it is simply wound over the lower set of coils before the others are placed in the slots.

FIG. 77.— Core of a large armature showing construction for good ventilation (*General Electric Company*).

The coils must be a close fit in the slots, in order to prevent any possibility of chafing. If necessary, strips of fullerboard or treated wood should be inserted at the sides or bottom of the slot, to make the coils a tight fit. As each top coil is put in place it should be driven into the slot, the protecting cells then cut off, and folded over it, and fiber wedges driven into the wedge grooves. The slots on a large-sized machine are too long to allow one wedge to be used, so that one or more must be driven in from each side of the slot to furnish complete protection for the face of the coil. The armature should then be tested for grounds, before the connections are soldered.

After the winding is completed, the armature may be banded temporarily at both ends. Then drive wooden wedges loosely in between the commutator necks, all around the armature to insure even spacing. After this drive them in tightly, to force the necks and coil ends into tight contact and hold them rigidly in place. With two-piece coils, connecting clips are placed over the leads at the rear end, and wedges driven in between these in the same manner. The connections to the necks, and the rear end connections, if any are used, can be soldered. This soldering should be done on the side of the

FIG. 78.—Large direct-current engine type armature showing method of ventilation (*Westinghouse Electric & Mfg. Company*).

machine instead of the top, as a better joint can be made in this manner, and there is less liability of the melted solder running along the necks and short-circuiting the commutator segments.

Before removing the wedges the armature should be mounted in a lathe, or if no suitable lathe is available, in its bearings with the field frame removed, and the soldered connections turned down. If the armature is mounted in its bearings, a suitable tool holder must be fastened to the frame, or some rigid support. The commutator may then be turned down and given its final polishing at the same time. Now knock out the wedges from between the leads, and round off the sharp corners with a file.   When the bare copper is not covered with insulation, insulating material can be inserted between the adjacent leads to prevent accidental contact.   At the rear end, this usually takes the form of asbestos tape which can be interwoven between the leads or of canvas hoods, sewed in place.   At the front end, the necks may be separated at the tops by strips of heavy fish paper, bent over the tops of the leads so as to be held in place by the band wires.   Where the

FIG. 79.—Large direct-current engine type armature partly wound with strap coils (*Westinghouse Electric & Mfg. Company*).

necks are quite long, additional separators may be inserted half way up from the commutator.   These may be in the form of fiber buttons or may merely consist of heavy twine, interwoven between the long commutator necks.

Banding Wire.—Bands of steel wire are ordinarily placed over both ends of the armature, and frequently another over the connections to the commutator necks.   No bands need be used over the surface of the core, as the wedges are sufficient to retain the body of the coils in place.   The coils can be protected from the mechanical pressure of the banding by layers of surgical tape separated by strips of cement paper, over which the bands are wound. The wire should be wound on under heavy tension, secured by clamping it between blocks of wood. These blocks can be held from moving by heavy straps of wire, fastened to some rigid object—usually the machine frame. If desired, a spring balance may be inserted, which will give the

FIG. 86.—Armature of a 350 kw., 250-volt, engine type generator showing the core construction for good ventilation and the use of copper strap coils (*Fairbanks-Morse & Company*).

exact tension that is being applied. This should run between 300 and 400 lb. The bands should be firmly soldered in place. When it is desired to secure extra mechanical strength, the wire is sometimes wound on two or three layers deep, each layer being soldered separately. The proper banding of a large armature by this method is often a serious problem on a repair job. A sectional band wire such as shown in Fig. 82, is therefore convenient. When using this type of banding, the two ends of any section are keyed together into an

Fig. 81.—Completed armature of a 350 kw., 250-volt, direct-current engine type generator, lapwound for 8 poles with equipotential connections.   Four coils per slot are used (*Fairbanks-Morse & Company*).

Fig. 82.—Tool for use in applying section bands on large armatures.

open loop and then applied to the armature. In making the final connection the special clamp shown in Fig. 82 is needed. The two jaws of this clamp grip the ends of the band and by means of the handle whose lower end is formed into a cam, the jaws can be forced together so as to interweave the loops of the band wire and permit the steel key *B* to be inserted. In this operation the clamp can be held in any position by inserting

Fig. 83.—Large direct-current armature partly wound with strap coils. Note the insulating strips between end connections and double insulation in slots (*Crocker-Wheeler Company*).

the pin *A* through the movable jaw and beam. For other details of banding see Chapter VI, page 146.

Balancing Large Armatures.—After the armature is banded it is ready for balancing. Suitable balancing ways may consist of heavy steel beams with polished steel plates mounted on their upper edges. The surface of the polished plates must be accurately leveled. The shaft should rest on the inner surface of a polished steel ring, which in turn rests on the polished plates. In this way, an almost frictionless bearing surface is obtained, and the armature tends to roll until the heaviest part is at the bottom. Melted lead can be poured into recesses in the spider, or cast-iron weights bolted to the spider arms to correct any unbalanced condition, until the armature will lie with any part uppermost. The armature should then be thoroughly cleaned with an air blast and

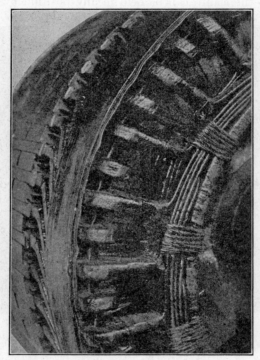

Fig. 84.—Method of cross connecting a large direct-current armature having a lap winding (*Westinghouse Electric & Mfg. Company*).

sprayed inside and out with black finishing varnish. Special care should be taken to reach all exposed parts of the core, to prevent rusting.

Rotary Converters.—There is no essential difference in the winding operations as described between rotary converters, and other direct-current machines. At the rear of the armature, however, taps are brought out from the coils at regular intervals.   On a three-phase machine, this will be two-thirds of the pole pitch; on a two-phase machine, one-half the pole pitch, and on a six-phase machine one-third the pole pitch. These taps are connected to the collector rings.   A two-phase or a six-phase rotary converter cannot be wound with a wave winding on account of the necessity of having an equal number of coils between taps on the armature.

Three-wire Generators.—Practically any standard generator can be adapted for use as a three-wire machine by the

Fig. 85.—Completed armature for a large 3-wire direct-current generator (*Crocker-Wheeler Company*).

addition of suitable collector rings and balancing coils.   These coils are entirely self-contained and may be installed apart from the generator.   The collector slip rings are usually much smaller than those of a rotary converter, as each one carries only a fraction of the unbalanced current.   The current which they carry is largely unidirectional, only enough alternating current flowing to excite the core of the balancing coils. They are accordingly made of iron to avoid the blackening from electrolysis which takes place when the direct current flows from copper to carbon.   They may be placed at either end of the armature, but are usually placed at the end of the commutator, for greater convenience (see Fig. 85).

IV. WINDING RAILWAY, MILL AND CRANE TYPES OF ARMATURES

The methods of winding and insulating armatures for railway, mill, mining and crane types of armatures are practically the same, since the service is somewhat similar and the windings must stand up against much hard usage and abuse of the motor. Thorough insulation and protection against vibration and chafing of the insulation are essential points in the winding of these armatures and must be given more attention than in any other.

Railway Type Armature Coils.—This type of armature coil is completely formed and impregnated with insulating compounds. It needs no shaping when placed on the armature.

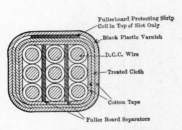

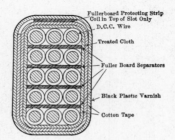

Fig. 86.—Wire wound coils showing single coils arranged in vertical layers.

Fig. 87.—Wire wound coils showing single coils arranged in horizontal layers.

It is usually advisable for the repairman to purchase these coils from the manufacturer of the motor which is to be repaired. Usually the coils are made up of two or more single coils wound with round wire or copper strap. These single coils are separately wound but grouped together for mechanical reasons in handling and insulation. The windings of these motors are of the wave or two-circuit type, except for the largest sizes of mill or locomotive motors. The insulation for coils and core and the details of the winding of railway armatures as given here, are the recommendations outlined by a writer in the *Electric Journal*, Vol. VII, No. 10.

Wire Coils.—The coils for smaller machines are made of double cotton-covered wire. The single coils which form a complete coil are insulated from each other by fish paper or fullerboard separators and may be arranged radially or circumferentially in the slot as shown in Figs. 86 and 87. The leads from wire wound coils are secured along the diamond end and leave the coil one after the other, each being firmly tied and taped in position so that there is no possibility for them to chafe against one another. They are reinforced with cotton sleeves.

Strap Coils.—Most of the larger railway motors have the armature coils made from rectangular conductors instead of round wire, as with this form of conductor a greater proportion of the slot space may be filled with copper, without

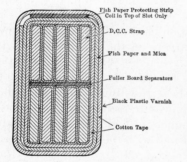

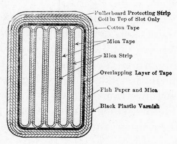

FIG. 88.—Section of slot showing strap wound coil of two turns.

FIG. 89.—Section of slot showing strap wound coil of one turn.

sacrificing the insulation requirements. The pressure on the insulating surfaces is also more evenly distributed, as with the round wire the pressure bears on a line, while with the rectangular conductors it is distributed over a flat surface and is much less liable to injure the insulation. Figs. 88 and 89 show a cross-section through two-turn and one-turn coils, respectively.

The one turn coil readily lends itself to bringing out the leads in position to enter the top and bottom of the commutator necks respectively, by the use of the standard form of diamond end. A two turn coil requires a special turn at the rear end of the coil, in order to bring the leads out in the proper position. By the use of this form of coil, all the advantages of the strip winding can be secured for the smaller machines on which more than one turn per slot is usually required.

In some large motors, coils of the rectangular types are made in two pieces, and are known as two-piece coils. Their advantage lies in the fact that if a coil becomes damaged, only one-half of the complete coil need be removed to overcome the defect. As damage to the coils nearly always occurs on the outside of the armature, this type of coil is peculiarly adapted to railway type armatures. It requires, however, a soldered connection at the back, in addition to the usual soldered connection at the commutator, and hence is used only on the large motors where the saving of copper for repair parts would be great.

Coil Insulation.—The insulation used on motors of the type under consideration depends largely on the type of coil used. Where double-cotton-covered coils are used there is little advantage in using materials for the remainder of the slot insulation which have higher heat resisting ability than the cotton strands which are in immediate contact with the conductors, since it is necessary under the circumstances to limit the temperature to values consistent with the cotton insulation. For this reason on certain types of mill motors, where the temperature conditions are exceptionally severe, asbestos covering is used instead of the cotton, with mica insulation around the complete coil, cotton being used only in the protective taping over the outside.

With strap wound coils it is possible to use built up mica in immediate contact with the conductors and cotton only on the outside protective coverings, where it is in contact with the air or the relatively cooler iron. Hence the copper can be safely worked to a higher value and continued overloads and abuse will not be so liable to cause breakdown. The coils should be vacuum impregnated before insertion in the armature. This process renders them thoroughly moisture and oil proof and prolongs the life of the coils over that of unimpregnated ones, especially where they are subject to moisture, acid fumes and deleterious gases. It is applied to all railway type coils except those for mine locomotives, whose armatures are usually impregnated as a whole after the winding is completed.

Insulating the Core of Railway Armatures.—In this type of armature it is advisable to supply extra protection at every point of special electrical or mechanical stress such as where the coils leave the slots, where the leads leave the coils and where the leads cross one another or cross the ends of the coils. Before applying the core insulation, the core should be thoroughly cleaned with an air blast and burrs taken off with a file. When wire wound coils are used the coil supports have curved surfaces and should be insulated with treated cloth in strips or with layers of rope paper and treated cloth.

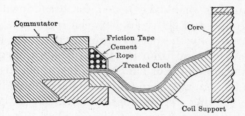

Fig. 90.—Insulation of support for front coils of railway armature.

Slits should be made in the strips where necessary to make them lie smooth as over the end bell, care being taken that the slits in the successive layers are staggered. These strips should be bound together with shellac and ironed smoothly into place. They should be built up to a thickness of about one-eighth inch (six layers of rope paper and five layers of treated cloth are sometimes used) over the entire support and to the level of the bottom of the slots and the commutator necks at each edge. Where this would require an excessive amount of insulating material, as occurs in the rear of the commutator on certain types, a bed of rope can be built up, as shown in Fig. 90, and bound in place with an insulating cement. A final layer of friction tape can be applied over all the insulation, great care being observed to make the layers lie smooth, and to build up a firm support for the coils where they leave the slots.

On the cores for strap wound coils, the coil supports are usually straight and insulated with built-up mica bushings or with heavy bands of treated cement paper. No tape is used in this case, but the bushings are arranged to come up level with the bottom of the slots.

On both wire and strap wound armatures, the slots for about an inch at the ends may be slightly wider than the coils. In such cases narrow strips of heavy fish paper, projecting slightly from the slots, should be inserted for additional protection to the coils at this point. The slots should be further insulated with regular fish-paper cells for the mechanical protection of the coils.

Inserting the Coils.—Before starting to wind the armature, the commutator should be tested for breakdown with 5000 volts to ground and 200 volts between segments. Mark two slots, separated by the proper throw, with chalk for the first coil. Then count off from the bar opposite the center of the first slot, the commutator bars into which the leads from these slots must fit. In a lap winding these bars should lie adjacent. In a wave winding, the number of bars between them must be determined. (See page 105, Chapter IV.) The first coil is then placed in these two slots, the bottom half being driven into the lower half of the slot, and the top half being merely caught in its proper slot, as it will have to be removed later, to allow a coil to be inserted beneath it.

Wire Coils.—In wire wound armatures the lower leads should be taped with friction tape when necessary to make the insulation continuous from the coil to the commutator. These leads should then be laid along the coil supports of the armature core in smoothly fitting rows and the bare ends driven into the proper commutator necks. Heavy insulation is needed between the coil ends and the upper and lower leads and between the upper and lower coil ends. This may be of different form in different types of armatures. In one type treated canvas strips may be inserted so as to furnish extra insulation between the ends of adjacent coils and between the coil ends and the lower leads   In addition a friction cloth strip, doubled over a piece of rope, may be inserted at each end between the upper and lower coil as the coils are inserted, the rope fitting in the point of the diamond. The coils should be shaped with a fibre drift and rawhide mallet so as to fit snugly against one another at both ends. It is

Fig. 91.—Inserting the top sides of coils in an armature. The leads of the bottom coil sides are shown connected to the commutator. Note the band of insulation between end connections.

essential that they be made to fit closely together when first inserted, otherwise the armature will bulge at the ends. Any attempt to shape the coils in a completed armature is liable to injure the insulation.

After all the coils have been inserted and the top parts of the throw coils have been replaced, the ends of the canvas strips which project up between the coil ends should be trimmed off level with the top of the coils at both ends of the armature. Those strips which project out from beneath the coils, should be turned up over the coil ends and bound in place with friction tape. This tape when wound completely across the upper surface of the coil ends, serves as a protecting and insulating layer between the coils and the upper leads.

Another method of providing extra insulation on some armatures is to slit two strips of treated canvas and insert them between the lower leads and the coil ends with the slits staggered. No strips are inserted at the rear end and no insulation is required between the ends of adjacent coils, beyond that on the coils themselves. Strips of friction cloth and rope may be inserted between the upper and the lower coil ends, and the canvas strips folded over the ends of the coils and covered with friction tape as just described. In this case, however, strips of fish paper should be slipped over each coil and wedged between the coil ends close to the core, for further protection to the upper leads.

Before connecting the upper leads to the armature they should all be tied together with bare copper wire and the coils subjected to a break-down test of 3600 volts. Any defective coil must be replaced. The armature can then be trued up. This can be done by tapping down with a mallet all the high coils as located by holding a piece of chalk so that it will rub against the high parts when the armature is revolved. A somewhat better method is to squeeze the coils into place by means of a flexible metallic strap and turn-buckle. The latter method is less liable to damage the insulation and all the coils receive uniform treatment so that a better balance of the armature results. Both ends must form a compact mass. Where end room is especially short, as in mine motors, a special form can be used on the rear end of the armature so as to press all coils against this when being inserted to give uniformity to the arrangement.

Where the top of the coil is above the top of the commutator, there is sometimes difficulty in keeping the leads properly separated in bringing them down to the commutator. In such cases a canvas strip may be interwoven over every other one, making it possible to have two layers of leads on the vertical part. The leads are then inserted into the slits in the proper commutator necks and copper wire dummies driven over them, to prevent any possibility of a portion of the leads being removed when the necks are turned down. Both leads and dummies should be tinned and make a driving fit in the necks.

Strap Coils.—The leads of strap wound armatures are formed to shape and, therefore, require little bending during their installation. The coil supports of the two turn strap coils are shaped and insulated in a manner very similar to that for wire wound coils. In addition a bed of the insulating cement is made over the insulation at the rear of the commutator into which the lower leads are forced as they are inserted into the commutator necks. They are thus held rigidly in place after the paste hardens. Strips of treated canvas or of friction cloth folded over fish paper and mica should be threaded between the upper and lower coil ends, at each side of the machine, as the coils are inserted. A length of rope should also be threaded through the diamond point at each end. Between the coil ends and the upper and lower leads, strips of treated canvas with slit edges should be inserted so that the openings will be staggered. The edge toward the core must be shaped to fit up between the coils and furnish added protection to the leads. After all the coils have been inserted, the upper leads may be bent up slightly, and the edges of the various insulation strips cut off even with the commutator. Friction tape should then be wound smoothly over the treated canvas, holding it in place, and forming a bed for the upper leads. These leads can then be bent down and inserted into the proper commutator necks.

Coil supports for one-turn strap coils, whether two piece or one piece, are straight, and can be insulated with built up mica forms, or strips of fish paper or treated cement paper, shellaced and tied in place. Insulating cement should be plastered over the insulation back of the commutator, to hold the leads from the individual coils in place. Separate the ends

7

of the coils by two thicknesses of treated canvas, threaded in place as the coils are inserted.

The coil supports for two-piece coils may be insulated in the same manner as the one-piece coils. The end bells for this type of armature, however, are usually separate from the core and are not put in place until the winding is complete, so that the winder has plenty of room to work on the rear end of the coils. The winding operation can be greatly facilitated by the use of a steel winding jig, consisting of a slotted disk with a hub bored to fit the armature shaft. The number of slots should be equal to the number of single coils in the armature, and the thickness of the disk equal to the width of the connecting clips. As each coil is placed in the armature slot, the straps composing it should be placed in the proper slots in the jig and in the commutator necks until all the lower half of the winding is in place. The leads on the upper and the lower half should be separated by a couple of thicknesses of treated cement paper, or by a layer of fish paper and mica. After all the coils are in place, the straps which are to be connected together at the rear end lie one above the other in the slots of the jig. These can be cut off even with the surface of the jig, a temporary band wrapped around the coil ends, and the jig removed. Copper connector sleeves should then be slipped over the coil ends and wooden wedges driven in between them. The connectors may then be soldered and the coil ends turned down at the top and side. Next knock out the wedges and interweave asbestos braid between the connectors to prevent accidental contact. The end bell, properly insulated with moulded mica or moulded paper, can then be bolted into position.

Connections with Dead Coils.—If in a four-pole motor with a two-circuit winding there is an even number of single coils in a complete coil, one single coil in the armature must be cut out in order that the winding may be made continuous. This coil is called a dead coil, because it is not connected to the circuit. It is necessary first to determine the number of single coils in a complete coil, by dividing the number of complete coils or slots by the number of commutator bars. If there are more leads from each side of the coil than there are single coils, each single coil is composed of two or more wires in parallel and these must be treated as a single lead. In strap coils each strap corresponds to a single coil. The coil is cut out by cutting off the leads on both sides of a single coil about an inch from where they separate from the coil. Then carefully tape them up. The body of the coil of course, must be left in the slot for uniformity of the winding.

Hooding and Banding.—As a final protection to the armature coils, heavy hoods may be put on over the ends of the coils, covering the armature from the commutator to the core and from the core to the end bell. At the commutator end the hood may be of woven asbestos sewed to a conical shape, and impregnated in a moisture and oil repelling compound. It should be put in place while wet. The small end should be drawn up over the commutator, turned inside out, and firmly tied over the leads and commutator necks with heavy twine. The body of the hood must then be turned back over the armature. If the commutator necks are lower than the level of the core, another layer of twine should be wound over the hood near the commutator and a band of canvas sewed over the whole. Then stretch the hood tightly back over the armature and tie with twine.

Around the rear end of the armature, a band of canvas may be wrapped so that the greater part of the strip extends out over the shaft, only enough being wound over the armature to permit a secure fastening. This may be bound in place with a band of twine wound tightly in the groove between the coil ends and the end bell. The canvas should then be turned back over the armature and bound smoothly in place.

The number and size of bands depends upon the size and speed of the armature. All armatures should have bands on each end, placed as far out as possible, so as to cover the greater part of the coil ends. When such a band would be quite wide, two separate narrower bands may be wound on each end. These bands should be insulated from the coils by three turns of canvas tape separated by treated paper which extends at least one-eighth inch beyond the band on each side. The bands around the body of the core in the band grooves should be insulated from the core and coils by strips of fish paper. They should also be put on with a tension of about 350 pounds sufficient to make a good firm band and to bring the coils down so that they will not project above the surface of the core at any point. The individual turns of the banding should be well soldered together and held at several places by thin copper clips placed before the banding was started. For other details of banding see Chapter V, page 146.

After the banding is completed, the mica insulation between the commutator bars should be undercut to a depth of about one-sixteenth inch, with a special milling cutter. The entire armature except the commutator, can now be sprayed with an air-drying finishing varnish.

CHAPTER IV

MAKING CONNECTIONS TO THE COMMUTATOR

Before starting to insert coils in the slots of the armature, the commutator should be tested for grounds. This can be done by touching one lead of a high-voltage transformer (1200 to 2000 volts) to the shaft and moving the other over the surface of the commutator and at the edges. If there is no arcing, the commutator is properly insulated. The winder can now insert the coils. As each coil is put in place the sleeving on the ends of the lower leads should be fastened to the wire by a few turns of friction tape and these leads inserted into the slits of the proper commutator bars. In case the coil has two or more start and finish ends, care must be taken that the different-colored sleeves are connected to the commutator always in the same order.

Locating First Connection to Commutator.—Before connecting the first coil to the commutator, the winder must examine the setting of the brushes, to see whether they are centered between pole tips or opposite the center of the pole. When the brushes are centered between the pole tips, the start end of each coil must be connected straight out to the bar opposite the slot in which the beginning of the coil is located. When the brushes are opposite the center of the poles, the start end of the coil must be swung a certain number of bars (equal to 90 electrical degrees) to the right or left of the bar opposite the slot in which the beginning or bottom side of the coil is located. The number of bars right or left (equal to 90 electrical degrees) can be determined by the following formula: Total number of commutator bars ÷ (Number of poles × 2). If this number is mixed such as 6.5, use the next higher whole number as 7. The reason for these connections of leads is that the coils must be commutated or short-circuited by the brushes while the coil sides are in a neutral position or outside the pole flux.

The spacing of the brushes from the heel of one brush to the heel of the next for a lap winding will be equal to the number of commutator bars divided by the number of poles.

Testing Out Coil Terminals.—After the commutator pitch has been determined, take the bottom lead of one coil and connect it to a commutator riser, using the same throw as employed on the old winding in case it is being duplicated. After the position of the first lead has been determined, the remainder of the bottom leads can be connected in rotation. When all the bottom leads are in place, a lighting out test should be made to see if the leads are connected to the proper bars. A short circuit and ground test must also be made at this time.

For a lighting-out test, place one terminal of the lamp tester on a commutator bar, and with the other touch the top leads of several coils until the lamp lights. This will locate the top side of the coil corresponding to the bottom side connected to the test lamp. If the lamp lights on more than one lead, it indicates a short circuit between coils. In an armature containing twice the number of commutators bars as there are armature slots, the same procedure is followed in locating the two leads of the same coil.

Commutator Connections for a Lap Winding.—After all the beginning ends of the coils or the ends for the coil sides in the bottom of the slot have been connected to the commutator and all the coils tested out for open circuit, short circuit and grounds, the finish ends or the ends of the coil sides in the top of the slot, can be connected to the commutator   In the case of a coil wound with one wire or two wires in parallel, the finish end of coil No. 1 is connected to the commutator bar next to that to which the start end is connected. Thus, if for coil No. 1 the beginning end is connected to bar No. 1 the finish end will be connected to bar No. 2. The beginning end of coil No. 2 will also be connected to bar No. 2 and its finish end to bar No. 3 and so on until for the last coil the finish end will connect to bar No. 1 and close the winding (see **Fig. 97**).

On the armature of some large direct-current machines a commutator is provided which has twice or three times as many commutator bars as slots or winding coils. The object of this is to improve commutation and prevent sparking by commutating only a part of the current at a time. In a case where the commutator has twice as many bars as slots the coils are made up with two wires-in-hand when winding. For the case where there are three times as many bars as slots, coils made up with three wires-in-hand when winding are used. The coils in either case are placed in the slots the same as those wound with one wire but connected to the commutator differently.

In the case where the number of bars is double the number of slots and coils, the start and finish ends of the coils will have two wires. For coil No. 1 connect the start ends as follows: One wire to bar No. 1 and the other end to bar No. 2; for coil No. 2, one end to bar No. 3, and the other to bar No. 4; and so on. When connecting the finish ends proceed as follows: For coil No. 1, connect one end to bar No. 3 and the other to bar No. 4; for coil No. 2, one end to bar No. 5 and the other end to bar No. 6 and so on until for the last coil one of the finish ends will connect to bar No. 1 and the other to bar No. 2. In this case, each brush will cover two bars.

When there are three start and three finish ends to each coil and three times as many commutator bars as slots, proceed in the same way by connecting the start ends to adjacent bars and the end of one coil to the start of the next. In this case each brush will cover three bars.

Requirements of a Lap Winding.—A lap winding can be wound on an armature having any number of slots provided each slot will accommodate two coil sides for each commutator bar and the number of bars is an even multiple of the number of slots. When the total number of coils is not exactly divisible by the number of pairs of poles the winding pitch can not be equal to a pole pitch. This, however, is not an obstacle except where it is desirable to use equipotential connectors. When the winding pitch can not be equal to a pole pitch it is made so as nearly as possible. When the front and back pitches are specified to be odd for a lap winding, the coil pitch in winding spaces is meant and not the slot pitch. It will be found that with the usual type of form wound coils, the pitches for back and front are necessarily odd, because one side of the coil is in the bottom of a slot and the other side in the top of the slot. The terminals of the coil side in the bottom of the slot are usually considered the start ends and the terminals of the side in the top of the slot the finish ends.

Commutator Connections for a Wave-Winding.—For a wave winding, the start and finish ends of coils are connected to the commutator differently than for a lap winding. In the case of a coil wound with one wire, having one start and one finish end, these are not connected to adjacent commutator bars as in a lap winding, but a number of bars apart. When the coils are inserted in the slots the start ends of the coil

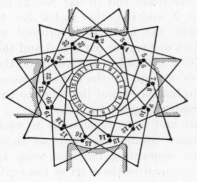

FIG. 92.—A 4-pole, wave winding for an armature having 13 slots and 13 commutator bars.

sides in the bottom of the slots should be connected to the commutator as in the lap winding when each coil is placed. When ready to connect the ends, the commutator pitch must be determined. The formula for commutation pitch in numbers of bars is ($y_k = y_1 + y_2) \div 2$.

Where y_1 is the front pitch and y_2 is the back pitch of the coil, each counted in winding spaces.

With a double layer winding or two coils per slot, there will be two winding spaces per slot.

In the case of a 4-pole, double layer with 13 slots and 13 commutator bars, y_2 equals 7 and y_1 equals 5. Then $y_k = (5 + 7) \div 2$ or six bars. With a back pitch of 7 winding spaces and a front pitch of 5 winding spaces coil No. 1 would lie in slot No. 1 and slot No. 4. Its start end would be connected to commutator bar No. 1 and its finish end to bar No. 7. Coil No. 2 would lie in slots No. 2 and 5. Its start end would be connected to bar No. 2 and its finish end to bar No. 8 and so on until coil No. 13 in slots Nos. 13 and 3 would have its start end connected to bar No. 13 and its finish end to bar No. 6.

It will thus be seen that in a 4-pole machine the finish of one coil is joined to the commutator and to the start of another which lies under another pair of poles. (See Fig. 92.) The finish end of the latter coil is connected to the commutator bar adjacent to the one to which the start of the former coil is connected. In Fig. 92 it can be seen that the coils referred to are the ones connected to commutator bars, No. 1, 7 and 13. In other words the two coils are connected in series with their start ends under different north poles and their finish ends under different south poles. This explains why the wave winding is called a series or two circuit winding.

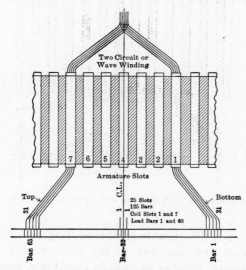

FIG. 93.—Wave winding with an odd coil throw and an odd throw of coil leads.

Practical Method for Locating First Connection to Commutator for a Wave Winding.—When there are an odd number of leads per coil, or in case of a dead coil an odd number of coils remain, the following procedure will locate the first

connection to the commutator. Locate the center line between the slots of the coil throw. If the throw of the leads of
the coils is an odd number of bars, this center line will fall on
a commutator bar. If it is an even number, the center line
will fall on the mica between bars. In either case the bar or
mica so located is the starting point for laying off the connections to the commutator.

If there are an odd number of bars in the throw of the leads,
take one less than the number of bars and count off half of this

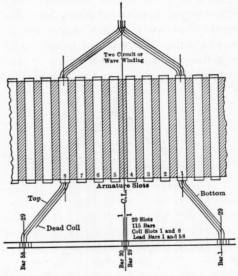

Fɪɢ. 94.—Wave winding with an even coil throw and an even throw of coil
leads.

number in each direction from the starting bar, and this will
give the first and last bar of the commutator throw. If
there is an even number of bars in the throw, count off half
the number in each direction from the starting mica. A
check is to count from the first to the last bar, and see if it
agrees with the information given. As the first coil put down
will have an odd number of leads, the center one of the top and
bottom leads should be placed in the first and last bar of the
throw as determined.

When there are an odd number of coils per slot and an even number of slots, a somewhat different method is required. This, however, seldom occurs. In such a case, if the lead throw is an odd number of bars, the center, as indicated by the coil throw, will line up on the mica and, if an even number of bars, it will line up on a bar. If there is an odd number of bars in the throw, take one less than the number of bars and count off half this number to the left and one more than half to the right, and this will give first and last bar of the commutator throw. If there is an even number of bars in the throw count off half the throw to the right and one less than half to the left. If there are two leads in the first coil, No. 1 lead should lie in No. 1 bar, and if there are four leads in the first coil, No. 2 lead should lie in No. 1 bar.

Winding conditions with odd number of commutator bars	Center line of coil lines up with
Coil throw and lead throw even...........	Mica and tooth
Coil throw odd, lead throw odd...........	Bar and slot
Coil throw even, lead throw odd..........	Bar and tooth
Coil throw odd, lead throw even..........	Mica and slot

Requirements for a Wave Winding.—For the wave or two-circuit winding there should always be an odd number of commutator bars. With an odd number of slots on the armature core, and an odd number of coil sides per slot, a balanced wave winding with no dead coils is possible. The actual number of coil sides per slot can be determined by counting the terminals of each taped up coil in the slot. There may be only two taped-up coil sides in the slot but each coil may be wound with three wires in-hand while winding. In such a case there will be six coil sides per slot for a two-layer winding.

Progressive and Retrogressive Wave Windings.—When a wave winding passes once around the complete armature and has its start and finish ends connected to the commutator as shown in Fig. 95 (at left), it is said to be a progressive winding. When after passing once around the armature the start and finish ends are connected as shown in Fig. 95 (at right) it is said to be retrogressive.

The conditions under which a wave or series winding can be used are shown by the formula: $K = \dfrac{kp}{2} \pm 1$.

Where K is the number of commutator bars, p the number of poles and k a whole number. When the minus sign is used the winding will be progressive and when the plus sign is used it will be retrogressive in a case where the number of commutator bars is odd.

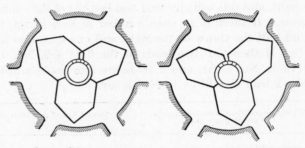

FIG. 95.—The illustration at the left shows one turn of a progressive wave winding; the one at the right a retrogressive wave winding.

Wave Winding with Dead Coils.—For a wave winding, as already mentioned, the number of commutator bars must not be a multiple of the number of poles, otherwise the winding would close after it has passed once around the armature, instead of advancing or falling behind one commutator bar as required by the wave winding. In other words, there must be as many coils in series between adjacent commutator bars as there are pairs of poles. Also with two or more coil sides per slot, the total winding pitch of the end connections (front pitch + back pitch) should be a whole number. It frequently happens that is found to be a fraction. By dropping the fraction when the number is odd, a wave winding can usually be connected with a dead coil. A rule which is often used by engineers to determine when a wave winding is possible without a dead coil is that given in another paragraph, namely:

Number commutator bars $= \dfrac{kp}{2} \pm 1$; where p is the number of poles and k must be a whole number. When an even number of coil sides per slot are used and an odd number of commutator bars, there will always be a dead coil. Also when there are an even number of slots on the armature core, an odd number of commutator bars, and an odd number of coil sides per slot are used, there will always be a dead coil.

Another rule for a possible wave winding is that the total number of slots times the number of coil sides per slot may be any number divisible by the number of poles.

When it is found that a dead coil must be used, one coil, (any one) on the armature should be cut back a short distance from the commutator and taped up with friction tape. The other coils can then be connected as in any other wave winding. That is, connect all the leads of the bottom sides of the coils to the commutator first, then connect the leads of the top sides of the coils the proper commutator pitch away from the bottom leads.

When there are twice as many commutator bars as coils in a wave winding, each coil is wound with two wires and there are two start ends and two finish ends. In making connections to the commutator the two start ends should be connected to adjacent bars and the two finish ends to adjacent bars, spaced the proper commutator pitch apart.

Cutting Out Coils of a Retrogressive and Progressive Wave Winding.—In Fig. 96a is shown a portion of the winding diagram of the armature, for the case of a retrogressive winding with a connecting pitch of 1 to 49. If the burned out coil is between commutator bars 47 and 95, disconnect it from the commutator at a and b and cut it at c if it has more than one turn. Then connect commutator bars 46 to 47, and 94 to 95 and disconnect the coil between bars 95 and 46 at a' and b'. Or connect bar 95 to 96 and 47 to 48 and disconnect the coil between bars 96 and 47 at a'' and b''.

For the case of a progressive winding with a connecting pitch of 1 to 50, the winding diagram is shown in Fig. 96b. If the burned out coil is between commutator bars 3 and 52, disconnect it from the commutator at a and b and cut it at c, if it has more than one turn. Then connect bars 3 to 4 and 52 to 53 and disconnect the coil between commutator bars 52 and 4 at a' and b'. Or connect bars 2 to 3 and 51 to 52 and disconnect the coil between bars 51 and 3 at a'' and b''. For definition of retrogressive and progressive wave winding, see page 107, Chapter IV.

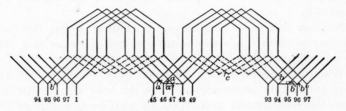

Fig. 96a.—Method of cutting out a damaged coil in a retrogressive wave winding.

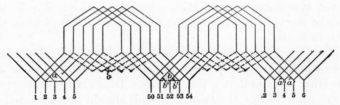

Fig. 96b.—Method of cutting out a damaged coil in a progressive wave winding.

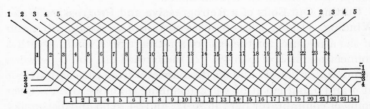

Fig. 97.—Double layer winding for a 4-pole armature having 24 slots and 24 commutator bars. The connections for this diagram are given in tabulated form on page 111.

Tables for Placing Coils and Connecting Them in a D.-C. Armature Winding.—To avoid mistakes in reading a complete winding diagram and to avoid the necessity of making such a diagram, Fig. 97, it is advisable to furnish an inexperienced armature winder with a table for laying the coils in the slots and also a table for connecting the proper leads to the commutator. These tables can be made up as follows:

TABLE FOR PLACING COILS IN ARMATURE SLOTS—LAP WINDING

Coil number	Place sides of coil in	
	Winding space numbers	In slot numbers
1	1 and 12	1 and 6
2	3 and 14	2 and 7
3	5 and 16	3 and 8
4	7 and 18	4 and 9
5	9 and 20	5 and 10
6	11 and 22	6 and 11
7	13 and 24	7 and 12
8	15 and 26	8 and 13
9	17 and 28	9 and 14
10	19 and 30	10 and 15
etc.	etc.	etc.
24	47 and 10	24 and 5

This table is for a four-pole, double layer, lap winding on an armature having 24 slots and 24 commutator bars. By giving the throw of the coils both in winding spaces and in number of slots the winder will not become confused when either is used in referring to the winding. A table of connections to the commutator for this winding is made up as follows:

TABLE FOR CONNECTING COIL LEADS TO THE COMMUTATOR—LAP WINDING

Coil number	Connect terminals of coil	
	Start end to bar number	Finish end to bar number
1	1	2
2	2	3
3	3	4
4	4	5
5	5	6
6	6	7
7	7	8
8	8	9
9	9	10
10	10	11
etc.	etc.	etc.
24	24	1

Such tables are particularly useful in the case of a double layer wave winding where each coil is wound with two or more wires in-hand. The following tables for a four-pole, double layer, wave winding with two terminals per coil, 15 slots and 30 commutator bars, will illustrate their usefulness in such a winding:

TABLE FOR PLACING COILS IN ARMATURE SLOTS—DOUBLE WAVE WINDING

Coil number	Place sides of coil in	
	Winding spaces numbers	In slots numbers
1	1 and 8	1 and 4
2	3 and 10	2 and 5
3	5 and 12	3 and 6
4	7 and 14	4 and 7
5	9 and 16	5 and 8
etc.	etc.	etc.
15	29 and 6	15 and 3

TABLE FOR CONNECTING COIL LEADS TO THE COMMUTATOR—DOUBLE WAVE WINDING

Coil number	Connect terminals of coil	
	Start ends to bars numbers	Finish ends to bars numbers
1	1 and 2	15 and 16
2	3 and 4	17 and 18
3	5 and 6	19 and 20
4	7 and 8	21 and 22
5	9 and 10	23 and 24
etc.	etc.	etc.
15	29 and 30	13 and 14

Wave vs. Lap Windings.—The wave winding is mostly used on the smaller types of direct current machines of multi-polar construction. This winding has but two paths through the armature, regardless of the number of poles, and half the coils in the armature are connected in series in each path, whereas the lap winding has as many paths as there are poles, and a correspondingly smaller number of coils in series. For instance, in the case of a four-pole armature, wound with coils of the same number of turns and same size conductors; if all are connected in a wave winding, the armature will be suitable for double the voltage at half the current that would be used if the same armature were connected as a lap winding. Thus on small machines, where the number of turns is necessarily limited, the wave winding is usually much cheaper and easier to use. The wave winding is widely used in armatures for railway, hoist and crane motors.

The limitation in the use of the wave or series winding is in the main the amount of current which can be carried by one armature circuit. Since the wave winding consists of two circuits, the current per circuit is equal to one-half the total armature circuit of the machine. Where the value of this current exceeds that which has been found to be consistent with good practice, (up to 250 amperes per circuit in non-interpole machines and up to 550 amperes in interpole machines) then it becomes necessary to arrange more circuits on the armature, each circuit carrying a part of the total current. In this case the lap or multiple winding is usually employed, which as explained has a number of circuits equal to the number of poles of the machine. However, the choice of wave or lap windings is usually not only determined from the amount of current to be handled but is greatly influenced by the requirements for good commutation and by the size and design of the armature to be wound.

It is customary with some motor manufacturers to use wave windings wherever the current to be handled permits the use of a conductor of a sufficient size to form it into a wave shaped coil and where the number of coils in the slot does not become too large. The latter condition is objectionable on account of the space required for insulating the coils. Other manufacturers employ the lap winding wherever possible, that is, in cases where the number of turns per slot does not become too small. As a general rule, it can be said that the wave winding often works out to advantage in cases of comparatively large machines for low voltage whereas the lap winding

8

is preferable in cases of large or small machines for high voltage as well as for small machines for low voltage.

Except under the special conditions named above, such as heavy current to be handled by the armature, machines of high voltage, and small machines of low voltage where the lap winding has advantages over the wave winding, there is little choice between the wave or lap winding for those machines where the number of poles may equal the number of circuits of which the winding may be made up. It may be said that in this case, American practice favors the lap winding and European practice the wave winding.

It might be pointed out further that in a wave or two-circuit winding all of the coils between two diametrically opposite points on the winding are in series with each other while in a lap winding only the coils between adjacent pole centers are in series. Therefore, under similar conditions, the voltage in a wave winding will equal the voltage of a lap winding multiplied by the number of pairs of poles. The voltage between the commutator segments will also vary in the same ratio. In order to obtain the same voltage of the machine the relative number of coils in the two types must vary inversely with the number of poles and the size of the coils in the wave winding must increase in proportion. Where the size of armature coil does not become excessive nor the voltage between segments too great to permit good commutation, the wave winding can be used. These conditions, however, limit this type of winding under ordinary conditions to four or six pole machines. In cases where the number of poles is larger the lap winding has a wider application for direct-current armatures.

In regard to the selection of the proper type of winding for direct-current and alternating-current machines, Henry Scheril, formerly a member of the engineering department of the Crocker-Wheeler Company, has made the following comment (*Electrical Record*, January, 1919):

The selection of the proper kind of winding depends upon the capacity of the machine, the voltage and speed. Wave windings are used on machines of small capacity. They are also being used for low speed and medium ratings. On small

high voltage machines, like the railway motor, the wave winding is being used to advantage because it has only two sets of
brushes and it can be inspected very easily. Wave windings
are also used for the rotors employed in induction motors. In
all other cases, lap windings are to be preferred.

Lap Windings for Direct-current Armatures.—In general,
the ends of a coil of lap winding in a direct-current machine
are connected to the adjacent commutator bars. The sides
of the coil are spread over and placed in the slots of the armature corresponding to the distance equivalent to 180 electrical

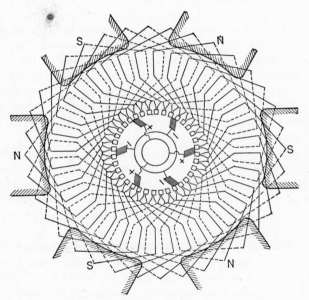

Fig. 98.—Lap or parallel winding for a 6-pole machine.

degrees. That is to say, if one side of the coil is under the
center of a north pole, then the other side of the coil will be
placed in a slot having a similar position under the adjacent
south pole. This brings one to a consideration of the winding pitch. The pitch is the number of slots spread over the
periphery of the armature corresponding to the arc equal to the
distance between two similar points of two consecutive poles.

For instance, if a machine has 72 slots and eight poles, the full pitch will be $72 \div 8 = 9$, and the coil will lie in slots of one and ten.

In a direct-current machine the lap or multiple winding has a number of paths for the current to travel through the winding from positive to negative, equal to the number of poles. It becomes necessary, sometimes, to wind a machine with what is known as the "short chord" or fractional pitch winding. In this kind of winding, using a fractional pitch, the coil is spread over the distance which takes in less than the number of slots between two similar points on two consecutive poles. The use of this kind of winding on a direct-current machine is made when there is a desire to improve the commutation. That is, because with a fractional pitch winding the emf., due to inductance of the armature, is lessened at the time of commutation. In direct-current machines it is not advisable to use a shorter pitch than about 90 per cent. of the full pitch. If this figure is exceeded then the advantages which this winding would give are practically eliminated and liable to bring about worse results.

All interpole machines are built with lap windings and equalizer bars are used. The setting of the brushes on interpole machines must be done very accurately because their position is fixed once and for all, but due to irregularities in manufacture, in order to eliminate any possibility of poor commutation equalizer connectors are being used.

Lap Windings for Alternating-current Machines.—Practically all alternating-current machines use windings having a short pitch. The reasons for using the short pitch winding, especially on alternating-current machinery, are many. To begin with, most manufacturers standardize their frames, standardize their shields, standardize the clearances between the rotary elements and the stationary elements. In some machines, the clearances between the windings and the shields, especially in machines carrying heavy currents, and also in high voltage machines, become very small due to the form of end connections which are being used in lap windings. It has been found that by using the short pitch winding, the end connections can be shortened considerably and thus obtain more clearance. Another reason for using the short pitch winding in alternating-current machinery is because if the machine is to be designed with existing punchings, there is a possibility that in designing the winding, one may get too many turns by using the full pitch due to a greater number of slots than required. By reducing the pitch from full to fractional, the same results are brought about as when the number of slots is reduced. In alternating-current machinery, short pitches are used as low as ⅔ of the full pitch. Practically all two-speed induction motors have ⅔ pitch.

Wave Windings for Direct-current Armatures.—The series or wave winding consists of coils spread over the per-

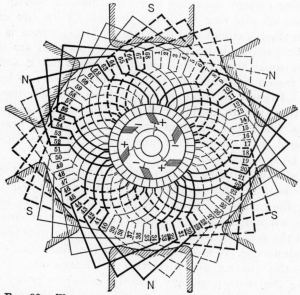

Fig. 99.—Wave or two circuit winding for a 6-pole machine.

iphery of the armature in the same way as the multiple winding but with the ends of the coil in the direct-current machines connected to the commutator bars whose relative positions correspond to about double pitch. From the nature of this winding, there are only two paths for the current to flow from positive to negative brush independent of the number of poles. Now since the winding goes around the armature several times, depending upon the number of slots, in order that the winding may not close upon itself, the number of coils in series must be one more than, or one less than the number of poles. Since this winding has only two circuits, regardless of the number of poles, only two sets of brushes are needed. However, when this winding is being used on machines of large capacity, there will usually be as many sets of brushes as there are poles. The purpose of this is twofold. One is to reduce the size of the commutator and the other is to reduce the brush density.

Wave Windings for Alternating-current Machines.—In alternating-current machines wave windings are mostly used in rotors of slip ring induction motors. They are either single or double circuit and their use for that purpose is twofold. One reason is because the end connections are much easier to make than in the case of the lap winding and the second reason is because of certain definite ratios to be obtained. Double or triple wave windings are also used on alternating-current machines of very low voltage and high currents where lap windings are found to be not practical because of the form of end connections. All wave windings should be symmetrical.

For a wave winding in an alternating-current motor the number of slots (plus or minus one) is chosen so as to be divisible by the number of poles. If the number of slots is plus one, the winding is called progressive, since after traveling once around the stator it returns to the starting slot plus one. If it is minus one, it is called retrogressive since the circuit returns the winding to the starting slot minus one. In this winding the correspondingly placed conductors under adjacent poles are connected in series with the circuit proceeding from pole to pole several times around the stator. The circuits are then interconnected to give the required phase relations.

Single vs a Number of Independent Windings.—Most machines are built with a single winding with the exception of some three-wire generators, having double windings, the two windings being independent of each other. All alternating-current machines are built with windings so that they can be easily changed from multiple circuit to single circuit. That is to say, the design of a winding for an alternating-current machine is made such that if it is built in two circuits, for say 220 volts, that same machine can have the windings reconnected for 440 volts.

Double or triple windings, either lap or wave, have been found to give much trouble in direct-current machines, especially in commutation. Sparking at the commutator becomes very pronounced and the commutator wears down very rapidly. For this reason this kind of winding is not widely used on direct-current machines.

Lap Windings vs Multiple Wave Windings.—Although they have not been much used in the past, multiple wave windings, sometimes called series-parallel windings since they are wave windings with more than two circuits, have some advantages. The points in favor of their use are outlined as follows by Albert A. Nims of the engineering department of the Crocker-Wheeler Company (*Electrical Record*, February, 1919):

There seems to be no reason for avoiding wave windings with more than two circuits on ratings where they would be desirable, provided they be made perfectly symmetrical. This condition would bar out a four circuit winding on a six-pole machine. Arnold, who is generally regarded as the originator of this type of winding, did not always insist on complete symmetry, but the writer believes that the unsuccessful experiences with series-parallel windings in the past has been largely due to an incomplete understanding or observance of the laws of symmetry of armature windings.

In windings with circuits equal in number to the poles multiple or lap windings are ordinarily used. They possess the advantage of having each coil commutated at only one brush, and also the disadvantage of having each circuit under a different pole, or pair of poles. If the field strengths under the various poles are not identical, the induced emfs in the various circuits are not the same. Undesirable currents, which may be of considerable magnitude because of the low resistance of the winding, then circulate between the different circuits, overloading some brushes and causing them to spark, and uselessly heating the armature. The brushes may be protected by diverting these currents through internal equipotential connections, but the useless heating of the armature still remains. This, however, is usually not excessive compared with the heating of other losses, so that this winding may be called standard today.

Series-parallel wave windings with circuits equal in number to the poles possess the disadvantage, common to all series wave windings, that the terminals of each coil lie under two different brushes, which are of the same polarity and, therefore, connected by a low resistance conductor. That is, a coil is commutated by two brushes and the connector between them and there is a tendency for selective commutation or unequal division of the current among the brushes to occur, especially in large non-interpole machines. This generally results in sparking at some of the brushes. They are eaten away so that the effective position of their contact surfaces are changed. Other brushes then get more current than they should and eventually all the brushes are damaged. Series-parallel wave windings do have the advantage that each circuit is influenced by all the poles, so that the induced emfs in all circuits are equal and there is little tendency for circulating currents to occur due to unbalanced induced emfs. To eliminate the disadvantages and combine the advantages of these two classes of windings, multiple wave windings have been used, particularly on four-pole machines. Although they are "special" and, therefore, cost more than standard windings, they accomplish their purpose admirably. There seems to be no reason why they would not be equally successful on machines with six or more poles.

Use of Equalizer Rings.—Equalizer rings are being used on lap windings only on large multipolar machines, where unbalanced conditions in the magnetic circuit are liable to cause circulating currents between the several paths through the armature. This condition will occur for instance in the course of operation where the air gap will not be uniform so that the emf induced in a coil opposite a small gap will be larger than that induced in the coil which is opposite the large gap and this difference in the emfs will bring about a circulating current which will flow between the windings and thus interfere with the performance of the machine. This condition will also occur if the machine has been in operation any length of time, the inequality of the air gap being brought about by the wear in the bearings. The same condition will occur if the brushes are not spaced properly. In a wave winding, each circuit has its conductors pass under all poles and, therefore, there is no necessity of using equalizer rings.

CHAPTER V

TESTING D.-C. ARMATURE WINDINGS

The common causes of trouble in armatures are practically the same as in any electrical circuit, namely, a short circuit in or between coils, an open circuit, reversed coils and grounds. Of all the faults inherent to armatures, probably the most dangerous is the short circuit between coils. If it is not detected and remedied as speedily as possible, the result in most cases is the burning out of the coils affected, and possibly the whole armature.

Causes of Short Circuit in an Armature.—There are numerous ways in which a short circuit of coils may occur. In the case of wire-wound coils, it sometimes happens that one of the turns forming the coil becomes twisted during the process of inserting the coil in the slot, and in order to force the winding down to an even depth, the turn of wire was driven down upon other turns, cutting through the insulation and causing a short circuit between turns of the same coil. When this occurs, the resistance of the coil is reduced, allowing more current to flow, increasing the temperature of the coil and eventually causing a deterioration of insulation on other wires at that point. In the majority of cases this results in short-circuiting the entire coil upon itself.

Also a frequent cause of trouble is the short circuit between coils This is often caused on the back end of the armature by oil soaking into the coils by leakage from the out-board bearing, which, together with the dust that will invariably work in between the windings, break down the insulation and cause an electrical leak between coils. A short circuit may also result from the top and bottom armature leads coming in contact with each other. A short circuit between commutator bars is often the cause of burned out coils. In soldering leads to the commutator, great care must be exercised not to

122

allow any of the molten solder to run down behind the bars, as this very frequently short circuits the bars. A good way to avoid this is to raise the back end of the armature a trifle so as to allow the solder to run to the front where it can be easily removed.

Tests for a Short Circuit in an Armature.—Probably the best way of detecting the presence of a short circuit in the armature of a motor in operation, is to carefully watch it when starting as soon as faulty operation is noticed. Sometimes the armature will not start upon the first few points of the rheostat, and will then take an excessive current. This will cause it to run with a slow and unsteady motion (especially at low speeds), due to the fact that every time the short-circuited coil comes under the influence of a pole, it will have a tendency to retard the motion of the armature. By running the motor for a short time, the bad coil will heat much more than the others, and its location can usually be detected by passing the hand over the end windings.

When a short circuit is suspected in an armature, the machine should be shut down at once and the necessary repairs made. One sure method of locating a short-circuited coil is to disconnect all the leads from the commutator and test out the coils with a test lamp. A test lamp consists of two wires about 10 feet long, connected to a 110-volt circuit with an incandescent lamp connected in series in the circuit. This method requires a great deal of work in unsoldering all the leads, which may not be necessary since in the majority of cases, the seat of the trouble will be found in the commutator itself, due to short circuits between bars.

A rapid test often used to locate the trouble without disconnecting any of the wires on the commutator during the test, is the bar to bar test. This test can be applied to armatures with any style of winding connections, for there will be exactly the same drop of potential between any two adjacent commutator segments no matter which scheme of connection is used. Fig. 100 shows the connections necessary for a test of this kind. A steady current, taken from a 110-volt circuit should be sent through the armature at opposite sides of the commutator. The brushes *B* should only be wide enough to

cover one bar.   *C* is a fiber block holding the copper contact
points, so spaced as to rest on adjoining segments as shown.
Adjust the lamp bank until the voltmeter gives a readable
deflection when *C* is in contact with what are supposed to be
good coils.   The deflection of the voltmeter will depend upon
the difference of potential between the bars.   If everything
is all right, practically the same deflection will be obtained
all around the commutator regardless of what pair of bars *C*

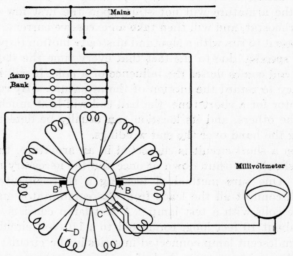

Fɪɢ. 100.—Connections for testing out armature coils with a millivoltmeter.

may rest upon.   Pass the contact points over each pair of
bars and note the deflection on the voltmeter.   When the
short-circuited coil, to which the bars are connected, comes
under the contacts there will be very little if any movement of
the needle, because there will be little or no drop through the
coil   A more satisfactory test for use on a removed armature
is the transformer test discribed on page 125.

When the coil at fault has been found in this manner, its
leads should be disconnected from the commutator, together
with the leads adjoining it on either side.   The commutator
should now be tested by use of the test lamp to determine if
the bars to which the coil was connected are short-circuited.

The banding wires should be removed from the armature next, and the defective coil taken out by raising the top sides of other coils clear of the armature as far around as the bottom side of the damaged coil, when it can be lifted out. In many cases the insulation on the wire of the coil has reached such a stage of deterioration that a new coil will be necessary, in which event a new one should be formed with exactly the same number of turns and size of wire as the old one. Care should be taken not to wrap a thicker layer of tape on the new coil than was on the old one, for if this is done trouble will be experienced in forcing the coil back into the slot. The finished coil should be given a coat of insulating varnish. It is a good plan to re-insulate the armature slots also, before returning the coil. If the commutator is free from short-circuits, the coil may be replaced, the raised coils returned to their slots, and the leads soldered to the commutator again.

Testing for Short Circuits and Open Circuits with a Small Transformer.—While the method of testing between adjacent commutator bars with a millivoltmeter will indicate short-circuited or poorly soldered leads by a low reading and open-circuited or poorly soldered leads by a high one, it often occurs that an armature is rewound and reinstalled with considerable time and labor and found to be defective after all. The millivoltmeter or drop of voltage method merely measures the resistance of each coil but when an armature is subjected to magnetic induction, an emf is induced in its windings which will cause current to flow in the turns that are short-circuited. When one turn in a coil has been forced so hard against another that the insulation is broken and the turns become short circuited, the millivoltmeter test may not serve to detect the short circuit and as a consequence the turns, and probably the coil, would be destroyed by the immense current which would flow in the short-circuited turns when running in the magnetic field of the machine.

A simple way of detecting such defects is by the use of a small transformer often called a "mill" or "bug" and constructed as shown in Fig. 101. When this transformer is applied to the armature core as shown, the alternating flux produced by it flows through the core and produces an emf. in

the coils.   If the winding is correct no current will flow as
the voltages will balance each other.   If, however, a coil is
short-circuited, a current will flow in the turns that are short-
circuited.   To locate the defective coils take a sharp piece of
steel or a knife blade and pass it around the commutator so as
to short circuit in succession, the coils which have one side
under the transformer.   A decided sparking, indicating a
potential difference between the bars, shows that the coil is
in good condition.   Absence of sparking indicates either

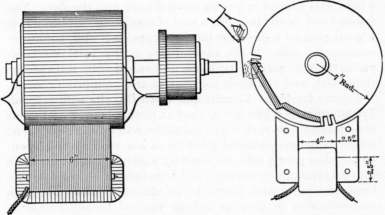

Fig. 101.—Method of testing an armature for short circuits and open circuits
in coils by use of the special transformer shown.

an open circuit or a short circuit.   The latter can be readily
determined by running a light piece of sheet iron over the
surface of the armature core so as to bridge the slots in succession.   If there is a short circuit in one of the coils which
has one side under the transformer, a local current will flow
through this coil generating a magnetic flux which will attract
the piece of sheet iron.   If it is held away slightly it will be
made to vibrate very rapidly.   The coil will also heat very
rapidly and if the transformer is large enough for the armature
being tested, the coil will be burned out completely.
   In case there is no sparking at the commutator when the
coils are short-circuited as described above and there is no

local magnetic flux when moving the piece of sheet iron over the slots of the core, an open circuit is indicated.

A transformer of the dimensions shown in the accompanying illustration can be operated on a 110-volt, 60-cycle circuit and will serve for testing many sizes of armatures. The one illustrated was made up by E. W. Copeland (*Electrical World*) using 60 turns of No. 6 magnet wire. When using such a transformer it should be fastened under the armature so that there is just enough clearance between the transformer and armature core that neither will touch. Current should always be off while placing the transformer and also when it is not in use.

When testing an armature with a small exploring transformer, the number of poles in the machine must be taken into consideration. In a two-pole armature, a single short circuit may heat up two coils, in a four-pole armature, four coils and so on. A good way to locate the defective coil is suggested by Maurice S. Clement (*Electrical Record*, November, 1918) by applying the telephone receiver test. In applying this test the terminals of a telephone receiver are placed on adjacent commutator bars which are connected to one of the affected coils, and the volume of sound transmitted to the receiver noted. The same should be done to all the other affected coils. A short circuit will have a greater volume of sound than a perfect coil.

Causes of Open Circuits in an Armature.—An open circuit may result from a number of causes. In the first place, when the armature was wound, the coil may have been driven into position in such a manner that one of the wires was strained or partly cut in two. The momentum of the armature, and constant vibration of the machine will finally break the wire, and in this way form an open circuit. Sometimes an open circuit of this kind will only show up when the armature is up to speed, the centrifugal force causing the wires to separate, thus opening the circuit. When the motor is at rest, the wires will come together again, and a test will reveal nothing. This condition is known as a "flying" open circuit, and occurs quite frequently. The same state of affairs may result with a short circuit between overlapping coils. An open circuit may also be caused by the armature leads being drawn too tightly when they are soldered to the commutator. This will cause a break due to expansion and contraction of the wire from the constant heating and cooling.

Another common cause of open circuits is poor workmanship when the leads are soldered to the commutator. If the lugs or risers are not perfectly tinned before attempting to solder the leads into them, the solder will not take hold over the entire area, and a lead may be held in place only by a thin film of solder on the outside surface. When the current through the armature is heavy, the contact area between the riser and the leads may not be sufficient to carry the necessary current without excessive heating. This will melt out what little solder there is, and an open circuit will result. Sometimes a commutator will become so hot from excessive brush friction, resistance drop, overloads, or the like, that it may throw solder, and cause an open circuit.

Tests for an Open Circuit in an Armature.—The symptoms of an open circuit are often very prominent. A vicious greenish-purple spark will usually appear at each brush as the open-circuited coil passes from one pole to the next. This spark has a tendency to leap out from the brush and follow around the commutator for quite a distance. The bars to which this coil is connected will be found to be burned and roughened, and the mica insulation between eaten out to a considerable depth.

In a lap wound armature the position of an open-circuited coil is easily located, because each end of the coil is connected to adjoining bars. In a wave winding this is not the case. Each end of a coil is connected to a bar removed a certain distance around the commutator from the other, depending of course, upon the number of poles and the winding pitch employed.

If an open circuit exists in an armature for any length of time, the burned condition of the commutator bars will usually indicate where the trouble is located. Both lap and wave wound armatures may be tested for open circuit by a testing transformer, by use of the ordinary test lamp, and a bar to bar test, or by ringing out between adjacent bars with a magneto.

If the test lamp is used, test the commutator from bar to bar and note the brightness of the lamp on each pair of bars. When the bars are reached to which the open-circuited coil is connected, the light will dim considerably, and may go out, depending upon the resistance of the winding. When more than one coil is open-circuited, the winding will be divided into two or more sections, and the test lamp will only light when the test leads are in connection with the bars in each section.

The testing set described for locating short circuits (page 124) may also be used for open circuits. Proceed in the same manner as when testing for short circuits. When the contact points C (Fig. 100) are connected to the open-circuited coil (indicated at D), there will be a violent throw of the needle, because the voltmeter will then be connected to brushes B through the intervening coils. When C is moved to the next segments, there will again be no deflection, thus locating the break definitely.

If an open circuit results from a lead breaking off at the commutator, it is an easy matter to solder it back again. When the break occurs within the coil itself, a new one must be substituted, as described for the short-circuit test.

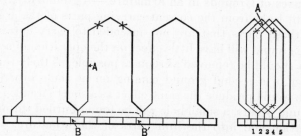

Fig. 102.—The illustration at the left shows method of bridging a coil of a wave winding. That at the right for cutting out a coil of a lap winding.

Cutting out Injured Coils.—In case of emergency, the bad coil can be cut out of circuit and the commutator bars connected together by a wire large enough to safely carry the current. This wire should be well insulated from the other leads, as any connection with them would constitute a short-circuit. In Fig. 102 the method of bridging out a coil in a

9

wave winding is shown. When one of the coils is short-circuited as shown at A, the top side of the coil is disconnected from bar B, and the bottom side from bar B' Jumpers should be soldered in as shown by the dotted line. The ends of the coil leads can then be cut off close to the armature core and taped. The coil should be cut completely in two at X and X', and the ends taped. This will prevent self-induced currents from being generated within the coil, which might cause heating and injure the insulation on other good coils. In Fig. 102 (at right) the method of cutting out a coil in a lap winding is shown. The coil is open-circuited at A. The top side of this coil should be disconnected from bar 3, and the bottom side from bar 4. In this case the jumper must be run from bar 3 to bar 4. The dead coil can be taped up the same way as the series or wave coil mentioned above.

One coil cut out of an armature will not perceptibly affect the running of a motor, and several of them can usually be cut out with safety, providing they are not bunched together. It is not wise to cut out too many coils, as this increases the heating and speed of the armature and lowers the efficiency of the machine.

Causes of Grounds in an Armature.—A ground occurs when current leaks from the current carrying parts of the armature into those parts that are not intended to carry current. A single ground will have little effect on the operation of a motor, but it should be removed as soon as possible, as there is always danger of a second ground coming on at some other point, which would produce the same effect as a short circuit. When a ground occurs, a small hole will be found burned through the insulation and into the iron parts of the armature. Across this carbonized insulation, current will pass. Grounds occur very frequently on the ends of the armature core at the points where the coils leave the core. If the bend has been too sharply made, or has been hammered too hard, the sharp edge of the core will cut through the insulation. To avoid this, the slot insulation should extend at least one-quarter to one-half inch past the end of the core on each end.

Grounds also frequently occur in the commutator, caused by oil creeping up on the mica ring. Combined with the copper and carbon dust from the commutator, this forms a good path for leakage of current.

Tests for Grounds in an Armature.—A ground can usually be located by using the test lamp.   Disconnect the leads from four of the commutator bars on one-quarter of the circumference.   This will determine the section of the winding in which the ground is located.   Raise the leads of the defective section out of the commutator.   Place one wire of the test lamp on the shaft, and with the other, test each coil separately to locate the ground.   Sometimes the trouble may not be in the armature, but may be caused by a grounded commutator. If the coil is at fault, it should be removed and reinsulated.

Reversed Coils.—A reversed coil, that is, one with the leads to the commutator reversed, frequently occurs.   A practical way of locating a reversed coil is to pass a current through the armature at opposite points.   The lamp bank and connections of Fig. 100 can be used for this test.   Then with a compass or small bar of magnetized steel explore around the armature to determine the direction of magnetism from slot to slot.   When the compass is over the reversed coil, the needle will reverse, giving a very definite indication of the coil which is connected wrong.   The leads of this coil should simply be reversed.

Use of a Bar Magnet and Millivoltmeter to Locate a Reversed Armature Coil.—In armatures where both leads of a coil are taped together, and led out from an identical point, there is considerable danger of getting the leads crossed while connecting, thus reversing the direction of flow of the current in that coil.   Such a reversal will in all cases "light out" as though perfect when tested with a lamp, but will cause bucking when the machine is run.   A reversed coil of this sort is unusually difficult to locate and in many cases a whole machine has been stripped because ordinary methods of testing failed to locate the trouble.

An efficient test which has been used by J. G. Yoerns (*Electrical Record*, September, 1918) is illustrated in Fig. 103. It will be noticed that a millivoltmeter is used rather than a voltmeter because of the greater sensitiveness of the former. Both terminals of the meter are connected to adjacent commutator bars. Next, take a piece of metal which has been magnetized and move it in a direction corresponding to the revolving of the armature, directly above the coil to which the meter is connected. It is well to keep in mind the fact that if a clockwise motion is used on the first coil, the same direction must be retained on all remaining coils, otherwise the meter reading will be backward. On the downward stroke of the magnetized bar and as it approaches the coil to be tested, magnetic lines of force will travel from the bar to the coil, thence to the meter, causing the needle to fluctuate slightly. If the needle jumps ahead on the downward stroke, it will jump backward on the upward stroke, and vice versa. The reversed coil will read opposite from the others. To change the direction of the fluctuations of the needle, either reverse the meter terminals or reverse the motion of the magnet.

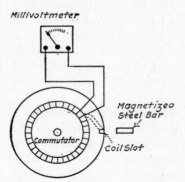

FIG. 103.—Method of using a magnetized bar and millivoltmeter to locate a reversed armature coil.

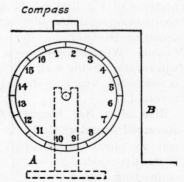

FIG. 104.—A convenient method for using a compass when testing for a reversed coil.

Use of a Compass to Locate a Reversed Armature Coil.— In connecting up small armatures with lap windings wound on by hand with four or more leads coming out of each slot, the leads may be easily confused as already mentioned so that some of the individual armature coils will be reversed. E. C. Parham (*Electrical Record*, August, 1918) has, therefore, suggested the use of the testing device shown in Fig. 104. While several reversed coils distributed around the armature may not cause sufficient effect to excite suspicion, they are likely to give trouble in time. It is conceivable that if alternate coils were reversed, a highly improbable condition, the armature would be inoperable because then there would be an equal number of coils tending to turn the armature in opposite directions.

The accompanying diagram (Fig. 104) shows a simple cheap method of readily locating any reversed coils that may exist. The armature rests in a support *A* that permit of rotating the armature as the test progresses. A strip of copper *B* is bent over the armature, as indicated, and a compass placed upon it. Current from an incandescent lamp test circuit is then applied to adjacent commutator bars that are connected to the coils that lie in the slot that is immediately under the compass. Suppose that the compass needle is deflected to the right on touching bars 1 and 2 and bars 2 and 3, there being two coils per slot. Rotate the armature until the next slot comes under the compass and touch the test points to bars 3 and 4 and then to bars 4 and 5, and so on all round the commutator.

The compass deflections obtained should be always in the same direction. Any pair of adjacent bars touched by the test points causing a reversed deflection, includes a coil the leads of which have been brought down to the commutator in reversed order. In order to test the effectiveness of the method, it is necessary to only apply the test points to adjacent commutator bars in reversed order and observe that the compass deflection is thereby reversed.

Locating Low Resistance or Dead Grounds.—It is often difficult to locate a low resistance or "dead ground" in a low resistance armature owing to the very low resistance of the windings themselves. In such cases the following method can be used:

First, short circuit all commutator bars by winding several turns of bare copper wire around them; then apply a source of energy, direct current being preferable, to the commutator and shaft. The voltage to be used depends upon the resistance of the "ground." This produces a circuit from the commutator through the grounded coil to the ground and out through the shaft, thus setting up a field around the conductors in this coil. By applying a small piece of iron to the surface of the armature core and gradually moving it around, the grounded coil can be located by means of its field, which will attract the iron.

The same method can also be applied to alternating current windings although not quite so readily. For example, in the case of a three-phase, single-circuit, Y-connected armature, first disconnect the Y, splitting the winding up into three separate circuits. Then test out each circuit with a magneto

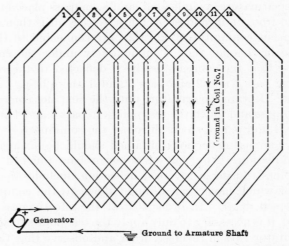

Fig. 105.—Method of locating grounds in an armature winding.

or test lamp. Next apply a current to one end of the grounded circuit and to the shaft. Assume that there are 12 coils as shown in Fig. 105, coil No. 7 being the grounded coil while coil No. 1 is connected to the line as shown. There will then be a circuit through coils Nos. 1, 2, 3, 4, 5, 6, and 7 which can be readily detected with a piece of iron as already explained, while coils Nos. 8, 9, 10, 11, and 12 are dead. It is then, of course, obvious that if coils Nos. 1, 2, 3, 4, 5, 6, and 7 carry a current while coils Nos. 8, 9, 10, 11, and 12 carry no current, the ground must be in some section of coil No. 7, the circuit being completed at that point.

Use of a Telephone Receiver in Testing for Short Circuits, Open Circuits and Grounds in an Armature.—The telephone receiver on account of being very sensitive to sound, makes a convenient testing instrument in a repair shop. The ways it can be employed to discover a short circuit, open circuit, or ground are given here as used by Maurice S. Clement (*Electrical Record,* December, 1918).

This testing device can be used either with alternating current or direct current. If alternating current is to be used, a test lamp and a pair of leads from a 110-volt circuit are connected to the commutator as in Fig. 106, from one-fourth to one-half of the circumference apart. Next, take the receiver which has about two feet of two-wire telephone cord attached and hold it to the ear. With the other hand press the receiver leads firmly to the commutator,

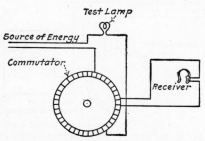

Fig. 106.—Connections for using a telephone receiver for locating short-circuits and open circuits in an armature winding.

taking care to touch adjacent segments. Move from one lead of the test lamp to the other segment by segment and repeat the operation until the commutator has been circled.

If the wire in the coils is of too low a resistance to make a buzz in the receiver, put a rosette fuse in place of the test lamp and cut a rheostat in series with the fuse. This will bring the resistance up sufficiently to make a buzz in the receiver. A low buzz indicates a good flow of current; if no sound whatever can be heard from two commutator bars, there is a dead short circuit. An open circuit is indicated by a very loud buzz. A cross connection will produce a defective sound on three segments. These three leads should be taken off and reconnected immediately and the receiver test once more applied.

For a dead ground which persists in remaining invisible, place one side of the receiver line to the shaft, as in Fig. 107, and the other side of the test line to the commutator, then, with the receiver to the ear, buzz each segment. The grounded coil will buzz louder than the rest.

If direct current is to be used, the source of energy should be a battery. A buzzer connected in series on one side of the battery completes arrangements.

Sometimes, when testing an armature with a transformer, a single short circuit will heat up coils in two, four, six or eight places, according to the polarity of the winding. By applying the receiver leads to the bars connected to each coil thus affected, a short circuit can be located quickly.

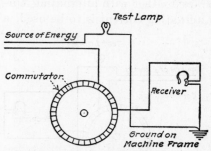

FIG. 107.—Connections for using a telephone receiver for locating grounded coils in an armature winding.

Testing for Reversed and Dead Field Coils.— In multipolar machines the polarity of field coils can be tested with a carbon filament lamp. By placing the lamp while lighted between the pole tips, the loops of the filaments will draw close together or separate far apart depending upon the direction of the magnetic flux. A dead pole can be quickly found in this way.

Another very simple and positive method for testing the polarity of field coils is by means of two ordinary iron nails. To do this, pass a current through the field coil winding and place the nails on two adjacent poles. If the polarity is right, they will attract each other and if wrong they will repel each other. This method can be used also for detecting a dead coil.

The Commutator.—Trouble in a commutator may be traced to either a short circuit or a ground. In a commutator a short circuit may be caused by any of the following: Particles of metal touching two adjacent bars, or mica burned away allowing current to arc across. In an undercut commutator be sure the slots between bars are thoroughly free from all dirt before testing. A grounded commutator must invariably be removed from the shaft, and the damaged part well cleaned and reinsulated. In a case where a motor has been through a

FIG. 108.—Testing switchboard in a large repair shop.

fire, the segments will in nearly all cases be undamaged, but the mica will be burned beyond future use, and in such a case refilling will be necessary.

Testing Equipment for a Repair Shop.—In addition to the facilities necessary for testing out armatures and machines for short circuits, open circuits, grounds and the like, every repair shop must be equipped to test and load motors of different sizes requiring voltages from 110 to 2300. A voltage of from 1200 to 1500 volts is needed for testing an armature for grounds. A transformer is therefore required with taps and connections so that the voltage can be varied from about 500 volts up to 2500 volts.

For testing for short circuits and open circuits a small transformer with specially shaped laminations about which a coil of wire is wound should be available (see Fig. 101 on page 126). When applied to an armature with a short-circuited coil, the defective coil will show up by getting hot.

For testing out circuits for opens, and to match up ends of coils when inserting them in the armature core, a test lamp and terminals is convenient. A magneto is also used for this purpose. In the case of testing for open circuits, two leads connected to a 110-volt circuit with a lamp connected in series in one of the leads is sufficient. For selecting coil terminals or "lighting-out" an armature winding while in the machine to discover trouble, a 6- or 12-volt automobile storage battery provided with two leads having snap testing clips and a lamp in series with one lead, is a convenient outfit that can be taken about the shop and to any job.

At least one portable ammeter and one voltmeter are needed and one ringing out magneto and a pair of head telephone receivers.

For testing motors a small switchboard wired so that connections can be made on the front by plugs and the voltage increased by using jumpers, is a convenient outfit that saves much time in making a test. This switchboard should have mounted on it, a voltmeter, ammeter, frequency meter and the necessary switches to connect and operate both motors and generators on either direct or alternating current.

CHAPTER VI

OPERATIONS BEFORE AND AFTER WINDING
D.-C. ARMATURES

Before an armature goes to an experienced armature winder and after it leaves his hands, there are certain steps in the process which can be properly termed "before" and "after" operations. In a case where a damaged armature must be completely rewound, these operations may be outlined as follows:

Operations before winding	Operations after winding
Stripping off old winding.	Testing out winding.
Cleaning slots and ends of core.	Soldering leads to commutator.
Filing burrs off slots.	Hooding armature.
Testing commutator.	Banding armature.
Repairing commutator.	Turning commutator.
Making new coils.	Undercutting mica of commutator.
Insulating ends of core and slots.	Balancing armature.
	Painting armature.
	Relining bearings.

Reference has already been made to a number of these operations in connection with the procedure in rewinding machines as outlined in Chapters III and VIII. The details that are given here refer to the requirements in all cases, with references to other Chapters where the operation has been taken up as a special subject.

Stripping Off an Old Winding.—In this operation when band wires must be removed, they should be cut or filed in several places. When a chisel and hammer are used care must be exercised not to mash down the armature teeth. The next step is to unsolder the leads to the commutator and clean out the slits in the commutator necks carefully. By pulling out

139

the top sides of the proper number of coils according to the throw, the bottom sides can be reached that will allow the coils to be removed easily. (See Chapter III.)

Cleaning and Filing Slots.—After the coils have been removed, all old insulation must be thoroughly taken off the core and the slots. A solution composed of 25 per cent. alcohol and 75 per cent. benzole is good for loosening the varnish of old insulation so that it can be scraped from the slots in the armature. This will produce no bad effects on the laminations or on the winding when the armature is rewound. Alkali solutions such as caustic soda will also loosen the insulation without injury to the laminations, but will creep between the laminations and after the armature is rewound the alkali fumes are liable to damage the insulation. A tool made from bar steel one by one-sixteenth inch, of suitable length and drawn down to a long thin point like a chisel answers very well to remove old insulation after it has been softened, and will also give very satisfactory results without the use of any chemicals whatever. After removing the insulation in this way a file drawn through the slots will remove small pieces of insulation and smooth off all roughness. The edges of the slots should be filed to remove sharp edges and burrs that would injure the new coils while being placed in the slots. The entire core should then be thoroughly cleaned with a blast of compressed air.

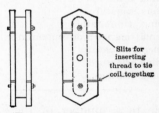

Slits for inserting thread to tie coil together

FIG. 109.—Shuttle form for winding a coil that can be pulled into a diamond shape in a special pulling machine (Fig. 291).

Testing Commutator.—Details of this operation are given in Chapter XII as well as the steps in repairing a commutator, testing it out after reassembly, baking the insulation and tightening end rings.

Making New Coils.—This operation calls for an inspection of the old coils and winding data as outlined on page 57, Chapter III. In case of changes in speed or voltage it requires certain calculations which involve the size of wire to use. These calculations are given in Chapter X, page 240. When the size of wire is known the winding of the coils can be done on one of the forms shown in Figs. 109 to 114.

In making coils in large repair shops three methods are used, namely winding on a mould, on a former or on a shuttle. Mould coils are usually those made on a form rotated in a lathe with all necessary shaping done with very little pounding on the conductors. By formed coils is usually meant, those coils made over a stationary form with the bends

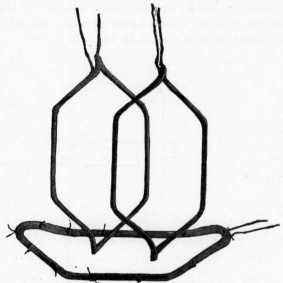

FIG. 110.—Three steps in the construction of shuttle wound coils (*Fairbanks-Morse & Company*).

(*a*) The coil at the bottom is shown as wound on a shuttle form using square copper wire. (*b*) At the left it is shown after being pulled into final shape, dipped in insulating varnish, thoroughly baked, and then taped. (*c*) The finished coil is shown at the right after four to six alternate dipping and baking treatments.

made by the use of levers and mallets to force the coil to the proper shape. Shuttle or "pulled" coils are first wound on a simple shuttle such as shown in Fig. 109 which is fastened to a lathe and then pulled on a coil puller to the shape required for the particular throw of the coil as shown in Fig. 110.

Forms for Winding Coils Like Those Previously Used.— A simple form that can be made from a pine board for duplicating the shape of coils previously used in an armature that is being rewound is shown in Fig. 111. The dimensions and general shape can be secured from a sample coil preserved from the old winding. In the illustration *A* is a small hole for mounting on a spindle. Small pins *B* are driven into the form to hold the coil in place while winding. *C* and *C'* are slots cut into the sides so that the several turns of the coil may be tied together with thread. This keeps the wires together after the coil is removed from the form. At the ends *D* and *D'* two pins are used in order to make the turn shown on the end section at the right in Fig. 111.

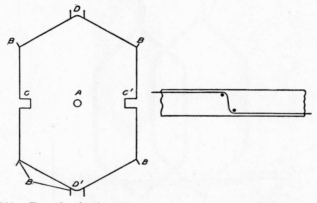

FIG. 111.—Form for shaping diamond armature coils to match old ones used.

Now mount the form on a spindle so that it can be revolved and wind on the required number of turns, using the pins as a guide. If the completed coil is to consist of two coils, take two wires and wind them together. When the proper number of turns have been made, cut off the wire and tie the coil with thread at *C* and *C'*. Remove the coil from the form and compare it with a sample if such a sample was preserved from the old windings. It is also well to try this first coil in the armature, and see that it has the proper span, and that the leads to the armature are long enough.

The following method for winding coils for small motors has been found convenient by Maurice S. Clement (*Electrical Record*, November, 1918) in those cases where a repair must be made on the job or coils made up where a coil winding machine is not available. The form is made up as follows: First take a flat piece of wood about three-fourths of an inch thick and plot out the shape of the coil. Then place right angle screw hooks, at all angle points. The screw hooks should point away from the center of the form. Mark out the center and run a breast drill through as far as it will go. Place the breast drill in a vise in a horizontal position with the coil form toward the left, taking care to place it so as to allow free

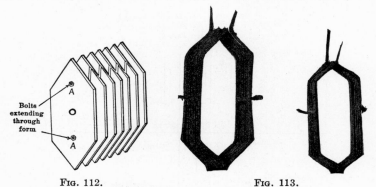

Fig. 112.   Fig. 113.

Fig. 112.—A six gang form for winding coils in series.

Six coils can be wound in series and removed in a group so they can be inserted in the slots of an alternating current motor stator without the necessity of makihg the series connections. This form can also be used to wind a single or double coil. It is built up in sections which are held together by the bolts at *A*. The slots in the divisions between sections enable the winding and removal of the coils in series.

Fig. 113.—Continuous jointless phase-group coils used on rotors of Fairbanks-Morse phase wound motors. These coils are wound on a form similar to that shown in Fig. 112.

movement of the handle. Turn the wire of which the coil is to be made, once or twice around a nail on the back of coil form, and lead the wire over the edge to the face of the form and turn the handle. The form can be revolved at any desired rate of speed and the wire run over all the screw hooks. Keep sufficient tension on the wire to permit each turn to lie snugly beside its predecessor.

This is a convenient way to wind coils, for the reason that unnecessary crossing of wires can be prevented. When the specified number of turns have been wound, twist a short piece of wire around each end of coil to hold it in proper shape.

To finish the operation, turn all screw hooks toward the center
of the form and slip the coil off.

Another hand-made form also recommended by Mr. Clement for use in winding larger coils than the one described
above is shown in Fig. 114.

Insulation of Core and Slots.—The insulation needed with
coils used in partially closed slots and in open slots of alternating current machines is given in Chapter VIII and in connection
with the winding of direct-current machines in Chapter III.

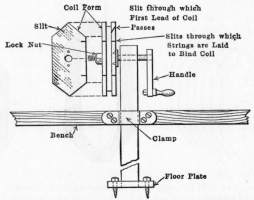

Fig. 114.—Construction of a convenient bench winder for forming armature
coils.

Testing Out the Winding.—Details of this operation both
before the leads to the commutator are connected and when
trying to locate troubles in the winding are given in Chapter V.

Soldering Coil Leads to the Commutator.—After the winding of an armature has been thoroughly tested out, the coil
terminals can be soldered to the commutator.   In the soldering operation great care should be taken that pieces of solder
do not fall or run down back of the commutator to later produce a short-circuit and cause the armature to be returned
for further repairs.   To prevent damage to windings, acid
fluxes should never be used in soldering a commutator.   A
solution of rosin in alcohol is recommended instead.   A tin
and lead solder is considered best in soldering leads to the
commutator but a pure tin solder is used in making all other

joints on the coils as the insulation is less liable to be damaged with this solder on account of its lower melting point. When tin is used the best results are obtained by working upon the side of the armature, so that the joint is level. After soldering, the armature should be mounted in a lathe and the rough solder on the necks of the commutator turned down, the commutator polished and the wiper rings turned to give the exact distance between bearings. In some armatures wedges are inserted in the slots above the coils. These extend above the surface of the banding grooves and should be turned down while in the lathe if they are used, so the banding grooves will present a smooth bed for the band wires.

Hoods for Armatures.—In order to protect armature end connections of railway motors and of mill motors that must be used in places where dirt and dust is liable to accumulate on the armature, a heavy hood is often put over the ends of the coils. For the commutator end a hood of woven asbestos is suitable. This hood is usually sewed in a conical shape and impregnated with a moisture and oil-repelling compound and fastened in place while wet. The small end should be drawn up over the commutator and turned inside out and firmly tied over the coil leads and commutator necks with heavy twine. The body of the hood should then be turned back over the armature. If the commutator necks are lower than the level of the core, another layer of twine should be wound over the hood near the commutator and a band of canvas sewed over the whole. The hood should then be stretched tightly back over the armature and tied with twine.

Around the rear end of the armature a band of canvas should be wrapped so that the greater part of the strip extends out over the shaft only enough being wound over the armature to permit a secure fastening. This should be bound in place with a band of twine wound tightly in the groove between the coil ends and the end bell. The canvas should then be turned back over the armature and bound smoothly in place.

In case the armature is to be banded with steel wire, two strips of cotton tape separated by a band of varnished paper should be wound over the hood and end connections near the core of the armature, as a base for the banding wires.

10

Banding Armatures.—In repair shops where banding machines are not available, the banding of armatures is done in a more or less indifferent way with the result that the banding may only perform a part of its function, namely, to prevent the coils from being thrown off the armature core. Unless the banding is placed on the armature with great care, there may be sufficient movement of the coils in the slots to wear the insulation and cause grounds. Such movement is also liable to cause breaks in the copper leads where they are soldered rigidly into the commutator. The details for banding an armature given in what follows, are taken from an article in the *Electric Journal* and represent good shop practice that can be followed in both large and small repair shops.

Shrinking Coil Insulation.—Since the coil insulation shrinks upon being heated, it is necessary to shrink it as much as possible before the final banding wire is applied. This is done by heating the whole armature to about 75°C. (167°F.), when the insulation becomes pliable and can be pressed down into permanent shape.

Temporary Bands.—The hot armature should then be mounted in a lathe and a protecting strip of cloth placed over the end windings. Wind a temporary banding wire over the coils with enough tension to draw them down into place, and fasten the ends by soldering tin clips over the wire. The armature should then be allowed to cool. After the temporary wires are removed the armature is ready for the permanent banding.

Banding Machine.—When a banding machine is used, the tension in the wire is regulated by passing it over a train of friction pulleys, mounted on the carriage. The friction of the pulleys can be adjusted to any desired value by the regulating screws. In the absence of such a device, fair results can be obtained by passing the wire two or three times around a round wooden banding stick approximately two inches in diameter and adjusting the tension by hand.

Core Bands.—When core bands are used, the grooves should be fitted with thin strips of tin, which protect the coils from the cutting action of the bands. In starting the permanent banding, wind a few turns at one end to secure the necessary tension. Then wind all the banding groups continuously, to eliminate the necessity of fastening the ends of each group as they are wound. The bands should be held together and the ends fastened by means of narrow tin strips (about 0.012 to 0.02 inch thick and 0.25 inch wide) placed under the wires and bent back over the top and held by pure tin solder. These strips should be inserted while the wire is being fed on and located about every three inches around the armature, with closer spacing at the beginning and end of each band. For the core bands, these strips should be placed in the slots and, being wider than the groove, they prevent any tendency for the bands to slide around the armature. The ends of the groups should then be cut and secured by being bent back outside one clip and inside the next one. Pure tin solder should be applied to the whole surface of the bands to form a solid web.

End Bands.—The end windings should be secured by groups of wire wound on insulating hoods to protect the coils. On the commutator end, strips of thin mica with overlapping ends are usually placed on the commutator neck and held in place with a few turns of twine. If a hood or head of canvas is to be used it should be wrapped around the neck, extending about an inch from the edge and turned inside out. After this end is secured with twine, the free end of the hood should be pulled back over the windings, bringing the outside of the hood at the surface and making a neat folded-under edge. This hood can be held temporarily with twine until the wire is applied. The other end of the armature should be similarly covered with a hood and banded.

Tension to be Applied to Band Wire.—The proper tension for banding wire when being applied varies with the size of wire and the construction of the end windings. When the end coils have no rigid support and extend out a considerable distance from the core, the tension should be gradually reduced, as shown in the accompanying table.

Wire.—The best material is a high-grade steel piano wire, having a final breaking strength of 200,000 lb. per sq. in. For temporary bands a cheaper grade can be used. The band wire should be tinned.

POUNDS TENSION FOR BANDING WIRES

Diameter of wire, in.	Core bands	End bands	
		At core	At end of wdg.
0.045	200	175	160
0.0641	300	250	225
0.0803	400	300	260

Solder.—Pure tin should be used, as this gives a band that will hold together for a longer time than half-and-half solder.

Flux.—About 1.5 lb. of powdered rosin, dissolved in one quart of denatured or wood alcohol makes a good flux.

Tin Clips and Strips should be of commercial sheet tin about 0.012 to 0.02 inch thick.

Precautions.—Use a band wire that is strong enough to prevent movement due to high speed and vibration.

Secure the ends of all band wires under the clips.

See that the bands are below the surface of the core to keep them from rubbing on the poles.

Before applying core bands, see that the tops of the coils are about $\frac{1}{32}$ inch above the band groove, so that the bands pull the coils down even with the core. If the coils are too high and the bands do not rest on the cores, loose bands will result when the insulation dries out.

Wind all core bands in one operation.

In soldering, use a 4-lb. clean iron, well tinned.

Bands to be effective should be kept tight. If they are allowed to become loose, grounded armatures and broken leads may result. It is considered good practice to reband new or newly rewound railway or hoist armatures after about 12 to 18 months as a safety-first measure; and to make renewals on old ones whenever the bands start to loosen. The service conditions—temperature and speed—largely determine the length of time that bands will hold tight. One large operating company rebands all armatures every two years.

Seasoning and Grinding a Commutator.—A new or reassembled commutator becomes "seasoned" that is the insulation baked out and all parts in their final set position, only after being in operation for a time with the necessary tightening and grinding. This is particularly true of a large commutator. Need of attention to a commutator will be indicated by roughness, high or low bars, flat sections resulting in poor commutation. If the commutator is in very bad condition it may be necessary to turn it down, but for ordinary cases a grinding tool is preferable and recommended such as shown in Fig. 115 (*Instruction Book*, Westinghouse Electric & Mfg. Co.).

Commutators should always be ground at from 100 to 120 per cent. normal speed. Turning requires a much lower speed; it should not be higher than 150 feet per minute.

Fig. 115.—Grinding device for truing commutators when they do not require turning down.

Before grinding a commutator, the machine should have been in service a sufficient length of time to bring the temperatures up to a constant value. Before grinding, the brushes should be lifted off the commutator as the copper and stone dust will rapidly wear them off. The dust will also become imbedded in the brush contact surface and later damage the commutator or cause poor commutation. The armature winding should also be thoroughly protected during this operation to prevent an accumulation of dirt and metal chips which may result in an insulation failure when the machine is again put in service. This protection can usually be obtained by using a circular shield of fullerboard, or similar material, around the commutator at the end next to the armature. This shield can be easily supported from the brush-holder arms and should extend from the commutator surface to an inch or two above the surface of the armature. It may also be desirable to put a temporary canvas hood over the armature winding. This protection can be best provided by carrying the copper dust away by means of a vacuum system. Even when this is done the armature should be protected as described. After grinding, the complete machine should be thoroughly cleaned by the methods already described. It may be necessary to repeat the heating, tightening and grinding one or more times before the commutator is in first-class condition. Emery cloth or paper should never be used for this purpose on account of the continued abrasive action of the emery which becomes embedded in the copper bars and brushes. Even when sandpaper is used the brushes should be raised and the commutator wiped clean with a piece of canvas lubricated with a very small quantity of vaseline or oil. Cotton waste should never be used and an excess of lubricant should be avoided.

The grinding device shown in Fig. 115 can be mounted in one of the brush-holder arms or brackets of a large machine. The grinding stones should be adjusted against the rotating commutator until a clean cutting effect is secured, but should be carefully shaped to the commutator surface before being placed in the grinding device. The stones can be moved across the surface of the commutator while it is running, by means of the handle shown at the right in the illustration.

Undercutting Mica of Commutator.—Several devices and hand tools are used for this operation. Details of their use and descriptions of the devices are given in Chapter XII, page 320.

Balancing an Armature.—After an armature has been wound, banded and its commutator trued it must be balanced. In the case of small medium speed armatures this operation can be successfully done on a pair of steel knife edges mounted parallel to each other and perfectly level. The ends of the armature shaft are placed on these knife edges so that the armature is free to roll. It is then given a slight roll with the hand and when it comes to rest, the bottom marked with a piece of chalk. This rolling and marking should be repeated several times. If the marks fall well distributed around the armature core the armature is in sufficient balance for service and can be placed in the motor. In case the marks fall close together or all on one side of the armature, it must be balanced by adding weight to the opposite side or removing weight from the heavy side. This is done in different ways depending upon how much the armature is out of balance. Before the weight is permanently fixed it must be determined exactly. This can be done by the use of slugs of lead properly attached and shaved down with a knife until the proper balance is secured. Frequently a nut or bolt head can be filed on the heavy side when the amount to be removed is small. Otherwise some method of attaching a piece of metal or solder must be devised equal in weight to the lead slug determined by the test.

For high-speed armatures and those machines where a perfect balance must be secured, the armature should be tested in a special balancing machine.

Painting the Winding.—The kinds of insulating varnish and impregnating compounds that should be used on an armature winding are given on page 176 of Chapter VII. Only good grades of insulation paints should be used on windings. When the winding is subjected to acid fumes, or the machine located in damp places the manufacturer should be consulted on the treatment that should be given the winding.

Relining Split Bearings.—The following suggestions (*Instruction Book*, Westinghouse Electric & Mfg. Co.) can be followed in renewing split bearings of the oil ring type. Melt the old bearing out of its shell and prepare an iron mandrel such as shown in Fig.

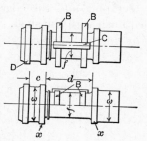

FIG. 116.—Mandrel for use when relining split bearings.

116 having the same diameter f as the shaft and dimensions c, d and e taken from the bearing to be renewed. Iron pieces BB and C should be attached by screws to the mandrel to form the oil ring slots and the horizontal inspection opening

in the top half of the bearing. The pieces *BB* should be tapered so that they will withdraw easily from the cast metal. A shoulder *D*, so placed as to fit against the end of the bearing shell serves as a guide.

For the Lower Half.—Warm the madrel and bearing shell and while both are still warm so as not to cool the metal too rapidly when pouring, place the mandrel in the lower half of the shell with the shoulder *D* tight against the end of the shell and the straight bottom portions of the pieces *BB* resting on the split plane of the bearing. Close the joints *x* with putty and fill the openings between the shell and the housing leading to the oil well with wet waste. Pour the molten metal, heated just enough to flow readily, into the space between the shell and the mandrel until the metal is flush with the split surface of the housing. The metal will harden very quickly and the mandrel can then be removed.

For the Upper Half.—Fill the openings in the upper half shell with putty and lay the mandrel in the shell with the split side up. Block the openings leading to the oil well with waste, and pour as described for the lower half. Remove the mandrel, smooth all rough edges in the bearing by chipping or filing, and chip the oil grooves in the lining of the upper half. The bearing surface of both halves should be eased off by scraping and the edges along the split surface should be filed flush with the shell.

CHAPTER VII

INSULATING COILS AND SLOTS FOR DIRECT-CURRENT AND ALTERNATING-CURRENT WINDINGS

On account of the fact that the voltage between commutator segments in a 110-volt direct-current machine is not often more than six volts, in a 600-volt machine not over 18 volts and in a 1200-volt machine a maximum of about 25 volts, the voltage between the conductors of an armature coil is relatively low. These conductors are usually provided with either a single, double or triple cotton covering, the triple covering being used when the voltage between the conductors is near the upper limit of 25 volts. Where the winding space is small a silk covering is sometimes used in small machines. After the coils have been formed and bound together to hold the strands in place, the entire coil receives a special insulation as a protection against breakdown between the copper of the coil and the iron of the slot in which it is laid. The insulation for small low voltage machines may consist of a wrapper of treated cloth or mica held in place by a layer of cotton tape wound so that it does not overlap. The end connections of the coil are then protected by an overlapping layer of cotton tape with cotton sleeves used on the leads as further protection. The entire coil is then dipped in an insulating varnish and baked.

Insulation for Armature Coils and Slots.—In addition to the insulation provided on the coils, it has been found necessary to pay particular attention to the insulation of the winding as a whole from the armature core. The insulation used performs two functions, namely, to provide mechanical protection and to serve as electrical insulation. The following classification can be made of the materials that are much used as slot and coil insulation:

For Mechanical Protection.—Pressboard, presspahn, vulcanized fiber, hard fiber, fish paper, rope paper, Japanese and Manila paper.

For High Temperatures and Electrical Insulation.—Mica, micanite, mica paper and mica cloth.

For Electrical Insulation Only.—Cotton tape and oiled or treated cloth which includes cotton or linen muslin, varnished cambric, varnished muslin, and empire cloth.

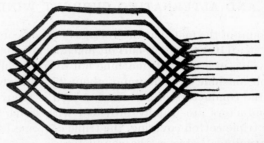

Fig. 117.—Type of wire wound coils used in stator of Fairbanks-Morse alternators (Fig. 155). These coils are thoroughly insulated and require only a non-abrasive material in the slot to give mechanical protection to the coils.

For Mechanical Protection and Electrical Insulation.— *Pressboard* or *fullerboard* is a material resembling cardboard and made from cotton rags and paper clippings. It varies from seven to 125 mils in thickness and when properly treated and varnished has a dielectric strength of about 500 volts per mil in thickness up to 25 mils and then reducing to about 200 volts per mil in the thicker sheets.

Presspahn is the name given to the pressboard which is made in Germany.

Vulcanized fiber also known as *hard fiber* is a dense hard material with a dielectic strength of about 200 volts per mil at thicknesses of from 50 to 150 mils. It is used wherever an insulating material of exceptional mechanical strength is needed such as wedges in armature slots and coil braces.

Horn fiber is a material made in different colors that has a high tensile strength and also a good dielectric strength (250 volts per mil when 10 mils thick) which can be increased by impregnation with oil or varnish.

Fish paper is made from rag stock and through a treating process becomes a hard fiber-like paper which is very strong. This material is not affected by heat and on account of this

and its mechanical strength is much used as cell lining in armature slots.

Manila paper is made from linen or Manila fiber producing a tough strong paper which when dry has a dielectric strength varying from 100 to 230 volts per mil in thicknesses of from 1.8 to 28 mils.

For High Temperatures and Electrical Insulation.—*Mica* is one of the very few materials which maintains a high dielectric strength at high temperatures. It is not, however, mechanically strong. Flexible sheets of mica are made up by sticking thin splittings of mica on one side of a sheet of paper or cloth with a suitable varnish in such a way that the joints

FIG. 118.—Different types of coils used in rewinding motors.

(1), (2), and (3) are wire wound direct-current coils. Two sections are shown in (1) before assembling the complete coil in (2). The coil in (3) is ready to be spread into a diamond shape in a pulling machine. (4) is a so-called mush or basket coil for partially closed slots. The coil as shown is ready for use in A. C. motors from about ½ to 15 hp. (5) is a completed strap coil ready for final treatment or dipping. (6) is a shuttle wound coil, three wires wide by eight wires deep in series for A. C. motors with open slots. This coil is spread into shape in a pulling machine. It is insulated with varnished cambric at the end where wires cross in winding. The coil at (7) is the same as (6) after being spread and insulated with tape.

are staggered. Such built-up sheets are known under different names, such as "Japanese Paper and Mica," "Fish Paper and Mica" and "Treated Cloth and Mica." These are also referred to as *Mica paper* and *Mica cloth*.

Micanite is a form of reconstructed mica made both in plate and flexible forms. The latter is used for armature slots and the former for commutator segment insulation. Its dielectric strength is very high ranging in the flexible form from about 600 volts per mil for five mil thickness to 500 volts per mil in

125-mil thicknesses. *Micanite paper* and *Micanite cloth* is also made with Japanese paper and with muslin.

For Electrical Insulation Only.—Cotton is used in the form of tape or cloth. When used primarily for its dielectric strength, it is treated with an insulating compound. After such treatment cotton cloth will withstand about 1000 volts per mil thickness. Because this insulation is flexible and tough it is much used as an insulation in the insulating of coils and other parts of electrical machinery. Since it is quite susceptible to damage and abrasion it is mostly used with a protective covering such as untreated cotton tape or friction tape or a tough paper such as fish paper. Different weights and thicknesses of cloth are used for insulating purposes such as cambric five mils thick; muslin eight mils thick; heavy cotton 11 mils thick; drilling about 17 mils thick; and duck about 30 mils thick. When duck is treated with linseed oil or varnish it is frequently used as a protective covering over coil supports, between coil ends and over the ends of armatures. Cotton insulating material when treated with an insulating compound, varnish or linseed oil, is known under several names such as *varnished cambric, varnished muslin, Empire cloth, Kabak cloth,* etc.

Any of the cotton materials can be cut into narrow widths for use as tape when insulation is more important than mechanical strength. Tape cut on the bias is used to tape-up coils of irregular shapes.

Descriptions and Uses of Insulating Materials.—In the following paragraphs the composition of the insulating materials already mentioned together with many others that are available are given with their various uses. This information is taken from a comprehensive classification of treated cloths, pressboards, fibers and papers by Hugh E. Weightman, Chief Engineer, Engineering Service Company, Chicago, Ill. (*Electrical Record,* July, 1919).

Treated Cloths.—The different kinds of treated cloths which are available are as follows:

Black varnished cambric	Yellow varnished cambric
Japanned muslin	Oiled muslin
Japanned duck	Yellow oiled canvas
Varnished silk	Yellow oiled cotton drill

Uses and Properties of Treated Cloths.—Each of the materials in the foregoing list has somewhat different insulating properties. Black varnish cambric is a varnish coated cloth used in the form of straight-cut tape for wrapping wire and cables and as bias cut tape for armature coils. It is usually supplied in 0.010-in. and 0.012-in. thicknesses in rolls about 36 in. wide. It is also supplied in ready cut tapes. The material is obtainable in two or more grades, the cheaper grades being used for phase insulation.

Japan muslin is unbleached muslin cloth treated with black japan and baked to produce a waterproof material of good insulating properties. It is used for wrapping where a coarse cloth is permissible and is usually supplied by the manufacturer in 0.017-in. thick by 30-in. wide rolls.

Japan duck is a high grade 8-oz. duck approximately 0.025 in. thick and of close weave. It is treated with japan and oven cured. It is chiefly used under the binding bands of railway motors as a protecting and moisture excluding fabric. This material is usually supplied in rolls 36 in. wide.

Varnished silk is made of Japanese silk treated with a high grade insulating varnish and oven cured. This makes a thin, tough insulating material of high dielectric strength which is used where light weight and a minimum of thickness is required. Varnished silk is also employed on meter coils and as insulation in airplane apparatus. The material in addition to being light does not become brittle in extreme cold nor gummy in heat. It is quite expensive and for that reason is not generally applicable. The usual thicknesses are 0.003 in. and 0.005 in. Sheets are 27 in. wide.

Yellow varnished cambric is a strong, closely woven cotton cloth having an especially soft finish and treated with high grade varnish. The varnish is baked in place, producing a material having a very high dielectric strength and a hard smooth surface. Its insulation resistance is usually not as high as black varnished cambric, especially at high temperatures. It is more easily handled than the black varnished cambric. It is usually supplied in rolls and sheets 36 in. wide and in tapes straight-cut or bias-cut, 0.010 in. and 0.012 in.

thick. This material is used for much the same purposes as black varnished cambric.

Oiled muslin is a linen finished cloth coated with oil and oven cured to set the film to a hard smooth surface. The product is a flexible cloth having high insulating properties and good resistance to deterioration through vibration or aging. It is used for a large variety of purposes, especially for wrapping armature coils and, in tape form, for taping coils and leads. It is supplied 0.007 in. thick in 36-in. rolls or in standard width tapes.

Yellow oiled canvas is a high grade duck treated with oil to produce a flexible waterproof material. It is used for pads under railway motor field coils and in similar places. This material is commonly obtained in one thickness of 0.045 in. in rolls 36 in. wide. It is also used for tarpaulins for generators, switches and such apparatus. Yellow oiled cotton drill is a light unbleached cotton drill treated with oil and oven cured to set the film to a firm surface. It is made 0.017 in. thick and in rolls 30 in. wide. It is often used for coil separators in transformers and regulators.

Pressboards, Fibres and Papers.—Fibers, leatheroids and such materials, are especially selected for their high insulating properties, and they are treated to render them more pliable and easily worked. The treatment does not appreciably affect the thickness except in the case of the shellacked materials. This treatment adds approximately 0.005 in. in thickness to the size of each sheet. When ordering treated material from the manufacturer the thickness always refers to the untreated material. The following kinds of this class of treated materials are available:

Pressboard	Varnished rawhide fiber
Japanned pressboard	Leatheroid
Oiled pressboard	Express parchment paper
Shellacked pressboard	Shellacked express paper
Varnished pressboard	Varnished express paper
Horn fiber	Red rope paper
Japanned horn fiber	Oiled red rope paper
Oiled horn fiber	Shellacked red rope paper
Shellacked horn fiber	Varnished red rope paper
Varnished horn fiber	Shellacked bond paper

Rawhide fiber
Japanned rawhide fiber
Oiled rawhide fiber
Shellacked rawhide fiber

Asbestos paper
Oiled asbestos paper
Varnished asbestos paper

Pressboards.—Pressboard is a specially prepared paper which is dense, flexible and easily worked. It readily absorbs oils and varnishes which render it less hygroscopic than in its untreated state. It is used very extensively as layer insulation and spacers in various types of generator, motor, transformer and regulator coils. Collars and shields on high-voltage transformers are also made of this form of insulation. One manufacturer carries this material in stock in the following sizes:

Thickness in inches	Size of sheets in inches
0.009	30 × 40
0.020	33 × 64
0.030	34 × 40
0.030	36 × 84
0.60	34 × 40
0.60	36 × 84
$\frac{3}{32}$	24 × 60
$\frac{1}{8}$	40 × 60

Japanned pressboard is used for separators and fillers in armature and field coils. It is made in the same sizes listed in the preceding paragraph. Oiled pressboard is used in the same way as japanned pressboard, and it is sometimes preferred since it is more flexible. It is supplied in the same sizes as given for pressboard. Shellacked pressboard finds its principal application as separators in bonding railway armature coils. The shellac upon the application of heat, melts, forming a close union between the separator and the coil. The principle thickness used is 10 mils or 0.010 in. although other sizes are available. This material is often made up locally by manufacturers. Any sizes previously listed are available.

Pressboard varnished and oven cured is used for fillers and separators. The usual sizes are available as listed above.

Horn Fibers.—Horn fiber is a tough flexible insulating material of high mechanical and dielectric strength. It is used for separators, slot channels, angles and joint insulation.

and wherever a high degree of flexibility is essential. This material can be bought in both sheets and rolls. All horn fibers are obtainable in the same thicknesses as listed for pressboard. Japanning greatly increases the flexibility and dielectric strength of horn fiber. One special application of japanned horn fiber is as fillers for bracket insulation and around rocker arms.

Treated with oil and oven cured horn fiber makes a superior dielectric material for general work. Shellacked horn fiber finds its greatest application as slot armors, it being customary to form the armors before shellacking. Varnished horn fiber is used for fillers and separators in preference to pressboard on better machines and especially on high speed units because it is more flexible and does not disintegrate as rapidly when subjected to vibration.

Rawhide Fibers.—Rawhide fibre is a harder pressed material than horn fiber and consequently lacks some of the flexibility of the latter. It is very tough and can be rendered more flexible by treatment with japan, oil shellac or varnish. Untreated it is used where toughness is essential and where great flexibility is not required. The thicknesses of the stock sizes of the different forms of rawhide fiber usually found on the market are: 0.005 in., 0.010 in., 0.015 in. and 0.020 in. Sheets or rolls are 40 in. to 48 in. wide. Sheets are usually 72 in. to 120 in. long. Japanned rawhide fiber has increased dielectric strength and is more flexible than the untreated fiber. It is used for the more simple shapes of slot armor and for fillers and separators. Rawhide fiber treated with a high grade oil and oven cured to produce a firm surface is used for the same purposes.

Shellacked rawhide fiber is used for the same purposes as shellacked horn fiber, where great flexibility is not required. Varnished rawhide fiber is the most flexible of the rawhide fibers and is used for fillers and separators.

Leatheroids.—In appearance leatheroid is quite similar to rawhide fiber. It is used for the same general purposes as the rawhide and horn fiber. It is, however, more resistant to heat, is more dense and molds more readily than either of the others. The usual thicknesses available in sheets or rolls

42 in. wide are 0.010 in., 0.015 in., 0.020 in., 0.030 in., 0.060 in., and ⅛ in. The sizes apply to all forms of leatheroids. The japanned leatheroid is used similarly to japanned horn or rawhide fiber where these materials are unable to stand the heat. Oiled leatheroid is used in place of oiled horn or rawhide fiber where a greater resistance to heat is desirable.

Paper Insulation.—Express parchment paper is a strong high-grade wood fiber paper selected to insure freedom from pin holes and metallic particles. It is used for layer insulation and in making up pasted mica sheets. The commercial sizes are as follows:

> Rolls 0.003 in. thick, 30 in. wide
> Rolls 0.005 in. thick, 32 in. wide
> Rolls 0.009 in. thick, 32 in. wide
> Sheets 0.005 in. thick, 30 in. × 35 in. wide
> Sheets 0.009 in. thick, 30 in. × 35 in. wide.

When it is shellacked, express parchment paper is used for armature and field coil bonding. The 5- and 9-mil sizes are most frequently used for this purpose. Varnished express parchment paper is used chiefly for slot insulation, its best recommendation being its glossy surface to which coils will not readily adhere when putting them in place. The same commercial sizes are available.

Red rope paper of a good hemp rope stock, selected to avoid pin holes and metallic particles is used in conjunction with parchment paper and other insulations in building up layer insulations. Treated with hot oil red rope paper is excellent for troughs, slot insulation, etc. Where heavy bar wound armature coils are used which are subjected to steam mold bonding shellacked red rope paper is usually used. The sizes listed for express parchment apply equally to these red rope papers. The 5- and 9-mil sizes of shellacked red rope paper are the most used. Red rope paper varnished and baked is used principally for slot insulation. As a rule it is made only in 5- and 9-mil thicknesses in sheets 30 in. by 55 in.

Shellacked bond paper is bond paper treated with a medium bodied shellac solution. It is used for separators in steam molds and is usually obtainable in rolls of any desired width. The thickness is 0.010 in. or 10 mils. Asbestos paper is used

11

in making layer insulations where heat resistance is needed. This material must be purchased under specifications having a test or inspection clause in order to guard against the presence of conducting particles of iron oxide.   It is furnished usually in rolls 36 in. wide and in the following thicknesses: 6 mil, 15 mil and 20 mil, $\frac{1}{32}$ in., $\frac{1}{16}$ in. and $\frac{1}{8}$ in.   Asbestos paper treated with hot oil and oven cured is used in railway motor, field and armature coils and in machinery operating at high temperatures.

When the asbestos paper is treated with a special black plastic varnish and oven cured it becomes a great moisture proof insulation and is used in forms for cores or spools.   It is used as a moisture-proof, heat-resisting insulation for motors intended for naval, mine or similar services.

Coil and Slot Insulation Used in One Large Repair Shop.— The following grades and thicknesses of coil and slot insulation is carried in stock and used by one large repair shop where all types, makes and sizes of motors are rewound.

Fish Paper: In sheets 4, 7, 10, 15 and 23 mils thick.

Fish Paper with Mica Splittings: In sheets 13 mils thick.

Fullerboard: In sheets 7, 10, and 15 mils thick.

Shellacked Fullerboard: In sheets 7, 10 and 15 mils thick.

Treated Cement Paper and Mica Splittings: In sheets 14 mils thick.

Barren Paper: In sheets 3 and 5 mils thick.

Empire Cloth: In sheets 9 mils thick.

Cotton Duck: In sheets 12 mils thick.

Cotton Tape: In widths $\frac{3}{4}$ and $1\frac{1}{2}$ in., 7 mils thick.

Treated Cloth Tape: In width $\frac{3}{4}$ in., 8 mils thick.

Under the different headings of Chapter III dealing with the windings of particular machines, details are given concerning the uses of the different insulating materials described here.

Micartafolium.—A special insulating material has been developed by the Westinghouse Electric & Manufacturing Company which is known as *micarta*.   In the form of *micartafolium* it can be used as a wrapping.   This insulation is used on the larger alternating-current armature windings, particularly those of alternating-current turbo-generators. It is also used for direct-current armature windings.   For commutators it is used between the bottom of the segments and the sleeve on the driving spindle. It is also used in direct-current machines for flash guards between the commutators and the armature winding of large units. For insulating studs and the capping of nuts and bolt heads it has also been found satisfactory. This type of insulation is made in sheets, blocks and tubes.

Thickness of Insulation Required in Slots.—Prof. Alfred Still in his book on Electrical Design, under the heading of slot lining points out that the insulation may be placed around the individual coils or in the slot before the coils are inserted. Part of the insulation may also be placed around the coils and the remainder in the form of slot lining. The essential thing is to have sufficient thickness of insulation between the cotton-covered conductors and the sides of the slot. In this connection the following figures are given by Prof. Still for the thickness of slot lining required for machines of different voltages. The thickness in inches is for one side only of the slot, and is as well the thickness that should be provided between the upper and lower coil sides in the slot.

Operating voltage for direct-current machines	Slot insulation—one side	
	A[1]	B[2]
Up to 250	0.035 inch	
Up to 500	0.045 inch	0.035 inch
Up to 1000	0.060 inch	0.055 inch
Up to 1500	0.075 inch	

For alternating-current machines

500 to 1,500, same as for direct-current machines		
Up to 2,000	0.080 inch	0.090 inch
Up to 4,000	0.120 inch	0.130 inch
Up to 8,000	0.190 inch	0.185 inch
Up to 12,000	0.270 inch	0.220 inch

Insulation of Formed Coils.—The practice of most motor manufacturing companies is to insulate coils for two or three ranges of voltage. In making changes in the connections of

[1] Prof. Alfred Still—Principles of Electrical Design.
[2] H. M. Hobart—Design of Polyphase Generators and Motors.

induction motors, therefore, where the changes involves an increase in voltage, it is important to know that the changes do not subject the coils to a voltage outside the range for which they were insulated. This precaution does not, of course, apply when reconnecting for a lower voltage.

Fɪɢ. 119.—Diamond shaped coil insulated and impregnated with compound ready for use (*Westinghouse Electric & Mfg. Company*).

The practice of one large manufacturer is to insulate coils for three ranges of voltage as follows:

I. Direct-current and Alternating-current Group Coils for Voltages up to 220.

For plain coils—other than phase coils:
1. Wound with double cotton-covered wire.
2. Binding paper over slot side, 0.003 inch thick.
3. 1½ turns treated cloth on slot side, 0.008 inch thick.
4. Cotton tape, one-half lapped all around, 0.004 to 0.007 inch thick.
5. Entire coil dipped in insulating compound and baked.

For phase coils the same insulation is provided and in addition a layer of empire cloth and tape over each end of the coil up to the straight sides. The diamond points are painted red to distinguish these coils from plain coils. Phase coils are used at beginning and end of each phase group.

II. Direct-current and Alternating-current Group Coils for Voltages up to 500.

For plain coils—other than phase coils:
1. Wound with double cotton-covered wire.
2. Binding paper over slot side, 0.003 inch thick.
3. 1½ turns mica and fish paper on slot side, 0.012 inch thick. This is made up of fish paper, 0.004 inch; three layers mica splittings, each 0.001 to 0.003 inch thick; Japanese paper, 0.001 inch thick. All shellacked together.

4. Cotton tape, one-half lapped all around, 0.007 inch thick.

5. Entire coil dipped in insulating compound and baked.

For phase coils the insulation of ends is the same as for 220 volts of the first group.

III. Alternating-current Group Coils for Voltages from 500 to 2300.

For plain coils—other than phase coils:

These coils are insulated the same as group II except 3½ turns instead of 1½ turns of fish paper and mica are used. A layer of treated cloth on the ends of the coils is also used.

For phase coils two layers of treated cloth and a layer of cotton tape are added.

Insulation for Coils used in 240-Volt and 500-Volt Direct-current Machines.—The following recommendations are given by Prof. Alexander Gray (Electrical Machine Design, Chapter IV on Insulation) for the windings of 240- and 500-volt direct-current machines.

For a 240-volt, double-layer winding with two turns per coil and four coil sides (eight conductors) per slot, the conductors being of strip copper wound on edge:

(a) After the copper has been bent to shape, tape it all over with one layer of half-lap cotton tape 6 mils thick. This forms the insulation between the adjacent conductors in the same slot.

(b) Tape together the two coil sides when they form one group (as in this case) with one layer of half-lap cotton tape 6 mils thick all around the coils. This forms the end-connection insulation and also part of the slot insulation.

(c) Bake the coil in a vacuum tank at 100°C. (212°F.) so as to expel all moisture, then dip it into a tank of impregnating compound at 120°C. (248°F.) and leave it there long enough to become saturated with the compound.

(d) Put one turn of empire cloth 10 mils thick on the slot part of the coil and lap the ends. This insulation should extend ¾ inch past the ends of the slot.

(e) Put one turn of insulating paper 10 mils thick on the slot part of the coil and lap it over at the ends. This paper should be long enough to also extend past the edge of the slot ¾ inch on each end. It is not put on for insulating purposes but to protect the other insulation which is liable to become damaged when the coils are being placed in the slots.

(f) Heat the coil to 100°C. (212°F.) and then press the slot part to shape while hot. The heat softens the compound and the pressing forces out all excess of compound. The coil can then be allowed to cool while

Fig. 120.—Coil taping and insulating department of a large repair shop.

under pressure and will come out of the press with such a shape and size that it will slip easily into the slot.

(*g*) Dip the ends of the coil in elastic insulating varnish.

For a 500-volt, double-layer winding having five turns per coil, and thirty conductors per slot, with the conductors covered with double-cotton coverings:

(*a*) Put one turn of insulating paper 5 mils thick around the slot part of the two conductors that form the individual coils. This paper should extend ¾ inch beyond the edge of the slot at each end. It forms part of the insulation between the individual coils in the same slot and also part of the insulation from winding to core.

(*b*) Put one turn of empire cloth 10 mils thick around the three coils that form one group and lap it over at the ends. Allow this insulation to extend as before ¾ inch at each end of the slot.

(*c*) Put one turn of paper 5 mils thick on the slot part of the coil and lap it on the top. As in the other cases allow the paper to extend over the slot length ¾ inch.

(*d*) Tape the ends of the groups of three coils with one layer of half-lap cotton tape 6 mils thick and carry this tape on to the paper for ½ inch to seal the coil.

(*e*) Wind the machine with these coil groups, putting a lining of paper 10 mils thick in the slot and then hold the coils down with band wires.

(*f*) Place the armature in a vacuum tank and bake it at 100°C. (212°F.) to expel moisture, then force impregnating compound into the tank at a pressure of 60 lb. per square inch and maintain this pressure for several hours until the winding has been thoroughly impregnated.

(*g*) Rotate the armature while it is still hot at a high speed so as to get rid of the excess of compound which will otherwise come out when the machine is carrying a heavy load.

(*h*) Paint the end connections with elastic finishing varnish, taking care to get into all the corners.

Coil Insulation for Induction Motor Windings.—The following recommendations are given by Prof. Alexander Gray (Electrical Machine Design, Chapter XX on A.-C. Insulation) for the coil and slot insulation of induction motors:

For 440-volt, wire-wound coils of double-layer windings:

(*a*) Double cotton covering on the conductors.

(*b*) A layer of empire cloth six mils thick between horizontal layers of conductors.

(*c*) One turn of paper 10 mils thick on the slot part of the coil to hold the conductors in layers.

(*d*) One layer of half-lapped empire cloth tape six mils thick all around the coil.

(*e*) One turn of paper 10 mils thick on the slot part of the coil to protect the empire cloth.

(*f*) One layer of half-lapped cotton tape six mils thick on the end connections to protect the empire cloth.

(*g*) The coil should be baked and impregnated before the paper and cotton tape are put on and dipped in finishing varnish after they are all put on to make it water and oil proof.

For a 2200-volt induction motor with strip copper coils and a double-layer winding:

(*a*) One layer of half-lapped cotton tape six mils thick on each conductor to form the insulation between the conductors.

(*b*) One layer of half-lapped cotton tape six mils thick all around the coil to bind the conductors together.

(*c*) One turn of micanite 20 mils thick on the slot part of the coil.

(*d*) Two layers of half-lapped empire cloth six mils thick all around the coil.

(*e*) One turn of paper 10 mils thick on the slot part of the coil to protect the empire cloth.

(*f*) One layer of half-lapped cotton tape six mils thick on the end connections to protect the empire cloth.

(*g*) Bake and impregnate the coil before the paper and the last taping of cotton tape are put on.   After that, the slot part of the coil should be hot pressed and allowed to cool under pressure.   Then the coil can be dipped in finishing varnish to make it water and oil proof.

Coil and Slot Insulation Employed by a Large Manufacturer.—The following insulation for coils and slots represents the practice of a large manufacturer specializing in the construction of motors and generators in a wide range of sizes and for all commercial voltages.

I. *For Small Direct-current Machines Using Wire-wound Coils:*
1. Coils are wound with double cotton-covered wire.
2. Dipped in varnish and baked to about 100°C. (212°F.) until coils are free from stickiness.
3. Taped with 6-mil linen tape.
4. Coils are then placed in armature and soldered to commutator risers.   After cleaning, the armature is dipped or sprayed with varnish and baked.
5. The final operation is to spray with shellac.
6. For slot insulation 10-mil pressboard is used.

II. *For Engine Type Direct-current Armatures Using Strip Copper Coils:*
1. Copper strips are taped with 6-mil linen tape, $\frac{1}{3}$ lapped.   Width of linen tape is $\frac{3}{4}$, 1 or $1\frac{1}{2}$ inch, depending upon size of the coil.
2. Coil is then dipped in good insulating varnish and baked until free from stickiness.

3. When coils are used in groups, the groups are taped with 6-mil linen tape ⅓ lapped.

4. Operation two is then repeated.

5. Coil is now ready to be inserted in armature slots. When armature is completed, and bands are on but before assembling in frame, the windings are saturated with air-drying varnish or it is baked until free from moisture. As a rule, machine is well baked by running under full load. It can then be sprayed with air drying varnish.

6. For slot cells, 10-mil pressboard is used not so much for insulation as for mechanical protection.

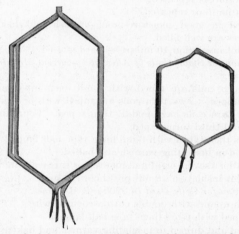

Fig. 121.—At the left, armature coil insulated for a 250-volt direct-current motor. At the right, stator coil insulated for a 220-volt induction motor (*Crocker-Wheeler Company*).

Variation from above practice depends upon the voltage. For high voltages, say 550 volts, the coil will perhaps be taped with 9-mil oil muslin half lapped and an additional varnish and baking treatment.

For mill motors the coils are usually insulated with flexible mica. The coil is heated in a form and connected in the secondary of a transformer. While the current passes through the coil, it is tightened so as to give the proper thickness, after which it is insulated with asbestos tape. Asbestos tape is used because of the severe duty to which these machines are subjected and because they are completely enclosed.

III. *General Method for Insulating Direct-current Field Coils:*

1. Coils are wound with double cotton-covered wire.

2. The coil is then taped with 6-mil linen tape about ⅓ lapped on the outside of coil. Width of tape one inch.

3. Coils are next placed in vacuum tank until free from moisture.

4. Dipped in good insulating varnish and baked.   Or if the varnish has air drying qualities, the coils are dried in air until free from stickiness.

IV. *Insulation for Stator Coils of Alternating-current Machines for* 600 *Volts and Under Using Wire-wound Coils:*

1. Coils are wound with double cotton-covered wire.
2. Heated and dipped in insulating varnish and baked.
3. Operation two repeated.
4. Taped with 6-mil linen tape half lapped.
5. Coil is then shaped.
6. Dipped in varnish and baked.
7. Operation six repeated.
8. Operation four repeated.
9. Dipped in good moisture-proof varnish and baked until all crevices are well filled.
10. For slot insulation 10-mil pressboard is used.

V. *Insulation for Stator Coils of Alternating-current Machines, Made up of Strip Copper:*

1. One-turn coils are taped with 6-mil linen tape one inch wide, half lapped.   Two turn coils are taped with one turn as above. Three turn coils have middle turn taped.   Four turn coils have first and third turns taped.
2. Coil is then taped with 6-mil linen tape half lapped.
3. Dipped in insulating varnish and baked.
4. Operations seven, eight and nine as for wire coils are then applied.
5. For slot insulation 10-mil pressboard is used.

VI. *Insulation for Coils Used in* 2200-*volt Machines:*

1. Coil is wound with double cotton-covered wire.
2. Wrapped with 6-mil linen tape half lapped.
3. Heated and dipped in insulating varnish and baked.
4. Operation three repeated.
5. Operation two repeated.
6. Coil is then formed.
7. Last tape is now removed from coil, which was put on in order to protect the first linen tape while the coil was being shaped.
8. Wrapped with 9-mil oil muslin half lapped and brushed with best quality insulating varnish.
9. Operation eight repeated.
10. Wrapped with 6-mil linen tape half lapped.
11. Coil is then dipped in insulating varnish and baked.
12. Operation ten repeated.
13. Operation eleven repeated.
14. For slot insulation, 10 to 20-mil pressboard is used and for insulation between layers 10-mil pressboard.

In making up coils for any kind of electrical machinery, the main thing to bear in mind is to apply such processes as to eliminate moisture from the coil.   Even for 2200-volt machines, except in special cases, the

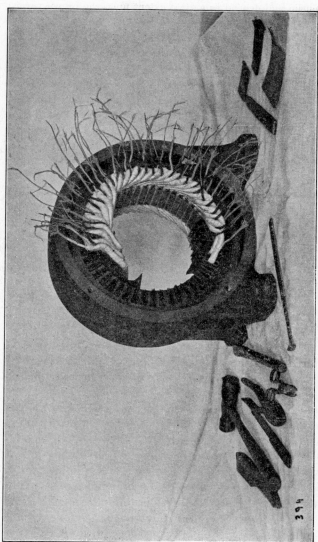

Fig. 122.—Partially wound induction motor stator showing taping at the coil ends and slot insulation. Winders tools are shown on either side of the motor. Retaining wedges are usually made of wood or fiber, but in a motor of one type a magnetic wedge is used, thus giving a closed slot characteristic with open slot advantages in winding. (*Roth Brothers and Company.*)

practice of the company employing the insulating methods described is
to use oil muslin and depend to a great extent upon the proper varnish
treatment.   After much experimenting with varnishes it has been found
possible to wind coils that will withstand high voltages equally as well as
insulated coils wound for the same voltages.

Insulation of End Connections of Coils. In a double-layer
winding, the voltage between the end connections of two
coils where they cross each other at the ends of the slot may
be about equal to the terminal voltage.   Suitable insulation
should be used at this point.   A belt of cotton duct is usually
used between the end connections for this protection, and also
to protect the coils from mechanical injury by rubbing against
each other.

Also the slot insulation should be allowed to extend out each
end of the slot a certain distance depending upon the machine
voltage.   Prof. Alexander Gray gives the following values as
typical of good practice.

Terminal voltage of machine	Length of insulation out of slot
Not over 800	0.75 inch
800 to 2500	1.25 inches
2500 to 5000	2.00 inches
5000 to 7500	3.00 inches
7500 to 11,000	4.50 inches

Coils for alternating-current windings must be wound to
stand the line voltage to ground.   In a Y-connected machine
the total insulation from copper to copper between two coils
should stand about 1.7 times this value.   The first coil of
each phase in a Y-connected machine has a voltage equal to
the line voltage to ground (volts between lines $\div \sqrt{3}$) against
which to insulate and should be given a protection equal to
the line voltage.   The first and last coils of each phase group
must also have extra insulation for protection at the points
where they cross.   These are called the phase coils.   One
layer of six-mil empire cloth on the end connections covered
with six-mil cotton tape half lapped in addition to the coil
insulation will give sufficient insulation to the phase coils
except in cases of voltages past 2300.   (See page 165 for
phase coil insulation for 2300 volts.)

Phase Insulation when Reconnecting from Two-phase to Three-phase and Vice Versa.—In reconnecting the winding of an induction motor from two-phase to three-phase or vice versa and in reconnecting a winding for a different number of poles to change the speed, it is necessary to rearrange the phase insulation because the spread of the coils per-phase, per-pole is being changed.

Mica Insulation for Armature Coils.—Mica has been found to be a first class insulating material. Its insulation resistance increases with temperature, a valuable characteristic for machines operating at high temperatures and in direct contrast with the properties of treated tapes, in which the insulation resistance and loss increases rapidly at temperatures above 100°C. or 212°F. It is unaffected by temperatures far in excess of those encountered in the modern, well-ventilated alternator. It is also impervious to the static discharges present in all high voltage machines. Furthermore, it is resilient and retains its resiliency indefinitely—thus helping to hold the coil tight in its slot.

Mica is a mineral obtained in the form of large crystals. These split readily into thin, parallel-sided laminæ, or flakes. The flakes can be pasted uniformly on cloth or paper to facilitate handling and to provide a mechanical support during application. In the form of a "wrapper," that is, pasted on large sheets of specially treated paper, mica is mostly used on the straight sides of each armature coil, to provide insulation between conductor and iron, the operating voltage of the machine determining the number of turns, or the thickness of this insulation wall.

All known insulating materials are relatively poor heat conductors. This is equally true of mica and treated tapes. Therefore, the tighter and the thinner the wall, the better the heat radiating characteristics of the coil. For the lower voltage machines the mica wrapper is applied as tightly as is possible by hand. For the higher voltage windings, 6600 and above, where the insulation wall must be relatively thick, special, patented machines are used which apply the wrapper under heat and pressure, and finish it to a solid, compact wall.

In general, all of the larger capacity generators have

relatively wide cores. Internal "hot spot" temperatures, considerably higher than those measurable by thermometer, exist.   On all such machines, each conductor of the coil is also insulated with mica tape.

Repairing Coils Damaged in Winding Process.—It often occurs that the insulation of a coil becomes damaged from chafing or from carelessness in the use of tools when laying the coils in the armature slots.   Such damage should be repaired at once to prevent possible trouble later which will make the repair more difficult and expensive.   To repair a damaged coil where the injury to it is only slight, the coil should be removed from the slot and all the insulation removed from the injured section.   Then apply an overlapping wrapper

Fig. 123.—At top, one whole and two damaged Eickemeyer coils taken from an elevator motor.   At bottom, fiber drifts, slot insulation, hammer, parallel jaw pliers and coil lifter.

of treated cloth and around this a protecting covering of cotton tape.   Glue down the ends of the tape securely and apply a good heavy coat of shellac.   The shellac can be dried quickly by touching a lighted match to it when the alcohol in which it is dissolved will burn with a blue flame.   Care must be taken that the tape is not burned in doing this.   In such a case the flame will turn yellow and should be smothered at once.   The heat of the burning alcohol is not usually sufficient to burn the tape.   After this the coil is dry and can be put back in the slot.   While this method of repair can be safely used in small armatures, it is not good enough for large armatures.   In the latter case a new coil should be used or the old one stripped and completely reinsulated, dipped and baked.

On account of the stiffness of the insulation on the terminals of formed coils, before connections are made to the commutator it is a good plan to soften the leads with "armalac" or a similar armature compound at the points where the leads leave the bottom coils in the slots. This will prevent breaks while handling the leads.

Voltage to use when Testing Coil and Commutator Insulation.—Under certain conditions the difference of potential between coils and the iron core of a machine may be equal to the terminal voltage. Under abnormal operating conditions it may even be greater. It is important, therefore, that the insulation of coils and commutator shall be sufficient to stand a voltage considerable larger than the terminal voltage of the machine without developing grounds. For this reason a high-voltage test is made on armature windings of both direct-current and alternating-current machines and the commutator of the former before the winding is finally completed.

The following values of test voltages that should be applied are given by Prof. Alexander Gray (Electrical Machine Design, page 34) based upon the standardization rules of the American Institute of Electrical Engineers.

Rated terminal voltage of machine	Rated output of machine	Testing voltage
Up to 400	Under 10 kw.	1000
Up to 400	10 kw. and over	1500
400 to 800	Under 10 kw.	1500
400 to 800	10 kw. and over	2000
800 to 1200	Any	3500
1200 to 2500	Any	5000
2500 and over.	Any	Double-rated voltage.

Some insulating materials will withstand very high voltages before used on coils. For instance, a good quality of oiled muslin will withstand as high a test voltage as 1500 to 2000 volts per mil for 9-mil thickness, however, when applied to coils, its insulating properties will diminish because of handling. This is, of course, the reason why so much insulation is used on coils, to protect them from becoming grounded. For coils that are to be used for machines below 2200 volts, no steps are usually taken to test coils before placing them in the machine. However, for voltages over 2200, the coils are tested before they are placed in the slots. For instance, coils that are to be used on machines of 6600 volts, are tested for ground at 20,000 volts by wrapping them with tin foil before placing them in the slots. Then they are tested with 15,000 to 16,000 volts after being placed in the slots. Finally a test of at least twice normal voltage is made for one minute.

Field Coil Insulation.—For the insulation of field coils, 10 mil paper, $\frac{1}{16}$ inch cardboard and 6 mil tape can be used where the field coil has a cardboard spool. The insulation can be applied in the order named using 2 layers of tape and paper with the paper next to the wires on the spool. The coils should then be baked in a vacuum tank and impregnated.

Varnishes and Impregnating Compounds for Coils.—The varnish used over the outside of insulated coils should be water, oil and acid proof and dry quickly in air forming a hard smooth surface. Such varnishes are made by a number of manufacturers.

Compounds for use in impregnating coils are also available in the open market and are usually an asphaltum or a paraffin base dissolved in a suitable thinning solution. It is important that the material will not attack copper, iron or insulating materials used and form a solid at all temperatures below 212°F. without contraction when changing from the fluid to the solid state. This material should not be applied at temperatures above the breakdown of cotton materials, that is, above a temperature of 248°F.

Because the desirable characteristics for a perfect varnish cannot be combined into one compound, a number of varnishes have been developed, each having its own characteristic. The purposes of some insulating varnishes of the Sherwin-Williams company are indicated in the accompanying table. Where more than one varnish can be successfully used the different types are indicated as first, second and third choices.

All of the varnishes mentioned in the table are of the baking type. However, insulating varnishes in general may be divided into several general classes, such as clear varnishes, black varnishes, baking varnishes and air-drying varnishes. The most marked difference between the clear and the black varnishes is the color, but owing to fundamental differences in the characteristics of the ingredients entering into their composition, there are also some differences in the physical properties of the varnishes themselves. As a general rule clear varnishes possess greater mechanical strength and resist oil better than black varnishes. An exception to this is the black elastic baking varnish shown in the table. Where extreme mechanical strength is required as on small high-speed armatures clear varnishes are almost always used.

TABLE SHOWING SUITABILITY OF INSULATING VARNISHES

Characteristics of clear and black baking insulating varnishes and uses for which they are recommended*	Clear varnishes			Black varnishes			
	Clear quick baking	Clear quick elastic baking	Clear elastic baking	Black quick baking	High Heat resisting baking	Black plastic baking	Black elastic baking
Dielectric strength...............	3	1	1	3	2	2	1
Mechanical strength..............	3	1	2	3	4	5	2
Flexibility......................	3	2	1	3	3	2	1
Plasticity.......................	..	..	..	..	..	1	..
Oil resistance...................	2	1	1	2	3	4	1
Water resistance................	2	2	1	2	2	1	1
Life under heat.................	4	3	2	4	2	1	2
Treating cloth, paper and thin fibrous materials.................	3	2	1	3	3	2	1
Treating fullerboard and heavy fibrous materials..............	2	1	2	2	3	3	2
Small high-speed armatures......	3	1	2	3	..	..	2
Intermediate-speed armatures.....	3	1	2	3	3	3	2
Large low-speed armatures.......	3	2	1	3	2	2	1
Field and stator coils............	3	2	1	3	2	1	1
Automobile-starting motors.......	..	1	..	..	..	..	..
Vacuum-cleaner motors..........	1	1	..	1	..	..	..
Washing-machine motors.........	..	1	1	..	1	1	1
Street railway and electric locomotive motors..................	..	..	2	..	..	1	2
Fan motors.....................	3	1	2	3	2	..	2
Magnetos and induction coils.....	..	1	2	..	..	..	2
High-potential apparatus........	..	1	2	..	..	..	2
Transformers...................	..	1	2	..	..	..	2
Average repair shop conditions...	..	2	..	..	2	1	..

* Numbers indicate order of suitability.

Black varnishes are not quite so strong mechanically as clear varnishes but are sufficiently strong for most purposes.

On stationary windings, as on alternating-current stator windings, the varnish is not subjected to centrifugal stresses and there is no advantage in using a clear varnish. Certain black varnishes are made from plastic materials and have the ability to withstand long-continued heating without hardening. Black varnishes as a rule are cheaper than clear varnishes and are more commonly used for that reason.

The chief difference between baking varnishes and air-drying varnishes is in the proportion of oxidizing ingredients contained. The baking varnishes are tougher, more elastic, more resistant to oil and water, and have longer life under heat. Speed in drying is always accomplished at the expense of these characteristics, and the air-drying varnishes are less durable and elastic than the baking varnishes. The air-drying varnishes find their principal field of usefulness on apparatus where severe conditions of usage are not encountered and for quick repair work.

Characteristics of Insulating Varnishes.—An important factor concerning insulating varnishes is that the dielectric resistance increases directly with the length of baking or drying period, the slow varnishes imparting the highest degree of insulation and flexibility and producing a tough, flexible film which may also be depended upon for mechanical strength and extreme durability. Black varnishes are claimed to be better for work where a transparent coating is not absolutely essential because they produce a more flexible and highly insulating film than clear varnishes of the same class. Varnishes should not crystallize under prolonged vibration, and their mechanical structure should be elastic and homogeneous. The accompanying table (page 179) gives the characteristics, uses, drying time and solvents of several varnishes.

Solvent Chart for Insulating Varnishes.—Since varnish is usually sold in concentrated form care must be taken in dissolving to avoid wrinkles or stringy drip forming on coils when varnish is too heavy. Benzine is preferable to gasoline as a solvent but gasoline can be used. The solvent and varnish should be approximately the same temperature and neither should be under 60°F. (15.5°C.). The chart on page 180 shows the percentage of 58 degrees benzine to be added to every

Characteristics of Varnishes (Mitchell-Rand Manufacturing Company)

Kind	Some uses	Characteristics	Time to dry, hours	Drying temp., deg. F.	Solvent
Clear baking varnish	Linen, canvas, cotton tapes, paper fiber coils, armatures, etc.	Penetrating and elastic; oil, waterproof and heat-resisting	6–8	212	Benzine
Black baking varnish	Motor repairs, coils, armature, transformers, ignition cables, asbestos	Prevents absorption of moisture, resists oil, heat, water and acid	4	275	Benzine
Clear air drying	Coils, molding fiber, etc.	Water, oil and acid resisting and insulating	4–20	Avg.	Benzine
Black air drying	Coils, general repair work	Water, oil and acid resisting and insulating	4–8	Avg.	Benzine
Clear finishing varnish	Finishing of apparatus	Oil and water resisting, flexible and insulating	1–3	Avg.	Denatured alcohol
Black finishing varnish	Motor frames, coils, laminations	Oilproof, tough and durable	1–3	Avg.	Denatured alcohol
Clear core-plate varnish	High-voltage electric machines, transformers	Water, oil and acid resisting. Heat conducting	{ 1 ½ }	Avg. 275	Benzine and benzol (9:1)
Black core plate	Insulation of armature and transformer lamination	Waterproof and acid resisting	{ 5–10 min. 1–2 min. }	Avg. 200	Benzine and benzol (9:1)

SOLVENT CHART FOR INSULATING VARNISHES (DOLPH MANUFACTURING COMPANY)

Observed specific gravity

Indicating the number of gallons of 58° benzine to be added to every one hundred gallons of varnish to reduce the varnish to the desired specific gravity. Example: To reduce from 30B to 32B—8 gallons; from 0.864 Dec. to 0.843 Dec.—18 gallons.

Dec. = Decimal Scale
B = Baumé Scale

Desired Specific Gravity.

Dec.	B	0.903 / 25	0.897 / 26	0.892 / 27	0.886 / 28	0.881 / 29	0.875 / 30	0.870 / 31	0.864 / 32	0.859 / 33	0.854 / 34	0.849 / 35	0.843 / 36	0.838 / 37	0.833 / 38	0.823 / 39	0.823 / 40
0.903	25	0															
0.897	26	3	0														
0.892	27	6½	3½	0													
0.886	28	10	7	3½	0												
0.881	29	14	10½	7	3½	0											
0.875	30	18	14½	11	8	4	0										
0.870	31	22	19	15	11½	8	4	0									
0.864	32	27	23	19½	15½	11½	8	4	0								
0.859	33	32	28	24	20	16	12	8	4	0							
0.854	34	37	33	29	25	21	17	12½	8½	4½	0						
0.849	35	43	39	35	30	26	22	17½	13½	9	4½	0					
0.843	36	50	46	41	36	32	27½	23	18	14	9	5	0				
0.838	37	57	53	48	43	38	33	28½	24	19	14½	9½	5	0			
0.833	38	65	60	55	50	45	40	35	30	25	20	15	10	5	0		
0.828	39	74	69	64	58	53	48	42	37	32	26	21	16	11	5½	0	
0.823	40	84	78	73	67	61	56	50	44	39	34	28	22	17	12	6	0

100 gallons of insulating varnish to bring it to the correct specific gravity. The most suitable gravity should be established by trial and the specific gravity kept constant at this value. With 63 degrees gasoline 15 per cent. less should be used than that shown and with 54 degrees benzine 10 per cent. more should be added.

Method for Making Tape from Cotton Cloth.—Maurice S. Clement has described the following method (*Electrical Record*, October, 1918) for making tape as used by a middle western electrical repair shop owing to a shipment of cotton tape being held up on account of war conditions. The repair job was urgent and the repairman was forced to make up an amount of cotton tape of different widths ranging from $\frac{1}{2}$ inch to 2 inches, sufficient to keep its maintenance men going until the order arrived. After considerable thought, the following was decided upon as a temporary remedy.

A bolt of white cotton cloth was purchased in a nearby dry goods store. The cloth was rolled tightly on a half-inch dowel and then marked off to the various widths on the outside. A band-saw was used to good advantage cutting the cotton cloth into tape; as this tape had no salvage edge, steps had to be taken to prevent it from unravelling. Both edges of each roll of tape were given a heavy coat of shellac and before it dried the alcohol was burned off. This has a sort of semi-baking effect which tends to strengthen the tape. It also prevents the tape from curling.

Drying Out Insulation of Direct-current Generators (*Instruction Book*, Westinghouse Electric & Mfg. Co.).—Drive the generator by a motor connected by a belt and short-circuit the armature beyond the ammeter using a very weak field excitation. If the generator is shunt wound, low voltage separate excitation must be employed; if compound wound the armature may be short-circuited through the series field coils. Direct-current generators are very sensitive when operated as series machine and there is danger of generating an excessive current. Consequently this method should be undertaken only by experienced operators.

The field coils may be dried by applying from some separate

source of excitation approximately two-thirds of the normal direct-current voltage.

There is always danger of serious injury to the windings when drying out with current since the heat generated in the inner parts is not readily dissipated; furthermore, coils containing moisture are much more susceptible to injury from overheating than when thoroughly dry. The temperature of all accessible parts should be carefully observed during the drying out process and never allowed to exceed 80°C. (176°F.), total temperature. Several hours or even days may be required for thoroughly drying out large machines. During the drying out process the temperature should not be allowed to drop below that of the surrounding air as moisture then condenses on the coil surfaces and the effect of the previous drying would be largely lost. At regular intervals during the drying out run, readings of the insulation resistance (see page 185) may be taken at regular intervals and plotted as a curve, using time for the horizontal scale and resistance for the vertical scale. The drying should continue until the resistance has begun to increase. If the insulation contains appreciable moisture the resistance will decrease during the first part of the drying out process.

Heating windings by current is more effective than any process of heating from the outside, such as enclosing the machine and heating the air by resistance or fires, because in the former method the inside of the coils becomes hotter than the outside and moisture is driven outward. With external heating the reverse is true.

Drying Out Synchronous Motors and Generators.—Synchronous motors and generators can be dried out by rotating the motor or generator at any convenient speed and short-circuiting the armature beyond the ammeters. The field should be excited so that the desired heating current will flow in the armature winding. For windings of 2400 volts or lower, the temperature, as measured by thermometers properly applied to the hottest accessible part of the winding should not be higher than 80°C. (176°F.). For 6600-volt windings the temperature should not be higher than 75°C. (167°F.) and for 11,000 to 13,200-volt windings not higher than 65°C. (149°F.).

The reason for specifying the lower temperature for the higher voltage windings is the greater difference in temperature between the inside of the coil and the outside (when the temperature is measured with a thermometer) in the coils having the thicker insulation.

If a low voltage (5 to 15 per cent. of normal) can be obtained from the taps on a transformer for example, the armature winding can be dried out by applying this low voltage to the armature terminals, the rotor remaining stationary. The field winding should be short-circuited and the temperature of the cage winding on the rotor should be watched. Less than normal current will be necessary on account of the absence of ventilation.

For medium sized alternators and synchronous motors a satisfactory way of drying out both field and stator windings is to connect the machine to an alternating-current circuit and run as a motor with fields overexcited at zero power factor. This method is both cheap and effective.

Drying Out Induction Motors.—Small motors can be baked in ovens. The temperature should be raised gradually taking several hours to bring it to the maximum value which should not be more than 80°C. (176°F.) at the hottest point. The temperature should be maintained constant for from one day to a week depending on the size and voltage of the machine and the history of its exposure to moisture. Induction motors can also be dried by operation at no load on low voltage (the primary current and heating increases as the voltage is reduced) or by a still lower voltage that will circulate a sufficiently heavy current with the rotor blocked. If a sufficiently low alternating-current voltage is not available, direct current may be used. There is always more or less danger of overheating the windings of a machine when drying them with current as the inner parts which cannot quickly dissipate the heat generated in them and which cannot be examined, may get dangerously hot while the exposed and more easily cooled portions are still at a comparatively moderate temperature. The temperature of the hottest part accessible should be measured during the drying out process and not allowed to exceed 80°C. (176°F.).

Insulation Test.—During the drying out of a machine, insulation resistance tests should be made at regular intervals and plotted in the form of a curve using time on the horizontal scale and values of insulation resistance on the vertical scale. The drying out should be continued until the resistance reaches it proper value. The insulation resistance is at best only a rough guide in determining the condition of the machine as to moisture and relative values in the same winding during a drying out run are of more value than the relative values of windings in other machines.

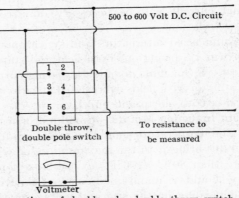

FIG. 124.—Connections of double-pole, double throw switch and 500-volt voltmeter for measuring insulation resistance.

A megger is also sometimes used for testing the condition of the windings during the drying out prcoess.

The insulation resistance of a machine in good condition and at its operating temperature will usually not be less than the value given by the following formula:

$$\text{Insulation resistance in megohms} = \frac{\text{Machine voltage}}{\text{Rated Kva.} + 1000}$$

For example a 1000-Kva., 11,000-volt motor should have an insulation resistance, if clean and dry, of 5.5 megohms. The insulation resistance of field windings will, in general, be much higher in proportion to the operating voltage than that of the armature. Since large armatures have much greater areas of insulation, their insulation resistance will be proportionately lower than that for small machines. The insulation resistance of any machine will also be much lower when hot than when cold, especially when the machine is heated rapidly.

Measuring Insulation Resistance.—Insulation resistance may be measured with a megger or by the use of a 500-volt direct-current voltmeter and a 500 volt-direct-current circuit. Connect the voltmeter as shown in Fig. 124 and read first, the voltage of the line; then connect the resistance to be measured by throwing the double throw switch and read the voltmeter a second time. The insulation resistance is then calculated by the following formula:

$$\text{Insulation resistance } (R) = \frac{r\,(V - v)}{v \times 1{,}000{,}000}$$

Where V is voltage of the line; v the voltage reading with insulation in series with the voltmeter; r the resistance of the voltmeter in ohms which is generally marked inside the instrument cover, and R the resistance in megohms. A megohm is equal to one million ohms.

If a grounded circuit is used in making the measurement, care must be taken to connect the grounded side of the line to the frame of the machine to be measured and the voltmeter between the windings and the other side of the circuit.

CHAPTER VIII

REPAIR SHOP METHODS FOR REWINDING ALTER-NATING-CURRENT MACHINES

I. WINDING SMALL SINGLE-PHASE MOTORS

The complete stator winding of most small single-phase induction motors is made up of two windings; the main winding of many turns of heavy wire and what is known as the "teaser" or starting winding. The latter is necessary because a single-phase motor is not self-starting and, therefore, requires some means of producing a rotating field to overcome this deficiency. This the starting winding does. It is of smaller wire than the main winding and of high resistance.

The method of winding single-phase motors differs from that used for other alternating-current motors in that a skein winding is often used. That is, the winding coil is in the form of a skein of wire which is looped many times through several slots to form a pole of the winding. The details of this method of winding as given in what follows, are based on articles that have appeared in the *Electric Journal* by G. I. Stadeker and C. A. M. Weber.

Insulating Lining for Slots.—The slots should be lined with a protecting cell of fish paper cut to fit the slot. Inside this a cell of treated cloth should be placed cut so that its edges will project about $\frac{3}{4}$ inch beyond the entrance to the slot. In those slots which will contain both the main and the starting winding, an extra treated cloth cell should be inserted over the main winding to enclose the starting coils. End plates of fullerboard or fiber are used to insulate the core from the windings. The end connections of the main and starting windings should be separated by friction cloth.

Winding the Skein Coil.—In repairing a motor, the number of times the skein is to be looped through the slots and the length of the skein can best be obtained from a skein taken from the burned-out machine. In removing the old winding care should be taken to preserve one entire skein if possible. If this is impossible a satisfactory scheme for the repairman is by trial with a single wire. This wire should be laid in the slots exactly as the skeins of wire will be laid, proper allowance being made for the building up of the skein ends from slot to slot. The wire should then be removed and measured. Make up a trial skein of this length and wind it in the slots. Corrections if necessary can be made on the next skeins made up.

Inserting the Skein Coil in the Slots.—After the skein length and distribution have been obtained from the old motor, the

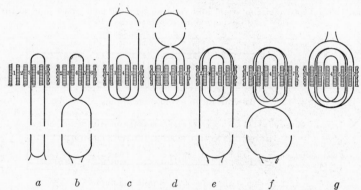

a   b   c   d   e   f   g

Fig. 125.—Successive steps in applying a skein coil for main winding of a split-phase, 60-cycle, 4-pole, 24-slot induction motor.

exact procedure in winding is as shown in Fig. 125 (*a*) to (*g*). The distribution of a 24-slot primary winding, indicating the number of times the main winding skein is wound into each slot, is shown in Figs. 126 to 129. The distribution in Fig. 126 is one commonly used. Other distributions may be used, but in all skein windings the wires in any slot must be a multiple of the wires in the skein.

A developed view of the primary or stator winding is shown in Fig. (125*a*), looking at the teeth with the first operation of putting the skein winding in slots 3 and 5 completed. The end of the coil thus formed should be firmly pressed against the core, using a rawhide or fiber mallet or a piece of smooth wood. A half twist is next made in the skein, as shown in

Fig. 125 (*b*), and the loop laid back over the winding and threaded into slots 2 and 6, as in Fig. 125 (*c*). The half twist is repeated, as in Fig. 125 (*d*), and the loop laid back in slots 2 and 6 for the second time, as in Fig. 125 (*e*). This second half twist, in Fig. 125 (*d*), must be in the opposite direction to the first one (Fig. 125 (*b*)), to bring the same side of the loop on top. Otherwise a twist will be put in the skeins, which will

Slot Number	1	2	3	4	5	6	7	8	9	10	11	12	13	14	15	16	17	18	19	20	21	22	23	24
Main Winding Distribution	1	1			1	1	1	1			1	1	1	1			1	1	1	1			1	1
Starting Winding Distribution			1	1					1	1					1	1					1	1		

Fig. 126.—Distribution of main and starting winding coils of a 4-pole motor showing skeins overlapped.

Slot Number	1	2	3	4	5	6	7	8	9	10	11	12	13	14	15	16	17	18	19	20	21	22	23	24
Main Winding Distribution	1	1		1	1		1	1		1	1		1	1		1	1		1	1		1	1	
Starting Winding Distribution			1			1			1			1			1			1			1			1

Fig. 127.—Distribution to avoid overlapping of skeins.

Slot Number	1	2	3	4	5	6	7	8	9	10	11	12	13	14	15	16	17	18	19	20	21	22	23	24
Main Winding Distribution	1•1	2	1		1	2	1•1	2	1		1	2	1•1	2	1		1	2	1•1	2	1		1	2
Starting Winding Distribution		2	1•1	2				2	1•1	2				2	1•1	2				2	1•1	2		

Fig. 128.—Distribution of an 8-pole machine.

Slot Number	1	2	3	4	5	6	7	8	9	10	11	12	13	14	15	16	17	18	19	20	21	22	23	24
Main Winding Distribution	1•1	1	1•1	1	1	1•1	1	1	1•1	1	1	1•1	1	1	1•1	1	1	1•1	1	1,1	1	1•1	1	1
Starting Winding Distribution		1	1		1	1		1	1		1	1		1	1		1	1		1	1		1	1

Fig. 129.—Distribution of an 8-pole consequent wound machine.

make it hard to wind smoothly, especially if it is looped back and forth many times. The half twist in Fig. 125 (*f*) is made in the same direction as that in Fig. 125 (*b*) By looping the turns into slots 1 and 7 the winding of the skein is completed. The winding of the second and subsequent coils is exactly the same as the first. The completed winding for a four-pole, 24-slot machine is shown in Fig. 130 (at top).

In split-phase starting, squirrel-cage motors the starting winding is connected across the line until approximately two-thirds synchronous speed is reached, when its circuit is automatically opened by a centrifugally-operated switch. The center of the starting winding is between the pole centers of

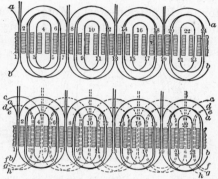

FIG. 130.—At top, complete main winding for a 4-pole, 60-cycle, split-phase induction motor. At bottom, complete main and starting winding for the same motor.

the main winding. Its distribution and the length of the skeins must be determined by trial as explained for the main winding. The starting winding is a resistance winding, consequently it is very important that its resistance in the

FIG. 130 (a).—Dissembled view of a single-phase repulsion induction motor.

motor be the same as it was originally, which makes the length of the skein important. The distribution of both the main and starting windings and the number of times the skein is to be wound into each slot are shown in Fig. 130 (lower diagram).

After all the slots have been filled the coils should be forced into position with a fiber drift, the insulating cells folded in and fiber wedges driven in the slots.

Winding for a Repulsion-start Motor.—For repulsion-starting, induction-running motors the primary winding is

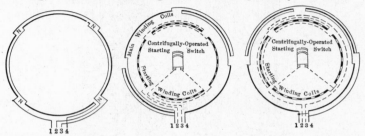

FIG. 131(*a*), (*b*), (*c*).—At left, primary connections for a single-phase, repulsion-starting induction motor. In center, connections for a 4-pole, split-phase motor. At right, same as in center but for a series-parallel connection of coils.

In the diagram at the left, *N* denotes neutral points. For a 220-volt circuit leads 2 and 3 should be connected together and leads 1 and 4 to the line. For a 110-volt circuit leads 1 and 2 should be connected in parallel to one line and leads 3 and 4 to the other. In the center diagram the coils are connected in series. To obtain clockwise rotation, leads 1 and 2 should be connected to one line and leads 3 and 4 to the other. For counter clockwise rotation, leads 1 and 3 should be connected to one line and leads 2 and 4 to the other.

complete, as shown in Fig. 130, and the coils are connected together, as indicated in Fig. 131 (*a*). Four leads are brought out, so that these motors may be connected externally for either 220 or 110 volts.

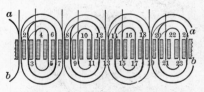

FIG. 132.—Hand-winding method for main coils of primary shown in Fig. 130.

Winding Small Motors by Hand.—A method sometimes employed in winding small motors of the induction type is known as hand-winding. The conductors are wound in the slots one at a time, beginning at the center of a pole, as shown in Fig. 132. This method is mostly used when the number of turns in the slots have no relatively large common divisor, thereby eliminating the skein-winding method. The hand-winding method should not be employed for the starting winding of a split-phase motor, because the resistance of the starting winding would not always be that required. A skein winding should be used.

Windings for Odd Frequencies.—It frequently happens that small motors must be wound for odd frequencies, such as 125, 133, and 140 cycles on standard 60-cycle motor cores. The number of poles of such motors is usually large, resulting in a small number of slots per pole. Using a 24-slot primary, wound eight poles, the slots per pole would be three and the distribution of the winding would be as shown in Fig. 128. Such a winding is very difficult to wind and in a case of this kind,

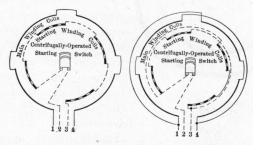

Fig. 133(a) and (b).—Connections for a single-phase, 8-pole, 24-slot, series-connected, consequent-pole, induction motor shown at left. At right, same for series-parallel connection.

a consequent-pole winding would be used with a distribution as shown in Fig. 129. This motor would be wound in the same manner as shown in Fig. 125 (a) to (g), but all the coils would be connected with the same polarity as indicated in Fig. 133.

Connections for Main and Starting Windings.—The coils of each winding are connected in series, as shown in Fig. 134. The leads of the starting winding are interrupted by a circuit opening device. Two circular stationary segments are used in one design of motor insulated from each other and from the frame and are mounted side by side on the bearing housing. At the start they are short-circuited by the rotating shoes which close the circuit of the starting winding until the speed reaches the point at which centrifugal force throws them off. This is ordinarily at about half speed. The main and starting windings are usually connected in parallel outside the machine. The direction of rotation is determined by the way the connections are made. To reverse the direction of rotation, interchange either the two main winding leads or the two starting leads; adopting the most convenient method.

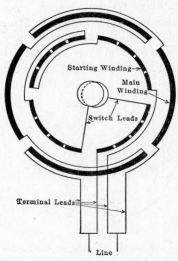

Testing Out Small Induction Motor Windings.—The windings should be tested for grounds with 1000 volts for one minute. Each winding should also be tested for short and open circuits by applying alternating current through a wattmeter. An excessive reading indicates a short circuit, while no readings show an open circuit. Polarity can be tested by applying direct current to the windings and testing with a compass. Adjacent poles should attract opposite ends of the needle. If the windings are correct, the end con: nections should be dipped in

Fig. 134.—Connections for single-phase motor windings.

a quick drying plastic varnish, which serves not only as an insulating medium, but excludes all dust and serves to stiffen the windings and make them moisture proof. After dipping, the windings should be thoroughly dried in an oven.

Windings for Small Polyphase Induction Motors.—The method of winding a small polyphase motor is similar to the winding of a single-phase motor. The slots are insulated with fish paper and treated cloth cells, and the skeins, which are also similar, are inserted into the slots as shown in the winding diagrams of Figs. 135 and 136. Each skein or group of coils overlaps the preceding one at the ends, as shown in Fig. 137, the ends of the coils being separated from one another by a layer of treated cloth. To produce a symmetrical winding, it may be necessary to remove half of the first skein before the last one can be put in place, in order to make them overlap in regular order. As the electrical characteristics of the machine would not be changed by so doing, the last skein can be allowed to overlap two skeins, while the first skein is overlapped by two others.

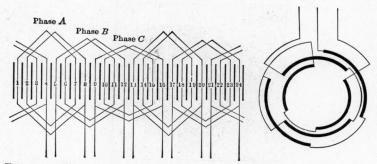

Fig. 135.—Winding diagram and connections for stator of small 3-phase motor.

The skeins are connected according to the connection diagram shown at the right in Figs. 135 and 136. The connections determine the phase and polarity of the machine. For instance, an armature having twelve skeins or groups of coils,

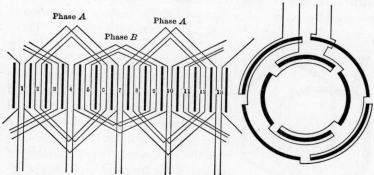

Fig. 136.—Winding diagram and connections for stator of a small 2-phase motor.

can be connected for six poles, two-phase, or eight poles, three-phase.

No starting winding is required for polyphase machines, and since they have a good starting torque there is no need for a

13

friction clutch on these machines. They should be tested
for breakdown between phases, and from each phase to ground,
and for short and open circuits, as described for single-phase
machines.

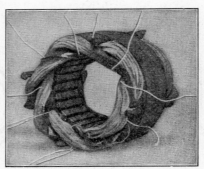

FIG. 137.—Stator of a small 3-phase motor completely wound with skein coils.

II. WINDING SMALL INDUCTION MOTORS WITH FORMED COILS IN PARTIALLY CLOSED SLOTS

Like the armatures of direct-current machines, the stators
of small induction motors are made with partially closed and
with open slots. The coils used with partially closed slots
are usually either of a diamond shape or of a square shape
such as shown in Fig. 138. These
coils are wound on forms as in the
case of direct-current coils using wire
having a double-cotton covering. The
coils when made up are not insulated
as a whole, since the turns of the coil
must be inserted in the slot one at a
time. The insulation between coils
and the core must therefore be placed
in the slots before the coils are inserted. The character of insulation
required and the methods of placing
the coils in the stator of motors
having partially closed slots and for those having open slots
are outlined in what follows according to recommendations
by a writer in the *Electric Journal,* Vol. VII, No. 9.

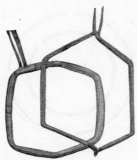

FIG. 138.—At left, a
basket or mush type coil.
At right a diamond type coil.

Insulation for Slots.—Clean the slots with a blast of air to remove all burrs and rough edges. Then cut a fish-paper cell large enough to just line the slot up to the opening and so as to extend at each end of the slot about three-quarters of an inch. This fish-paper cell possesses sufficient mechanical strength to protect the inner layer or cell of insulation which should be of treated cloth that have high insulating strength such as empire cloth or micanite. The inner cell should be cut large enough to extend beyond the protecting cell and the ends of the slot about one-quarter of an inch and up through the opening in the slot about an inch. The projections of this cell serve as a guide when inserting the coils and protect the wires from any possible abrasion when being inserted. The winding and the core should be insulated at the ends of the slots by a fullerboard ring and a fiber strip at each end. This will protect the overhanging ends of the coils from coming into contact with the core.

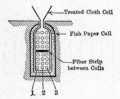

Fig. 139.—Slot insulation for a small induction motor having partially closed slots.

Basket Coils—One Coil per Slot.—Basket coils are wound to a shape corresponding only approximately to their final shape, as shown at the left, Fig. 138 It is important only that the total length of the loop be correctly proportioned so that the ends may be formed to the proper shape after the wires are in the slot. When a suitable form is not available, the coil may be wound around two pegs spaced the proper distance apart. Small pieces of tape should be fastened around the coil at convenient points so that the wires may be held together while they are being threaded into the slot. Basket coils are largely used with a one-coil per slot winding. This means that each side completely fills one slot, so that for a 48-slot core only 24 coils are required. In this class of winding, one end of the coil has to drop below the bottom of the slot in order to permit the adjacent coil to pass over it, while the other side of the same coil remains on a level with or only slightly below the top bore of the slot.

Winding a Three-phase Stator with Basket Coils.—Assume, for example, that a 48-slot core is to be wound for a four-pole, three-phase machine with a coil throw (in slots) of 1 and 12. Mark two slots to serve as a guide in placing the coils with respect to their proper span or throw. Any slot may be considered slot 1 and the other slot located by counting the throw in a clockwise direction. In this case (Fig. 140) the lower side of the first coil will go in slot 12. This side of the coil must now be laid wire by wire, inside the insulating cell in slot 12. The projecting edges of this cell can then be cut off close to the laminations, the ends folded over one another and the slot closed by driving a tight-fitting fiber

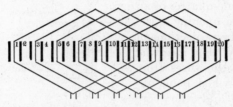

Fig. 140.—Winding diagram for motor using basket or loosely formed coils.

wedge between the outer cell and the tips of the teeth. This retaining wedge should not extend more than ½ inch beyond the core on either side, as it is liable to curl up and rub against the rotor. That part of the coil projecting beyond the slot should now be taped with a layer of treated tape and a covering of cotton tape for about half its length on each side of the core, and formed to drop below the bottom of the slot. This is known as the bottom part of the coil, as distinguished from the other side which will remain on a level with the slots known as the top part. In continuing the winding, the top part should be left out for the present, of slots 1, 3, 5, 7 and 9, since in completing the winding the coils in slots 2, 4, 6, 8 and 10, which drop below the slots, must be in place before these top parts can be inserted. These coils which have one side left out of the slot until the rest of the winding is completed, are known as throw coils. In the present case they are coils, 1–12, 3–14, 5–16, 7–18, 9–20.

The first coil that can be wound into two slots as a top and bottom coil is 11–22. The coil in slot 22, being a bottom coil, is inserted in the same manner as the coil in slot 12 already described, but is not taped or shaped until its other side is

threaded into slot 11. The ends can then be taped from iron
to iron with treated tape, in such a way as to overlap and seal
the projecting end of the insulating cell. This in turn should
be covered with a layer of cotton tape. The lower part of
the coil should then be shaped with a rubber or rawhide mallet
and fiber drift and treated with an insulating compound before

FIG. 141.—In this illustration the armature winder is shown inserting the
turns of a basket coil into partially closed slots of a small induction motor
stator (*Westinghuse Electric & Mfg. Company*).

the next coil is put in place. The drift and mallet used in
shaping the coils should have their sharp corners smoothed
off, and in no case should the coils be struck directly with an
iron tool.

Fig. 142 is a partially wound stator, showing the finished

shape of the coil ends. It is particularly necessary that both tapings should be applied as tightly as possible, as a failure to watch this point will result in the taping becoming loose and baggy when the coil is shaped. This is especially true if the slot is very deep as the process of dipping or shaping the bottom coil below the bottom of the slot has a tendency to pull the tape away from the laminations. To avoid this tendency it is desirable to use glue on those turns of tape that cover the projecting ends of the fish-paper cell.

Fig. 142.—A three-phase stator partly wound with basket coils.

During the operation of taping, the beginning and end of each coil should be brought out in such a manner as to lie on the side of the winding farthest from the bore of the stator and so placed that the beginning of one coil faces the end of the adjacent coil in a manner convenient for connecting. The method of winding just described should be continued until all the coils are in place. The winding is completed by placing the top parts of the throw coils in their respective slots.

Threaded Diamond Coil—Two Coils Per Slot.—The threaded type of diamond coil is wound with insulated wire, either on a form which finishes the coil to shape, or on a shuttle which winds the coil first in the shape of a loop, after which the loop is placed in a universal former or "puller." In this device (see page 457, Chapter XVII), the two straight sides are clamped between suitable jaws and are pulled apart the required distance, the coil assuming the shape shown on the right in Fig. 138. This type of winding is similar to the basket winding, in so far as the slot is insulated instead of the coil. On the other hand, the structure and the shape of the finished coils is identical with that of an open slot insulated coil. It is, therefore, not necessary to shape the coil after it has been placed in the slot as in the case of the basket winding. The slot insulation is practically identical with that of the basket winding with the addition of a fiber center strip to separate the upper and lower coils in the same slot. In this case, however, the slots should be laid out in groups according to a winding diagram, the number of groups being equal to the product of the number of poles by the phase of the motor. This grouping may be either uniform, alternate or irregular, according to the design of the winding. When the grouping is uniform, all groups consist of an equal number of slots, and contain an equal number of coils. In alternate grouping, every other group contains an equal number of slots and coils. In irregular grouping there is no apparent uniformity in the number of slots and coils per group.

Winding a Three-phase Stator with Diamond Coils.—In preparing to wind the machine, the slots forming the beginning of each group should be marked to indicate that the coils to be placed in them must be furnished with additional insulation at the ends. This is necessary as these coils form a boundary between phases, and consequently are subject to phase potential, whereas the potential between any other two adjacent coils is much less. Such coils are called the "phase coils" of the winding.

Taking as an example a 72-slot, six-pole, three-phase motor with a throw of 1 and 11. There will be $6 \times 3 = 18$ groups of four coils each, with 18-taped "phase coils" in the winding. The winding of the coils into the slots can be started by threading the bottom of the first coil into slot 11, the upper half of the coil being left up as a throw coil. The bottom parts of the next nine coils should be inserted in rotation, thus making ten coils left up as throw coils. The succeeding coil should be placed in two slots, 11 and 21. The rule to follow is, *that no upper part of a coil can be placed into a slot, the lower part of which is empty.*   After each bottom coil has been threaded into its cell, both the insulating cell and the coil should be raised to the top of the slot and the projecting sides of the cell cut off as close to the laminations as possible. The coil must then be forced back to the bottom of the slot. The edges of the insulating cell should be folded over each other and held in place by the fiber center strip.   The latter should be of a width to make a driving fit in the slot so as to hold the lower coil and cell firmly in place, and should be long enough to project out of the slot beyond the straight part of the coil.

Every fourth coil, in the present case, is one of the special "phase coils," and should be taped at the end from iron to iron with an overlapping layer of insulating tape and a protective layer of cotton tape.   The remaining coils may be left without any special insulation at the ends.

The placing of the upper part of the coil in the slot requires more care and skill, since the remaining space in the slot is just large enough to receive the coil with its wires lying parallel to each other.   Fig. 139 shows the cross-section of a coil three wires wide by four deep, the wire being threaded through in such a way that wire 1 is first passed through the slot, then 3 and finally 2.   This should be continued with each succeeding layer until the whole coil is in place.   The cell can then be folded in and the slot closed with a fiber wedge. The two coils must completely fill the slot.   If the insulation already mentioned is not sufficient to do this, additional filling strips of fullerboard, or treated wood, should be packed into the bottom or sides of the slot as may be required, until the coil is tight enough to prevent movement in the slot. The upper and lower parts of the winding outside of the slots must be carefully insulated from each other by a strip of treated duck cloth.   This strip should be wide enough to extend from the fish-paper cell to the portion of the coil farthest away from the slot, and should be threaded between the ends of the coils as they are inserted in the slots.

III. WINDING INDUCTION MOTORS HAVING OPEN SLOTS

The main difference between the coils used for a partially closed-slot and an open-slot winding, is that the latter are completely insulated before being inserted in the slots. They may, therefore, be wire or bar formed, and can readily be insulated for any commercial voltage. Consequently, motors of large size, or for voltages exceeding 550 volts are nearly always of the open-slot type. The insulation over the coils

FIG. 143.—Stator winding of a Fairbanks-Morse induction motor showing the type of coil used.

consists of a cell of treated cloth or mica over the straight part, and an overlapping layer of cotton tape over the whole coil. Extra insulation for high voltages (see pages 163 to 172) is made up by extra thickness or extra turns of the insulating cell. The phase coils receive an extra wrapping of treated cloth tape over the diamond ends in addition to the cotton tape, which, as a distinguishing mark, may be of a special color on these coils. After the final wrapping is completed, the coils should be dried in a moderate temperature in order to expel all moisture, then, while still hot, they should be dipped in an insulating compound and again subjected to moderate heat until the compound is thoroughly dried. This compound serves to fill up all the pores in the insulating materials and make the coils dust and moisture proof. Before inserting the coils in the slots the latter should be lined with cells of paraffined fish paper cut wide enough to project out of the top of the slot when folded, and to serve as a guide to the coils. These winding cells sometimes called "slippers" furnish mechanical protection only to the coils.

Winding a Two-phase Stator Having Open Slots.—Assume a stator designed for six poles, 72 slots, two-phase, with a coil throw (in slots) of 1 and 12. The total number of groups with uniform grouping is equal to the product of the number of poles by the phase of the motor, in this case will be 12, with six slots each. The groups should be laid off in a clockwise direction, the outside slots of each group being marked to receive phase coils, of which there are two per group. The coils can be inserted in regular order, beginning with the bottom part of phase coil in slot 12, and inserting phase coils wherever indicated. They should be driven into place by means of a fiber drift and mallet. Paraffin may be used as a lubricator, if necessary, as the coil should be a good driving fit in the protecting cell. The top parts of the first eleven coils, which are to be the throw coils will be inserted only temporarily until the bottom coils have been inserted into these slots. The remaining coils should be driven tightly into place, the projecting edges of the winding cell trimmed off close to the core and folded in, and the slot closed by driving a fiber retaining wedge into the grooves at the top of the slot. In some machines this wedge covers the entire face of the coil, while in others short wedges are driven in at each side, leaving the coil exposed at the middle of the core.

Testing the Windings.—After all the coils are in place on either of the types described, the winding must be carefully inspected for mechanical defects. All coils must clear the bore of the stator by at least one-sixteenth of an inch, and any coil which obstructs the bore should be tapped down with a mallet and fiber drift to give the allowed clearance. All cells must be intact and sound, especially at the bottom of the slots. If the punchings have been spread apart by driving in the fiber wedges, they must be closed up again. The punchings should also be inspected to see that no fragments project into the bore of the stator where the rotor will rub against them.

The winding should then be subjected to a break-down test to make sure that the insulation is sound at those points which in service will receive the most strain. These points are, from coils to iron, and from phase to phase. Connect all coils of the same phase together by a piece of copper wire. Then connect the terminals of a testingtransformer between the different phases and from each phase to iron and apply the required voltage for a length of time depending upon the characteristics of the machines. (See page 175, Chapter VII.) In case this test punctures the insulaton of any coil or the insulating cell in any of the slots, this insulation must be removed and replaced. If the puncture occurs in a top coil, it may sometimes be repaired by raising the coil out of the slot, removing the punctured insulation, and carefully replacing it with new material. If, however, a bottom coil or cell is punctured, it must be removed by raising the tops of the overlapping coils. The same procedure must be followed if a coil has to be replaced, as in the case of a burn-out due to a short-circuit. Such a process amounts practically to retracing the operation performed in the original winding until the injured coil is exposed.

Inserting a New Coil in a Winding.—In repair work where only one coil of a basket winding is burned out or damaged, and in general if the coils have been painted and are stiffened, rather than to remove all the throw coils, it is frequently easier to thread in a new coil. To do this cut the damaged coil at each side of the core and pull the wires out. New fish paper and treated cloth cells must be inserted. In emergency, fullerboard or rope cement paper may be used in place of fish paper. The treated cloth is variously known as treated cloth, oiled linen, empire cloth, etc. (See Chapter VII.) In this operation coils can be bent slightly to get them out of the way. Double cotton-covered wire of correct size and suitable length for rewinding must be used. The length and size can be obtained from the old coil by counting the turns and measuring the length of one. To make the wire thread in easily it can be rubbed with paraffine. If the coil consisted of two or more wires in parallel, that number should be used in rewinding. The number of wires in parallel is the number entering a given coil from any junction point of coil terminals. Great care must be exercised during the threading process to

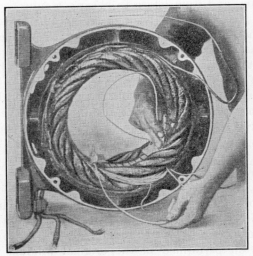

FIG. 144.—Method of threading in a new coil to replace a damaged one.

see that all the wires lie parallel in the slots and are free from kinks. Otherwise it will be impossible to get the full number of turns into the slot. In case a large number of turns are needed (more than 20 per slot) two or more lengths of wire may be wound at the same time and connected in series after winding, the joint being made outside of the slot. When the required number of turns have been inserted, the edges of the cells should be trimmed and folded in, the coil wedged in place and taped at each end. It should then be painted with an insulating paint.

Connecting the Coils.—After the ground test, the coils can be connected into groups, by joining together the beginnings and ends of adjacent coils until the group has but one lead at each end unconnected, which form the leads of that

Fig. 145.—The stator of an inductor motor with coils in place ready for connecting the pole-phase-groups and making end connections of such groups.

group. In doing this, the wires should be scraped clean and a sleeve connector of tinned copper slipped over them. They can then be soldered and taped. If suitable connectors can not be obtained (as may occur in making repairs), the stubs may be wrapped with fine bare copper wire and then soldered.

The terminals of the various groups should next be connected into proper phase relations (see Chapter XI) with double-braided rubber-covered wire or cable. The size of wire and the grade of insulation will depend upon the current and voltage. Joints in cables or wire larger than No. 6 should be made by wrapping with fine bare copper wire. Great care must be taken while connecting and soldering joints to protect the winding from the molten metal. After soldering, all joints and splices should be rubbed smooth with emery cloth and insulated with treated cloth tape, covered with one or more layers of cotton tape, and saturated with an insulating varnish or shellac. The connecting cables should then be arranged over the end of the windings in such a manner as to occupy the least possible space and yet keep them clear from the frame or end brackets.

Points to Consider when Connecting Coils.—The following points should be carefully watched in order to make a good job in connecting induction motor windings.

1. All wires should, if possible, be tinned before the connectors are put on. If this cannot be done they must be thoroughly cleaned by scraping.

2. All soldering must be thoroughly done, making a smooth and solid joint.

3. The wires of the joints should lap if space permits.

4. No acid flux should be used.

5. The wires or cables must be arranged in such a way as to occupy the least space and not obstruct ventilation.

6. Wires or cables must be clamped or tied down to avoid vibration.

7. Joints must be carefully insulated.

8. After connecting, the winding should be tested for electrical balance by causing a current to flow through it and comparing the voltage and current readings of each phase.

The windings on the side on which the connections are made, usually called the front side, are as a rule more rigid than those on the rear side, due to the fact that the connections exert a bracing effect. Since the windings in the rear lack this bracing effect, it is usually necessary with diamond windings to supply a supporting ring of insulated steel to which all the coils are laced with rope made of six- or eight-ply waxed ends. The inside diameter of this ring should just be large enough to make a good fit over the winding. If it is much larger than that of the winding, the coils will be under tension which will in time tend to loosen them from the supporting ring. Care should be exercised in lacing the coils to the ring, when the rope is led through ends of the coils with a steel needle, to see that no damage is done to the insulation.

Cleats and Terminals.—The wires that tap into the winding and extend to the outside of the frame are called the leads. To avoid the possibility of these leads transmitting jerks and vibrations to the soldered joints of the winding, they should be fastened to the frame by iron or porcelain cleats. Such cleats should also be used to support the leads from sagging wherever they pass close to the iron or moving parts.

Painting.—All of the windings, and especially the taped joints, should be thoroughly brushed with shellac or a finishing varnish. This material seals up any porous places in the insulation, and excludes dirt and moisture (see page 176).

IV. INDUCTION MOTOR SECONDARIES

The squirrel-cage secondary is the simplest mechanically, and at the same time is the most rugged and compact form of moving element to be found in any electric motor. The operating characteristics of a squirrel-cage rotor are dependent on its resistance. A winding of low resistance will have good efficiency and small slip, but will have poor starting torque for a given maximum current. A winding of high resistance, on the other hand, will have lower running efficiency and large slip, but will give a high starting torque with minimum current, and is suitable for mill or crane work where starting under heavy load is frequent and operation is for short intervals only. Where it is necessary, however, to start a heavy load with small starting current, and operate for long intervals with good efficiency, or wherever it is necessary to vary the speed or operating characteristics of the motor from time to time, a wound secondary should be used. The windings have a low resistance, and are connected in star with the open ends connected to slip rings. Adjustable external resistance can then be connected in series when starting, after which the rings can be short-circuited.

Fig. 146.—Squirrel-cage rotor for a 350-hp., 3-phase, 440-volt, 1465 r.p.m. induction motor (*Crocker-Wheeler Company*).

Squirrel-cage Secondaries.—The core of a squirrel-cage rotor is built up of laminated steel on a spider, and keyed in place with a feather key on the spider and ring keys at the ends.

Fig. 147.—Solid metal rotor "cage" winding of squirrel cage induction motor (*Fairbanks-Morse & Company*).

This rotor cage is made by casting end rings of copper or brass around the ends of the rotor bars which have previously been treated so that the metal of the bars is melted and fused together with the metal of the ring into a solid mass. This makes a rotor cage which is of one piece without joints. The iron core of the rotor was removed in order to obtain this photograph of the winding only, to show the characteristic structure from which the name "squirrel cage" is derived.

Ventilators are used on the rotors with wide cores. Rectangular copper bars are usually used, cut from soft drawn bar stock.

The end rings are made of copper, brass, or various grades of resistance alloys. The resistance of the ring, and consequently the characteristics of the motor, depend upon both the width and thickness of the ring, as well as its composition, and may be varied over a wide range by changing these dimensions.

Phase-wound Secondaries.— With wound secondaries either diamond or basket coils can be used. Partially closed slots are usually used and the slots are skewed, to prevent humming in single-phase designs. Wire-wound coils can be inserted in a manner as wire-wound, threaded-in coils for

Fig. 148.—Large induction motor rotor partly wound with two-part strap coils (*Crocker-Wheeler Company*).

direct-current armatures. The slots should be insulated with fish paper and treated cloth cells. The coil throw is determined by the number of slots per pole. The coils in each group should be connected in series, and the groups of each phase usually connected in series. The phases may be connected in star. Wedges are required to hold the coils in the slots, and the rotor should be banded and balanced in the same manner as a direct-current armature.

In rotors of large machines, the coils are generally form wound, of strip copper, and should be completely insulated before insertion in the slots. For partly closed slots the com-

14

plete coil may be composed of several strips, each completely insulated with a wrapper of treated cloth and a winding of cotton tape. In some types of machines, designed for especially heavy service, the insulation is composed of sheet micanite, wrapped with cotton tape. A cell of fish paper should be inserted in the slot for mechanical protection and the straps threaded in one by one. The cell may then be folded in and a wedge inserted. Wave windings are used for form-wound rotors.

Collector rings are made of copper or brass. If mounted inside the bearings, they are usually provided with lugs which are bolted through insulating washers to a ring in a small spider. If mounted outside the bearings, the leads are brought out through the hollow shaft and bolted to the rings.

V. WINDING LARGE ALTERNATING-CURRENT STATORS

The machines which fall under this heading include large induction motors used in industrial plants, engine and water-wheel driven generators, motor-generator sets, synchronous motors and frequency changers. While in many cases different types of windings are used, the method of winding the stators is essentially the same in all cases. Particular reference will be made, however, in the winding details to the usual construction and requirements of induction motors. The recommendations for insulation of slots, make up of coils and their insertion are those of a writer in the *Electric Journal*, Vol. VII, No. 12, and represent good practice both for closed and open slot construction.

Coils for Partially Closed Slots.—When it is necessary to replace the coils in large machines, they should be purchased from the manufacturer since it is very difficult to properly form and insulate a number of large heavy coils with the facilities available in an ordinary repair shop or at the location where the machine is operated, such as a generating station or industrial plant.

The partially closed slot requires a form of coil which can be either threaded-in through the slot opening or inserted from the end. As it is ordinarily impracticable to insulate the slots for the voltages commonly used on large machines by the methods used for threaded-in coils, it is necessary either to insulate each strand for the full voltage or to use some form of winding in which the complete coil can be insulated from ground and impregnated and then inserted into the slot from the end.

The former method may be used where strap diamond coils of a limited number of turns are to be used, and the voltages

FIG. 149.—Large induction motor stator partly wound showing type of coil used (*General Electric Company*).

are moderate. A standard application of this method which is much used on large induction motors consists of a four coil per slot winding. Two strap diamond coils for each slot are completely insulated and impregnated. The width and depth of the insulated coil are each equal to half the width and depth of the slot. The width of the opening at the top is one-half the width of the slot, and the winding process is the same as for an open slot winding, except that there are twice as many coils for the number of slots as in an ordinary winding.

Where a number of turns per slot are required with a partly closed slot a concentric shoved through coil can be used.

This may have as many turns as desired.   The coils may be
formed from double cotton covered wires, round in the smaller
sizes and square in the larger.   The wires should be cut off in
lengths equal to the total length of the coil plus enough to
allow for joints, and bound together in a long straight bar,
having the correct cross-section for the coil.   This bar is

Fig. 150.—Section of stator of water-wheel driven generator showing chain
winding.

then clamped by the middle in a forming machine, and the
ends are bent over suitable wooden forms to give the correct
shape to the finished end of the coil.   The two free ends should
be left straight, so that they may be shoved through the slots.

Coils for Open Slots.—Although the closed slot has some
advantages in the case of induction motors, the form of winding
necessary for more than four or at most six turns per slot, is

complicated and expensive to wind. The coils for an open slot winding are easy and cheap to form, to insulate and to install. A diamond winding can be readily chorded, and thus a standard frame and core can be used for different windings. In addition, a coil which can be completely insulated and impregnated before insertion in the slots is more reliable. Open

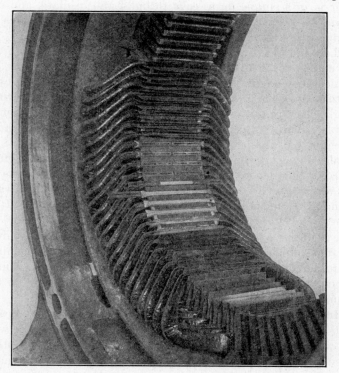

FIG. 151.—Partly wound stator of a 30-hp., 3-phase, 60-cycle, 685-r.p.m. induction motor (*Crocker-Wheeler Company*).

slot windings are used, therefore, for generators and synchronous motors, and for the large sizes of induction motors.

Both concentric (also called spiral or chain) and diamond windings can be used with open slots. Either type of coil (see page 3, Chapter I) is formed at both ends, and can be completely insulated and impregnated before assembling in the core. The concentric winding takes up less room where

the throw of the coils is great.   All the coils in a group are of
different size and shape, however, and the adjacent groups
must be of different length.   On account of the number of
different coils used, repairs are difficult to make and a larger
supply of extra coils must be kept in stock.   For this reason
the diamond winding is quite generally used.   A diamond
coil is of a simple form, easy to build and insulate, and one
form of coil is used throughout.   Repair parts can thus be
reduced to a minimum.

Lap and Wave Connections.—Either the lap or wave form
of diamond winding may be used.   The end connections, by
which the coil ends are connected into groups and the groups
into phases, are very much more simple with the wave winding.   This form of winding is, therefore, used whenever applicable.   The voltage between adjacent coil ends is much
greater, but as the coil must be insulated for full line voltage
under any conditions, this does not make any particular difference.   Where more than one turn per coil is required, however,
or where a series-parallel combination is necessary, the wave
winding is more cumbersome than the lap winding.   It is
accordingly used only with a one turn per slot coil, where all
the groups in a phase are connected in series.   The lap winding
is thus much more common as most high voltage machines
require more than one turn per slot.   The coils may be wound
from round or square wire or copper strap, depending on the
number of turns and the size of the conductor.

Insulation of Coils.—The insulation to ground is practically
the same for a given voltage for all types of coils.   The wire
in wire-wound coils should be cotton covered, and no other
insulation is needed between turns.   When the coils are made
up of two or more layers of conductors, however, the layers
should be separated by drilling, cotton tape or treated paper,
according to the type of coil used.   Strap conductors may be
insulated between turns with overlapping cotton or mica
tape.   In most cases, however, the tape is used over the ends
of the coils only, the straight parts being insulated by inter-
weaving an insulating cell of cement paper and mica between
them.   Where several straps are connected in parallel for
greater conductivity, they are ordinarily enameled, cotton

covered or taped to prevent eddy current loss. The several turns, whether connected in parallel or series, may be bound together with non-overlapping cotton tape and impregnated before being insulated from ground. While drying, the straight parts should be clamped in a press so that they will dry perfectly straight and without any interstices between the turns. The hardened impregnating gums then bind the dried coil into a compact unit.

The insulation to ground may consist of treated taping over the whole coil, with a protective covering of cotton tape. This material is widely used on the smaller machines, and for comparatively low voltages. For larger machines, however, and for high voltages, the customary insulation consists of a wrapper of cement paper and mica on the straight parts and treated tape or mica tape on the ends, with a protective layer of untreated cotton tape or mica tape on the whole coil, overlapping on the ends and non-overlapping on the straight parts. The entire coil may then be dipped twice in an insulating varnish, and dried thoroughly in an oven after each dipping. The requisite insulation for the high voltage machines can be secured by extra turns of cement paper and mica wrapper. Not over three and one-half turns is ordinarily used, however, on account of the difficulty of properly impregnating such a coil. Where this does not give sufficient insulation, two or more separate wrappers may be used, and the coil dipped twice in varnish and dried after the application of each wrapper (see pages 163 to 172).

Inserting Shoved Through Concentric Coils.—Windings using coils of this type may be divided into two classes, depending on whether the ends are bent down at one end or bent down at both ends. The winding processes are practically similar for both. Coils bent down at one end are used on both two-phase and three-phase machines, the two windings being practically identical with the exception of the end connectors. In a two-phase machine the alternate groups are of the same phase, that is, all the coils in each bank of coil ends belong to the same phase.

In a three-phase machine, with a winding of this type, every third group belongs to the same phase, and the groups of each phase alternate from one bank to the other. It should be noted in this case that the groups of the same phase do not lie adjacent to one another, but are separated by a distance equal to the pole pitch and that there are only three groups of coils per pair of poles.   Where the groups of each phase have one side adjacent to another group of the same phase, under the same pole, with six groups of coils per pair of poles, it is necessary to have three banks, to allow the end connections to cross one another.   In this case the coils of two of the banks must be bent down on both ends.   The ends of the third bank are, therefore, bent down also, to secure uniformity of the windings.

Considerable care is required in inserting coils of the shoved-through type into the slots.   The slots must be first cleaned from all foreign matter.   The coils should then be rubbed with paraffine, and the slots lined with paraffined fish paper, cut and bent to an exact fit.   The coil is thus made to slip easily into position, and at the same time is protected from damage by sharp edges of the iron.   A tight driving fit is absolutely essential with this type of winding.   If, on trial, the fit is too loose, strips of treated fullerboard or wood can be placed in the slot, or taped to the coils.

The smallest coil in each group should be placed in the slots first, and worked into them both sides at once, until the formed end comes within a short distance of the iron. Wooden distance blocks of appropriate dimensions can be used to secure uniformity.   The other coils may then be inserted in order.   All the coils of one bank should be inserted before the other bank is started.   Where a two-bank winding is used, and the coils are bent down at one end only, it is necessary to insert the coils of the different banks from opposite sides of the core.   By this method the winder forms only the straight end of the coils, and his work is very much simplified.   When a three-bank winding is used, however, the winder must bend down the ends of all the coils as he connects them.   In this case it is easier to insert all the coils from one end.   After all the coils are in place a fiber retaining wedge should be driven in over the top of each coil to hold it tightly in place, the fit being as close as possible without damaging the coil or spreading the lamination at the ventilating slots.

In forming the ends of the coils of both straight and bent down type, wooden blocks may be used over which to bend and shape the conductors. The inner layer should be connected first, the scheme of connections shown in Fig. 152 giving the best results. The connector consists of a copper sleeve, which is soldered over the ends, the joints being staggered, so that the coil ends will not be unnecessarily bulky. While making the joint it is advisable to protect adjacent conductors from the heat and solder by placing a layer of cloth or mica

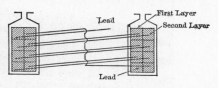

FIG. 152.—Connections when concentric coils are used.

between them. The finished joint should be smoothed off with a file or with emery cloth, and then insulated with treated cloth and friction tape.

Each coil, during assembly should be bent to correspond with the curve of the stator, so that no part of the finished coil will extend above the bore. A piece of insulating material, usually treated fullerboard, should be placed between the respective layers, which are then bound together with treated cloth and cotton tape. This serves both as insulation from ground and as mechanical protection for the coils.

In the process of connecting, care must be exercised that the ends of the same conductor are not joined together, thus producing a short-circuited turn. This can be prevented by testing out with a test lamp. As a precautionary measure, however, after the coils have been all connected, each one should be tested out with a testing transformer. This device (see page 126, Chapter V for construction) should be placed over one side of a coil and a thin piece of sheet steel over the other. If there is a closed circuit any place in the coil, a heavy current will flow, and the steel feeler will be strongly attracted to the iron of the core.

Bar and Connector Winding.—This type of winding consists of solid copper bars which are completely insulated and shoved

through the slots.   One or two bars may be used per slot.
Within an inch or so of the end, the bar is uninsulated and the
bare ends are tinned.   End connections of diamond or involute form, insulated and provided with tinned ends, are
used to complete the coil.   In order to facilitate the operation
of soldering, the ends of the connectors are slotted or drilled,

FIG. 153.—Section of the stator of a water-wheel driven generator showing
two-part bar coils, horn fiber slot insulation, wood wedges and ventilating
spaces in the core.

for without these openings it is difficult to force the solder
into the center of the joint.

In the case of a two-bar per slot winding, it is necessary
that the bar next to the rotor be shorter so that the joints
at both ends of the connectors will be accessible to a soldering
iron.   In this case, sufficient filling must be placed between
the two bars in the slot to allow the end connector to slip
over the top bar with sufficient clearance for taping.   In case

there is not sufficient room in the slot to allow of this filling, the top bars are cut away. The connector is shaped, as shown in Fig. 154, so as to allow it to slip between the lower bars and over the ends of the upper ones. All connectors must be soldered in place and the joints taped. With this type of winding repairs are very easily made, as any bar can be removed without disturbing the bars in any other slot, It is not adaptable to high voltages, however, on account of the limited number of possible turns. Furthermore, the end connections are very difficult to brace adequately.

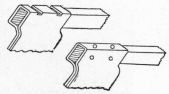

Diamond Coils. — On large machines a split frame construction is necessary. After

Fig. 154.—Stubs for bar and end connector winding.

the machine is completed and tested, the windings are removed by the maker at two points, in order to allow the frame to be disconnected for shipping. Some form of winding must, therefore, be used that can readily be disconnected and reconnected on arrival at its destination. This condition is most readily met by the open slot diamond coil. The diamond winding is by far the easiest to put in place, to remove when necessary without damage to the coil, to connect into groups and phases, to brace at the ends, etc. It is, therefore, much used on large or high voltage machines.

The assembly of wave and lap windings with these coils is practically the same, and the processes on the larger machines are similar to those employed on the smaller ones. The slots should be cleaned and lined with paper protective cells. The coils may then be inserted one after the other in order, no attention being paid to grouping, as the coils are all alike. On a large machine, the careful wedging of the coils in the slots is especially necessary, as the mechanical stresses that are brought to bear on account of the heavy currents in case of short-circuit, are very large. Hence the coil must fit very tightly in its place. If necessary, strips of treated cement paper, fullerboard or wood should be placed in the sides and bottoms of the slots to ensure a tight fit.

When inserting the coils, the first half of each coil should be driven tightly into the bottom of the slot with a fiber drift and mallet. The coil which goes over it must also be driven snugly into place. The fish-paper cell can then be cut off even with the top of the slot and folded over the coil. In order that this cell may not be torn by the wedge, a strip of treated fullerboard, the full width of the coil, may be laid

Fig. 155.—Stator of a 3-phase Fairbanks-Morse belted type alternator wound with the coils shown in Fig. 117.

into the slot, so that the wedge will slide over it readily, and at the same time compress the coil tightly into the slots. The wedges may, for convenience, be divided into sections 6 to 8 inches long and driven into position by means of a standard wedge driver or a blunt chisel. If the wedge is a very tight fit, the coil should be driven down with a drift just ahead of the wedge.

A four-coil per slot diamond winding used with partly closed slot cores, is assembled the same as any other diamond winding, with the exception that two coils lie side by side in both the bottom and top of the slot. The shape of the slot is such that no difficulty is encountered in inserting the second coil. This is essentially an induction motor winding, being used quite generally on both stator and rotor of large machines.

Double Windings.—On large induction motors, two speeds are sometimes secured by the use of two separate windings in the same slots, connected for a different number of poles. In this case the windings may be so designed that the coils for one speed lie inside the coils for the second speed. The two windings can be assembled at the same time, each pair of coils being treated as if it were a single coil of a one speed winding. Each slot thus contains four coils one above the other. In such cases it is quite common to have the two windings of widely different capacities, depending, of course, on the load to be carried at the separate speeds.

Testing Windings of Large Machines.—After the coils of the winding are all in place, their free terminals should be temporarily connected together, and a test made for break down to ground, with the standard voltage for the size and type of machine (see page 175, Chapter VII). After the coils have been connected into groups, and the groups connected into phases they should be tested for break down between phases, and for short-circuits between turns.

The break-down test consists of the application of the standard break-down voltage from the conductor to ground and from phase to phase. The test for short-circuit consists in placing an alternating-current magnet of the type shown in Fig. 101, page 126 over one side of the coil or group, and holding a light piece of steel over the other side of coil. If current flows in the coil, the piece of steel will be attracted. As no current can flow under normal conditions, this test is a sure indication of short-circuits. It cannot be applied where the groups are connected in parallel but must be made, in this case, before they are connected.

Connecting the Coils.—The number of groups in any machine may be either one or two per phase per pair of poles, depending on the arrangement of the coils and groups.   The coils of each group are connected in series but the groups in a phase may be connected in series, parallel or series-parallel, although for voltages of 2200 or higher they are nearly always connected in series.   The phases on a two-phase machine are never connected together inside the machine.

Stator windings of alternating-current machines may be connected either star or delta, the choice depending upon many conditions.   For machines of 2200 volts and over it is advisable to connect the winding in star because the voltage from any one terminal to ground is only (2200 ÷ 1.73) of the voltage between terminals and therefore the winding has a less chance to break down to ground.   However, this is not a strict rule for sometimes it is more convenient to have the stator delta connected for the reason that a smaller size of wire can be used and a larger number of turns.

On a concentric winding the groups are readily distinguishable.   In a diamond or involute winding, the number of coils per group must be counted off, and the groups temporarily connected by bending together the leads from a wire coil or by slipping a copper connector over the stubs from a strap coil.   They should be permanently connected by soldering the joints so made.   On most machines, the connectors between groups consist of insulated copper strap, with suitable openings at each end to slip over the group leads. All joints after being carefully soldered, should be smoothed up with emery cloth, so that no sharp-pointed edges are left to damage the insulation.

The connectors between coils, ordinarily called stubs, should be insulated with treated cloth tape, and a protective covering of untreated cotton tape.   Large stubs are sometimes covered with drilling caps, sewed to shape, and painted with insulating varnish after they have been fastened in place. Treated tape should be wound over the joints in the insulation. The thickness of the taping and other insulation, depends on the voltage of the machine.   The connectors between groups are ordinarily insulated and impregnated before they are put on the machine.   The joints between the connectors and the group leads should be insulated in the same way as the stubs.

Where double windings are used they are usually arranged for the connections to be made on opposite sides of the machine. Each winding may be connected as if it were entirely independent.

Bracing Needed for Heavy Windings.—The stresses occurring in the end connections of a large machine, due to magnetic reactions between current carrying conductors, are quite large. In addition, these effects are greatly magnified in case of a short-circuit on the generator. Some method of bracing these end connections is therefore necessary. This ordinarily takes the form of an insulated steel ring, to which the coils are tied with heavy twine. On a concentric winding a separate ring is used for each bank of end connections. On a diamond winding one ring at each end is sufficient. On a large machine, however, it is usually necessary to brace this ring by additional steel supports bolted to the frame.

VI. WINDING THE STATOR OF ALTERNATING-CURRENT TURBO-GENERATORS

Although the alternating-current turbo-generator falls in the previous group of large machines, on account of its winding being more or less special, it will be dealt with separately. There are special features of windings for this class of machines, owing to the high speed at which they are operated and the forced requirement that the inside diameter must be small on account of the centrifugal strains of the revolving field rotor. The generator core is therefore long requiring large coils frequently more than 10 feet long with a span from 30 to 40 inches and weighing as much as 100 pounds. One of the best discussions of the methods for winding an alternating-current turbo-generator has appeared in the *Electric Journal*, Vol. VIII, No 3. The winding details that follow have been taken from that source.

Coils for A.-C. Turbo-generators.—These machines have open slots and usually employ a diamond coil built up in two pieces for one or several turns per slot. The two-piece coil is used where the throw of the coils is very great, as in large size bipolar machines for 25 cycles. The one-piece coil is used on smaller machines, and in fact, wherever such a coil is not too cumbersome to handle, provided the complete coil can be passed through the bore. The coils of either type may be formed from cotton-covered strap or cotton-covered wire. Where a conductor of large cross-section is required, it is ordi-

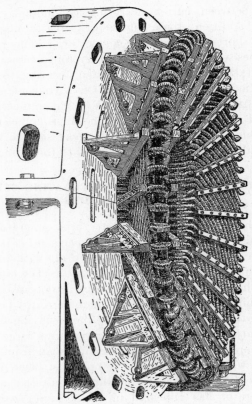

FIG. 156.—End of a large turbo-generator slowing method of bracing end connections to resist short-circuit stresses.

narily built up of a number of square copper wires in parallel, to facilitate bending and to obtain proper lamination. The individual strands are usually cotton covered. Most turbo-generators require more than one turn per slot in order to obtain the desired voltage. These several turns are bound together in a mechanical unit, insulated from each other and insulated as a group from the frame of the machine.

The coils may have their end connections bent down at any angle from zero to 90 degrees. The involute coils, of course, lie flat against the face of the frame. Diamond coils are always bent down at the ends from 30 to 60 degrees, both to provide ample clearance and ready access to the rotor, and in order that they may be more suitably braced, as shown in Fig. 156. Especial care should be taken to so shape the coil ends that cool air can circulate freely through them. Coils of several turns sometimes have the individual turns insulated separately after they leave the slots to give greater cooling surface to the ends.

Forming the Coils.—Except for conductors of large capacity, the conductors are formed from a single copper strap. The process of forming the coil is the same whether each conductor consists of one bar or several bars or straps in parallel. Each group of wires or straps which make up a conductor in the latter case may be formed as a single strap and then bound together with tape and treated as a unit. For a one-conductor coil, designated as an open coil, a strap of suitable length may be bent at the middle around a pin, forming a U with the sides separated very slightly. This loop should then be mounted directly in a mould. A steel pin through the bend of the U will serve to hold the point of the diamond vertical while the sides are bent to conform to the shape of the mould. Coils of several conductors are sometimes built in this same way, by forming the individual conductors in a group with a copper strip of the same thickness as the insulation inserted between them. The conductors should be separated and insulated from one another, and then insulated from ground the same as a one-conductor coil. The several conductors can be connected in series when placed in the machine.

A coil of more than one conductor formed from a single strap is known as a closed coil and requires several operations. The strap should be first wound around pins set in a flat table, to the required number of turns, and then given its final shape by forming over a mould. Throughout the entire operation the conductors must be kept apart by straps of metal to the same distance that they will be separated when insulated and placed in the machine. Two-piece coils can be formed from lengths of straight copper strap. The ends should be bent at a suitable angle to the straight part of the coil around two pins spaced a distance equal to the length of the straight part. The conductor may then be clamped in a mould and the ends bent into shape. The several conductors in a coil can be formed in the same mould, and separated by strips of copper strap.

Insulation for Turbogenerator Coils.—Since a turbogenerator may at times be subjected to very heavy overloads, the insulation should be as nearly heat proof as possible. For this reason, mica is much used. Where several conductors per coil are required, the insulation between conductors usually consists of flexible mica tape and mica cells. The individual conductors may then be suitably bound together. All coils should be impregnated with an insulating compound before the insulation from ground is supplied. The straight parts may be clamped tightly in metal clamps and impregnated, or may be impregnated without the clamps and placed in clamps to dry. Either method results in a compact, uniform construction so that the coil may be fitted tightly into the slot with minimum risk of damaging the insulation.

The insulation from ground usually consists of wrappers of paper and mica over the straight part. The coil ends should be insulated by layers of treated tape, with a covering of untreated tape, and the whole coil treated with insulating varnish. As in the case of engine type generators, if extra insulation is required additional wrappers of the paper and mica are frequently used, the coil being dipped and dried after each wrapper is applied. This makes the building of a high-voltage coil a long process, two weeks or more frequently being required for the completion of a single coil.

Testing Turbogenerator Windings.—Open coils may be tested for short-circuits by applying a suitable voltage between conductors. No short-circuit tests are usually made on the individual closed coils, but an over-voltage test should be applied after they are on the machine. All coils should also be tested for insulation by wrapping the outside with tin foil, and applying from two to two and a half times normal operating voltage across the insulation.

Inserting the Coils in a Turbogenerator.—Except for the great weight and large size of the coils which makes them more difficult to handle, the winding of a turbogenerator is in all essentials similar to the winding of an engine-type generator. The straight part of the coil should be waxed and laid over the slot opening, inside a paper cell with which the latter is

Fig. 157.—Turbo-generator stator partly wound using one-piece coils. The operator is binding the coils in position.

lined. In order to avoid bending the coil, a wooden drift as long as the straight part may be used to drive it into the bottom of the slot. The bottom halves of two-part coils should be inserted first in all slots in the span of one coil, the top halves being inserted later. One-piece coils should be inserted in regular order. After each top coil has been fitted into place, the cell which lines the slot may be folded over, and retaining wedges in short sections driven in place over the full length of the coil. Enough strips of extra material must be used in the slot to make the wedges fit tightly over the coil. The wedges may be driven in place by a tool of special shape, operated by a compressed-air hammer.

In order to get the bottom half of the last few one-piece coils into the slot, it is necessary to lift the top half of the coils which go in the same slots. With a full pitch winding this would mean one-half of the coils on a two-pole machine, and one-fourth the coils on a four-pole machine. With a "chorded" or fractional pitch winding, however, the number of throw coils is less. The throw of the coils can be readily seen in Fig. 157 which shows a generator partly wound with one-piece coils.

In some cases, the improved space factors that can be secured makes it worth while to use a one-coil-per-slot winding. This winding can be inserted in the same way as the two-coil-per-slot winding, except that alternate slots contain, respectively, front and rear ends of coils.

Bracing for Windings.—The instantaneous current which flows in case of a short-circuit to a turbo-generator or, in fact, any other generator, is very large and the magnetic stresses, which vary as the square of the current and the span of the end windings are consequently enormous in the turbo-generator. For this reason adequate bracing of the coil ends is of supreme importance. Greatest reliance is placed on metallic braces securely bolted to the generator frame. For involute coils, braces may be used that consist of U shaped clevises which are thoroughly insulated with treated tape and bolted to the machine frame at the ends through spacers. For diamond coils, the braces take the form of malleable iron brackets bolted to the frame. The coils should be rigidly secured to these braces by nonmetallic clamps, reinforced by brass plates, as shown in Fig. 156 and fastened to the braces by insulated bolts.

Connecting the Winding.—Turbine windings are almost always connected with one group of coils per pole per phase. The coils of each group are connected in series. In some cases these connectors are riveted as well as soldered in place.

The groups per phase may be connected in parallel or series, depending on the requirements of the machine. Ordinarily the series connection is used on machines of 2200 volts or higher. The end connections should be fully insulated and supported on the rear of the braces.

Break-down Test.—After all the coils have been placed in the core, their free ends should be connected together and the standard break-down voltage (see page 175, Chapter VII) applied from the copper to the machine. A similar break-down test should be applied between phases after the coils have been connected into groups. No further tests need be applied until the final load tests are run.

CHAPTER IX

TESTING INDUCTION MOTOR WINDINGS FOR MISTAKES AND FAULTS

After the coils have been placed in the stator of an induction motor and connected by the winder to give the required combination of phases, volts and poles, the next step is to connect the motor to a test circuit and note whether or not the current taken is the same in all the leads. If it is not, or the motor does not operate properly in other respects, the winding must be checked and tested for possible errors in connection of coils and for other defects. For an experienced induction motor winder, this is a simple job and one that is done very quickly. For the repaiman who has had less experience in connecting induction motors, the job is not so quickly performed. Yet it is not a difficult one when the procedure is correct. One of the most easily understood methods of procedure for checking induction-motor windings has been formulated by A. M. Dudley and published in the *Electrical Journal*. It is so simple yet complete that any repairman can with a little patience discover and correct even the most puzzling of errors and defects. It is given complete in what follows.

The errors which may occur in induction-motor windings have been arranged by Mr. Dudley in the approximate order of their occurrence as follows:

I. *Short Circuit and Grounds.*
  1. Short circuits or grounds of one or more turns in an individual coil caused by a break in insulation.
  2. Short circuit of a complete coil caused by connecting together the two ends of the coil. This is known by winders as "stubbing a coil dead."
  3. Short-circuiting a complete pole-phase-group.
  4. Short-circuiting one complete phase of the winding.
II. *Reversal of Part of the Winding.*
  1. This may be confined to a single coil or it may be a pole-phase-group or a complete phase.

III. *Open Circuits.*

   1. Caused by actually leaving the winding disconnected or open at some point.

IV *Placing One or More Coils too Many or too Few in a Pole-phase-group.*

V. *Using an Improper Group Connection.*

   1. For example, connecting in series when the winding should have been in parallel or *vice versa.* This is called "connecting for double or half voltage, respectively." A similar error would be connecting delta instead of star.

VI. *Connecting for the Wrong Number of Poles.*

   1. While this error comes under No. V, it is usually regarded as different and is sometimes difficult to locate unless it has been noticed that the speed of the motor when running light is not what it should be.

Testing for Grounds and Short Circuits.—Grounds of any description are located by "ringing out" between the copper

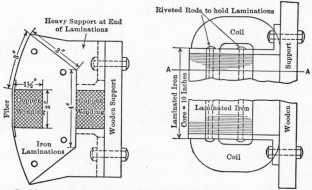

Fig. 158.—Section and plan views of a short-circuit detecting device for testing stator windings.

and the frame with a magneto or "lighting out" between the same points with an ordinary 110-volt lighting circuit test lamp. They are comparatively simple to locate and easy to repair by the use of insulating material used with the job.

Short circuits of a few turns or a single coil become hot in a short time if the motor is run light on normal voltage. Their presence can be detected by feeling around the winding with the hand immediately after starting the machine and noting if any coils are much warmer than others.

Short-circuit Detecting Device.—A device that can be used for detecting short circuits before the rotor is placed in the stator and without applying voltage to the winding itself, is shown in Fig. 158. It it somewhat similar to a large horse-shoe magnet except that the iron part is built up of laminations. It may also be considered a core-type transformer having the primary coil only and having one side of the iron core missing. The coil is excited with alternating current of a suitable voltage and then the complete device is passed slowly around the bore of the stator as shown in Figs. 159 and 160. The laminations of the stator core complete the magnetic circuit of the testing device and an alternating magnetic field flows in the stator core as shown by the dotted lines in Fig. 159. When moving the device around the stator bore, and it passes over a short-circuited turn or coil, such short-circuited turn or coil

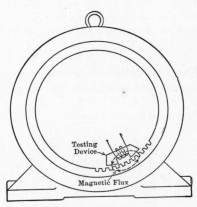

FIG. 159.—Method of using the short-circuit detecting device shown in Fig. 158.

immediately acts as a short-circuited secondary coil on a transformer of which the exciting coil on the testing device is the primary. As in any short-circuited transformer an increased current flows both in the primary and in the secondary coil and can be detected by an ammeter in series with the device or by the heating which immediately takes place in the defective coil in the winding or by the attraction which the other side of the short-circuited coil has for a strip of sheet iron. By passing the device slowly around the core and observing its behavior from point to point, short circuits can readily be detected. This refers particularly to short circuits in individual turns or in one complete coil. A short circuit of a complete pole-phase-group is more readily located by a compass test, and a short circuit of an entire phase can be found by a *balance test.* The balance test is made after the winding has been checked for grounds and short-circuited turns and has had the resistance of all the phases measured. If these checks indicate the proper number of turns in series, a comparatively low alternating voltage is applied to the winding of the stator without the rotor being in place. The current is then read in all the phases and if it checks up the same or *balances* as it is called, the machine is considered free of grounds and short circuits.

Fig. 160.—Testing stator winding for short-circuited coils by use of a small alternating-current magnet.

Reversal of One or More Coils or Groups.—It happens that individual coils or sometimes entire groups are connected in backward. If the error is confined to one coil it does not usually show up on the "balance" test and, of course, would not be found on the resistance test since the resistance is the same no matter whether the ends of the coils are interchanged or not. Such reversed coils or groups can be located by means of a polarity test with a compass. In this test the motor windings are excited by a comparatively low direct-current voltage so chosen that the current is limited to a reasonable value. If the windings are so excited and a compass is placed inside the bore and passed around slowly following the inner periphery, the needle of the compass will reverse in passing from a north pole to a south pole group and *vice versa*. If an individual coil is reversed it will show a tendency to reverse the compass needle when the needle is directly over that coil. If an entire pole-phase-group is reversed the compass needle will indicate the same direction of field on two successive groups. Also if a coil is left out of circuit or is "dead," as already mentioned, it will indicate an irregularity at the instant the compass passes directly above it. By checking the three phases of a three-phase winding separately, in this manner and marking the result inside the bore with chalk of different colors, it is possible to check for the reversal of an entire phase.

Open circuits are best checked by "lighting out." This test it made by connecting a 110-volt lighting circuit and an incandescent lamp in series with the winding. If there is an open circuit the lamp will not light.

Placing the wrong number of coils in two or more phase groups can hardly be deteced otherwise than by actually making a physical count. Since this is a simple matter, the check is best made in that way.

Using an improper group connection has in general the same effect as raising or lowering the voltage on a machine and can best be checked by operating the motor on what should be the correct voltage. If this voltage is considerably too high as would be the case if the winding was connected parallel when it should be series, or delta when it should be star, the motor will emit more than the ordinary amount of magnetic hum and will probably overheat in a short time even when not mechanically loaded. If the voltage is much too low, as would be the case if the winding was connected series, when it should be parallel, or star when it should be delta, the fact can be determined by trying a load on the motor. When the load comes on the drop in speed will be too great and the motor will pull out and come to a standstill on a load much less than normal.

Connecting for the wrong number of poles can most readily be detected by checking the no-load speed. (If it has a wound rotor, this must be short-circuited.) The no-load speed, being approximately synchronous, is very nearly equal to cycles × 120 ÷ number of poles. If this gives a result differing from that expected, the winding is connected for the wrong number of poles.

Order in Which Tests Should be Made.—The order in which these various checks should be performed is usually as follows: After the winder has completed the connection, the windings are checked against the winding diagram. The coils per group are counted and a visual inspection made for short circuits, open circuits and reversed coils. A balance test is made with low voltage to see if the separate phases show the same result. A high voltage test is then made on the insulation to ensure that the coils are not grounded between phases nor on the iron core. The machine is then assembled and the resistance of the completed winding is measured on all phases. If these checks are satisfactory the machine can be passed for a running light test without load. Sufficient voltage is put on the windings to start the motor up. If it comes up to speed without apparent distress or irregularity of any kind, the speed is checked and the temperature of the winding is tested with the hand all the way around the machine. If this is normal the voltage is raised to its normal value and the no-load current in all phases and the watts are read. If these values check with previous calculations or tests on duplicate machines the windings are considered to be correctly connected. If no data is available on the no-load current it may be considered reasonable if it does not exceed 40 per cent. and is at least 20 per cent. of full load current. The no-load watts running light may be considered reasonable if they are roughly in the neighborhood of seven or eight per cent. of the normal rating of the motor. If the motor does not readily come up to speed or the phases do not balance or there are signs of unequal heating in the winding or other distress, the rotor should be removed and the connections checked. If the error is not apparent and a source of direct current is available the compass test may be applied.

Connections for Applying Direct Current when Exploring A.-C. Windings with a Compass.—The accompanying diagrams show the methods for making connections for the use of direct current to excite the windings of an alternating-current motor so as to explore the windings by the use of a compass. When the winding is star connected, one lead of the direct-current circuit is joined to *A–B–C* connected together and

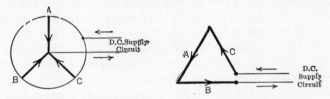

FIG. 161.—Method for checking 3-phase, star and delta connected windings with direct current.

the other lead to the neutral point. When the compass is held over the coils in the slots and moved around the stator, there should be three times as many poles as there are poles in the machines reversing alternately and spaced equally when the winding is balanced. In case of a delta-connected winding, it is only necessary to open the delta connection as shown in Fig. 161 at the right and connect the two ends to the direct-current leads.

CHAPTER X

ADAPTING DIRECT-CURRENT MOTORS TO CHANGED OPERATING CONDITIONS

The changes in direct-current motors which the repairman is most frequently called upon to make are: 1. Changes in speed. 2. Changes in operating voltage. 3. Changes to operate a motor as a generator and *vice versa*.

Changes in Speed.—A change in speed of a motor from 10 to 15 per cent. can usually be made by increasing or decreasing the air gap between the armature and fields. In general the per cent. changes in air gap required will be three or four times the per cent. change in speed. This will serve only as a rough check for use when measuring the air gap and considering the change of speed in this manner. To make this change with accuracy, it is necessary to have a magnetization curve for the design of the particular machine dealt with. However if the change in speed desired is not too great, the change in air gap will in most cases give desired results. The exceptions are those cases where the motor has been built to work high up on the saturation curve where the iron is practically saturated or very low down on the saturation curve where the excitation is practically all used in the air gap. The speed is increased by increasing the air gap and reduced by reducing the air gap.

It is usually easier to reduce the speed by change in air gap than to increase the speed. In the former case sheet steel liners or shims can be inserted next to the frame and different lengths of air gaps secured over a considerable range depending upon the length of the original air gap of the machine. If the air gap cannot be increased by removing such shims, it may be necessary to grind off the required amount from the pole faces. Such a grinding should not be done more than once if the operation will narrow the width of pole face to an appreciable extent. When the increase in speed is more than

237

can be secured by increasing the air gap, it may be possible to add a resistance to the shunt-field circuit. In such a case it will be necessary to check carefully the no-load and full-load speeds.

In the case of a shunt motor, a compound characteristic can be secured by increasing the air gap and then adding series turns to the field poles until the full-load speed is the same as it was before the change. For this purpose flexible copper cable can be wound around the shunt coil and bound in place. In reversing this change, that is, in changing a compound motor to a shunt characteristic, the air gap should be reduced and current shunted out of the series coils of the field until a constant speed range is secured.

An inefficient and emergency method of reducing the speed of a motor for a short time only is by the use of a resistance in the armature circuit. When a variable resistance is connected in series with the armature leads, it simply reduces the impressed voltage on the armature winding by using up a part of the voltage in the resistance. Since the speed of the motor is proportional to the operating voltage, the desired speed reduction can be thus secured.

In all cases where the speed of a motor is increased, attention must be paid to the armature construction so that the increased centrifugal strains on the coils and the banding due to the increase in speed will develop no serious defects, such as rubbing of coils on the fields, high commutator bars and poor commutation. When the increase in speed is 50 per cent. or more, the manufacturer should be consulted for advice as to the safety of the high speed for continuous operation.

Changes in Operating Voltage.—The speed of a direct-current motor varies directly with the operating voltage and (theoretically) inversely with the flux of the fields. When the operating voltage is increased on a motor, the excitation of the fields is also affected but on account of the saturation of the iron, the field flux is not affected in direct proportion so that the speed of the motor on an increase of voltage follows about in proportion to the increase. When the voltage is not increased or decreased more than 25 per cent. over the rated value for the motor, the correct speed can be obtained by a change of the air gap. In such a change the operating temperature of the field coils must be watched, since the temperature will vary about as the square of the voltage. A temperature higher than 160°F. will injure the insulation. To prevent this when the temperature of the fields is found to be around this figure, it will be advisable to rewind the field coils. In case the machine is operated on under voltage with the air gap as large as possible, a resistance can be used in the shunt field until the required speed is secured. On a compound motor, no-load and full-load speeds can be adjusted by changing the series field coils in either of the cases mentioned.

Operating a Motor on One-half or Double Voltage.—It frequently happens that a 220-volt motor must be changed to operate on 110 volts or a 110-volt motor on 220 volts. In the case of a 220-volt motor, it is usually possible to connect the shunt-field coils in two groups and then connect these groups in parallel. In such a case when the motor is connected to a 110-volt circuit, the voltage per coil will be the same so that the field flux will be the same, but the speed will be only one-half that on 220 volts. The speed can be brought up to normal by increasing the air gap as much as possible and using resistance in the shunt field as explained in a preceding paragraph. The rating in horsepower of a motor so changed will only be one-half of what it was before.

When a 110-volt motor must be changed to operate on 220 volts, the conditions are not so easy as in the previous case for if the smallest air gap with the shunt fields in series cannot be used, the field coils must be rewound. When operated in this way the motor will have double the horsepower rating on 220 volts that it did on 110 volts. The changes in the motor which have been mentioned do not require a change in the armature winding.

Changes in Armature Winding for Operating Motors on One-half or Double Voltage.—The most satisfactory way of changing a motor to operate on a voltage which is one-half or double the rated voltage is to rewind the armature to suit the new conditions. This is also the most expensive way and need not be resorted to when the change in voltage is not over 25 per cent. A direct-current armature winding can usually be changed for operation on a lower voltage in two ways. 1. By using new coils. 2. By reconnecting the old armature winding. When the armature is to be rewound for a different voltage, the number of turns in series between brushes will vary directly as the old voltage to the new. The cross-section of the wire for the coils will also vary inversely as the old voltage to the new. For instance if a 110-volt motor is to be operated on 220 volts, the armature conductors will be doubled in number and their cross-section made one-half, when the speed and horsepower rating will remain the same as before. When the size of wire previously used is known, one of one-half the cross-section will be three B. & S. gauge numbers higher.

A practical way of making these changes in armature windings in a repair shop is given on pages 243 to 260 as outlined by T. Schutter (*Electrical Engineering*, July and August, 1918) for the changes of one-half and double-voltage operation.

Size of Wire for D.-C. Armature Coils.—Before winding the coils needed in the repair of an armature it must be decided whether a lap or a wave winding will be used. In the lap winding there are as many current paths or circuits through the armature winding as there are poles with the coils connected in series in each of these paths or circuits. The wave winding has only two current paths through the armature winding regardless of the number of poles the machine has. In each of these two paths the coils are connected in series. Considering I the total armature current as given on the name plate of the machine and i the current in each circuit of the armature winding, the following formulas can be used to find the maximum current that can be carried by the coils of each circuit connected in series.

For a lap winding in which the number of circuits equals the number of poles or p,

$$i = I \div p$$

For a multiple lap winding, having two or more single lap windings in parallel,

$$i = I \div mp$$

In this case m is the number of single lap windings in parallel.

For a wave winding which has two circuits

$$i = I \div 2$$

For wave windings having more than two circuits, usually called multiple-wave or series-parallel windings

$$i = I \div 2m$$

In this case m is the number of wave windings used in the armature.

The permissible current density in armature conductors varies from 1500 to 3000 amperes per square inch. The cross-section or diameter of the wire for the armature coils can then be found by dividing the current in each section of the winding (i) by the allowable amperes per square inch. The value to use in the case of small machines should not exceed 3000; in intermediate sizes 2000; and in large sizes 1500.

When winding new coils in the repair of an armature it is necessary to determine the available winding space in the slot before deciding upon the number of turns and form of coil to use. In case the armature is to be rewound for changed conditions of speed or voltage reference should be made to Chapters X and XI where details to be observed are given for different changes in operating conditions.

Operating a Generator as a Motor and Vice Versa.—It is usually possible to operate a generator as a motor by setting

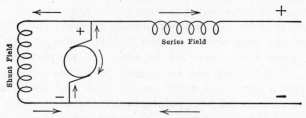

Fig. 162.—Direct-current generator with armature rotating clockwise.

the brushes for the correct rotation of the armature and with a backward lead instead of a forward lead when operating as a generator. To successfully operate a motor as a generator the air gap should be reduced to a minimum and the speed

16

increased where the voltage as a generator is to be equal or higher than the voltage as a motor. When the voltage is to be lower, the same speed and air gap can usually be used.

When a direct-current machine is changed from a generator to a motor, the current in both the armature and series field reverses. If, therefore, the machine is operated as a cumulatively compounded generator, it will also operate as a differentially compounded motor. In order to use a compound generator as a motor, it is usually necessary to reverse the connections of its series fields. The diagrams of Figs. 162 and 163 are self-explanatory.

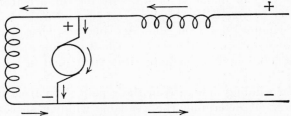

Fig. 163.—Differential motor with armature rotating clockwise and series field opposing shunt field.

Adjusting the Air Gap on D.-C. Machines.—When inserting the armature in any machine in which the bearings are independent of the frame, the air gap between the armature core and pole faces should be checked up. Any inequality of air gap will cause unnecessary friction and heating of the bearings and an unequal heating of the armature iron. The air gap may be adjusted horizontally in many cases by cross beams and jack screws on the bedplate and vertically by thin sheet liners inserted between the bedplate and the yoke. The air gap can be gauged during the operation by inserting a hardwood wedge on the front and back ends of the machine at different points, noting the distance to which the wedge enters each time. The adjustment should be continued until the air gap is the same around the entire circumference of the machine.

Motor Speed when Reconnecting a D.-C. Motor Winding Wave to Lap.—When reconnecting a wave winding to form a lap winding without changing the coils, or voltage, the speed of a four-pole motor will be increased twice, and the speed of an eight-pole motor increased four times. This is because the wave winding is a two-circuit winding while the lap winding has as many circuits as there are poles. The speed, therefore, varies directly as the number of circuits in the winding.

Change in Brushes when Reconnecting a D.-C. Motor from a Higher to a Lower Voltage.—When reconnecting a direct-current armature from a higher to a lower voltage, say 220 volts to 110 volts, the size of conductors must be doubled as the current will be about double its original value. The original brushes on the 220-volt machine must therefore be changed to handle this increase in current without heating and sparking. If twice as many brushes of the same size as before cannot be used, the size of brush must be changed to give twice the bearing surface. An increase in width of the brush should be avoided, the length being increased to get the proper bearing surface. A current density of more than 50 amperes per square inch will give trouble sooner or later in a reconnected armature.

For a four-pole motor originally 220 volts, changed to operate on 110 volts, the field coils should be connected two in series and these groups connected in parallel in order to get the same field current.

REWINDING AND RECONNECTING DIRECT-CURRENT ARMA-TURE WINDINGS FOR A CHANGE OF VOLTAGE*

When a direct-current armature is to be rewound or re-connected for a change from one voltage to another, the number of turns in series between brushes as explained on page 239 will vary directly as one voltage to the other and the cross-sectional area of the wire will vary inversely as the voltages. To illustrate, take the case of a 2-pole armature consisting of 24 coils, 20 turns per coil wound one wire-in-hand using number 19 B. & S. gauge wire, which has a cross-sectional area of 1290 circular mils. The armature has a 240-volt winding and is to be changed so as to operate on a 120-volt

* T. Schutter, *Electrical Engineering*, July, 1918.

circuit. This can be accomplished in two ways. First, by rewinding the armature; second, by reconnecting the present winding.

By comparing the original voltage with the new operating voltage, it will be seen that the new voltage is just half of the original voltage. If it took 20 turns per coil for 240 volts then it will take half of 20 or 10 turns per coil for 120 volts. As the machine is to do the same amount of work, it will carry twice the current at 120 volts that it did at 240 volts. For this reason the wire must have twice the cross-sectional area, or $1290 \times 2 = 2580$ circular mil area. This is equal to a number 16 B. & S. gauge wire, still using the same number of coils as before.

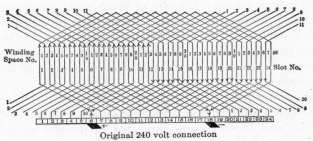

Original 240 volt connection

FIG. 164.—A 240-volt lap winding which is reconnected for 120 volts as shown in Fig. 165.

The other method is to reconnect the winding so that two coils are in parallel, and bridge two commutator bars. This will result in a winding of 12 coils, two in parallel, with 20 turns per coil. In Fig. 164 the original winding is shown, as it was wound and connected to the commutator. The armature core contained 24 slots and there were two coil sides per slot. The part of the slot which is occupied by a coil side is called a winding space. The odd numbered winding spaces are considered as being in the bottom of the slot and the even numbered winding spaces being in the top of the slot. The table for winding coils in Fig. 164 is given on page 245 and the connecting table for the original winding as illustrated in Fig. 164 on page 247.

By tracing the direction of flow of current through the windings from the positive brush to the negative brush, it will be seen there are two paths or circuits, each consisting of 12 coils in series, the two paths or circuits being in parallel with each other. This winding operates on 240 volts.

TABLE FOR WINDING COILS ON ARMATURE OF FIG. 164

Coil number	Coils are wound	
	In spaces number	In slots number
1	1 and 24	1 and 12
2	3 and 26	2 and 13
3	5 and 28	3 and 14
4	7 and 30	4 and 15
5	9 and 32	5 and 16
6	11 and 34	6 and 17
7	13 and 36	7 and 18
8	15 and 38	8 and 19
9	17 and 40	9 and 20
10	19 and 42	10 and 21
11	21 and 44	11 and 22
12	23 and 46	12 and 23
13	25 and 48	13 and 24
14	27 and 2	14 and 1
15	29 and 4	15 and 2
16	31 and 6	16 and 3
17	33 and 8	17 and 4
18	35 and 10	18 and 5
19	37 and 12	19 and 6
20	39 and 14	20 and 7
21	41 and 16	21 and 8
22	43 and 18	22 and 9
23	45 and 20	23 and 10
24	47 and 22	24 and 11

TABLE FOR CONNECTING COILS OF FIG. 164 TO COMMUTATOR

Beginning of coil number	To bar number	End of coil number	To bar number
1	6	1	7
2	7	2	8
3	8	3	9
4	9	4	10
5	10	5	11
6	11	6	12
7	12	7	13
8	13	8	14
9	14	9	15
10	15	10	16
11	16	11	17
12	17	12	18
13	18	13	19
14	19	14	20
15	20	15	21
16	21	16	22
17	22	17	23
18	23	18	24
19	24	19	1
20	1	20	2
21	2	21	3
22	3	22	4
23	4	23	5
24	5	24	6

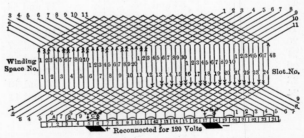

FIG. 165.—The 240-volt winding of Fig. 164 reconnected for a 120-volt circuit by connecting two coils in parallel and using wider brushes.

Reconnecting a Lap Winding.—In Fig. 165 the winding shown in Fig. 164 has been reconnected so as to operate on a 120-volt circuit.

As explained it will require one-half as much winding on 120 volts as it did on 240 volts. This can be accomplished by connecting two coils in parallel, and using wider brushes; that is, the brushes should be at least as wide as 1½ commutator bars and not more than two commutator bars. If it is possible to arrange for the use of the wider brushes, the commutator can be bridged, as shown by the jumpers *A, B, C,* etc., Fig. 165.

TABLE FOR CONNECTING COILS OF FIG. 165 TO COMMUTATOR

Beginning of coil number	To bar number	End of coil number	To bar number
1	5	1	7
2	6	2	8
3	7	3	9
4	8	4	10
5	9	5	11
6	10	6	12
7	11	7	13
8	12	8	14
9	13	9	15
10	14	10	16
11	15	11	17
12	16	12	18
13	17	13	19
14	18	14	20
15	19	15	21
16	20	16	22
17	21	17	23
18	22	18	24
19	23	19	1
20	24	20	2
21	1	21	3
22	2	22	4
23	3	23	5
24	4	24	6

By tracing the direction of flow of current through the winding it will be seen that the current flows in four circuits from the positive brush to the negative brush. In each path or circuit there are six coils in series, and the four paths or circuits are in parallel. This reconnection is equivalent to rewinding the armature with twice the size of wire and one-half the number of turns with which it was wound for 240 volts. Both Figs. 164 and 165 show lap or parallel windings.

Reconnecting a Wave Winding.—Fig. 166 represents a four-pole wave or series winding, consisting of 31 coils. The

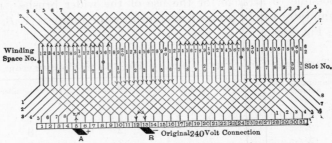

Fig. 166.—Wave winding for a 240-volt, 4-pole armature.

armature core has 31 slots, and there are two coil sides per slot. It is wound so as to be operated on a 240-volt circuit. The coils in this Fig. 166 are placed so that the beginning of each coil is placed in the bottom of the slot, and is represented by the odd numbered coil sides.

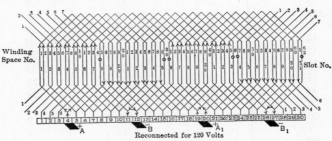

Fig. 167.—The wave winding of Fig. 166 reconnected so that there are four paths for current instead of two with four brushes instead of two. This winding can now be used on a 120-volt circuit.

By tracing the current from the positive to the negative brush, it will be seen that the winding is divided into two paths or circuits. To change this winding so that it can be operated on a 120-volt circuit, two methods can be used: First, reconnect the winding so that it will consist of four paths or circuits, and add another set of brushes as shown in Fig. 167. The

TABLE FOR WINDING COILS IN SLOTS OF FIG. 166

Coil number	Coils are wound	
	In spaces number	In slots number
1	1 and 16	1 and 8
2	3 and 18	2 and 9
3	5 and 20	3 and 10
4	7 and 22	4 and 11
5	9 and 24	5 and 12
6	11 and 26	6 and 13
7	13 and 28	7 and 14
8	15 and 30	8 and 15
9	17 and 32	9 and 16
10	19 and 34	10 and 17
11	21 and 36	11 and 18
12	23 and 38	12 and 19
13	25 and 40	13 and 20
14	27 and 42	14 and 21
15	29 and 44	15 and 22
16	31 and 46	16 and 23
17	33 and 48	17 and 24
18	35 and 50	18 and 25
19	37 and 52	19 and 26
20	39 and 54	20 and 27
21	41 and 56	21 and 28
22	43 and 58	22 and 29
23	45 and 60	23 and 30
24	47 and 62	24 and 31
25	49 and 2	25 and 1
26	51 and 4	26 and 2
27	53 and 6	27 and 3
28	55 and 8	28 and 4
29	57 and 10	29 and 5
30	59 and 12	30 and 6
31	61 and 14	31 and 7

additional brushes are marked A_1 and B_1. Second, connect two coils in parallel and still have two circuits in the winding. This, however, will necessitate the dropping of one coil, as shown by the heavy lines in Fig. 168. Only two brushes will be required as shown, if they can be set so that they cover at least $1\frac{1}{2}$ bars, the jumpers A, B, C, etc., can be omitted.

TABLE FOR CONNECTING COILS OF FIG. 166 TO THE COMMUTATOR

Beginning of coil number	To bar number	End of coil number	To bar number
1	28	1	12
2	29	2	13
3	30	3	14
4	31	4	15
5	1	5	16
6	2	6	17
7	3	7	18
8	4	8	19
9	5	9	20
10	6	10	21
11	7	11	22
12	8	12	23
13	9	13	24
14	10	14	25
15	11	15	26
16	12	16	27
17	13	17	28
18	14	18	29
19	15	19	30
20	16	20	31
21	17	21	1
22	18	22	2
23	19	23	3
24	20	24	4
25	21	25	5
26	22	26	6
27	23	27	7
28	24	28	8
29	25	29	9
30	26	30	10
31	27	31	11

The winding as shown in Fig. 167, is a four-pole lap or parallel winding, with four circuits or paths through the winding. The second method of reconnecting Fig. 166 so as to operate it on 120 volts is shown in Fig. 168. As previously explained, each two adjacent coils will be connected in parallel, and since there are 31 coils on the entire winding, one coil must be dropped. In this winding (Fig. 168) coil No. 2, shown with the heavy lines has no connection with the commutator.

TABLE FOR CONNECTING COILS OF FIG. 167 TO THE COMMUTATOR

Beginning of coil number	To bar number	End of coil number	To bar number
1	4	1	5
2	5	2	6
3	6	3	7
4	7	4	8
5	8	5	9
6	9	6	10
7	10	7	11
8	11	8	12
9	12	9	13
10	13	10	14
11	14	11	15
12	15	12	16
13	16	13	17
14	17	14	18
15	18	15	19
16	19	16	20
17	20	17	21
18	21	18	22
19	22	19	23
20	23	20	24
21	24	21	25
22	25	22	26
23	26	23	27
24	27	24	28
25	28	25	29
26	29	26	30
27	30	27	31
28	31	28	1
29	1	29	2
30	2	30	3
31	3	31	4

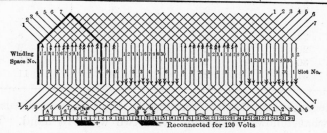

FIG. 168.—The wave winding of Fig. 166 reconnected for a 120-volt circuit by connecting two coils in parallel and using wider brushes. In this case one coil is dead as shown by the heavy lines.

There are 31 bars in the original commutator, so that by taking any two bars and putting a jumper across and considering them as one bar, it will be reduced to 30 bars. The connections will be made as shown by the following table:

TABLE FOR CONNECTING COILS OF FIG. 168 TO THE COMMUTATOR

Beginning of coil number	To bar number	End of coil number	To bar number
Coil 1 is not connected.			
2	28	2	12
3	29	3	13
4	30	4	14
5	1	5	15
6	2	6	16
7	3	7	17
8	4	8	18
9	5	9	19
10	6	10	20
11	7	11	21
12	8	12	22
13	9	13	23
14	10	14	24
15	11	15	25
16	12	16	26
17	13	17	27
18	14	18	28
19	15	19	29
20	16	20	30
21	17	21	1
22	18	22	2
23	19	23	3
24	20	24	4
25	21	25	5
26	22	26	6
27	23	27	7
28	24	28	8
29	25	29	9
30	26	30	10
31	27	31	11

Reconnecting Duplex Windings.*—The windings discussed in what follows are wound with two wires in hand. The

* T. Schutter, *Electrical Engineering*, August, 1918.

same results can be accomplished by two windings, using one strand (two simplex windings) at a time. In a winding of the duplex type there are usually twice as many commutator bars as there are slots and each of the two wires is connected to separate bars. The brush, however, will cover at least 1½ to 2 commutator bars, as shown in Fig. 169, which is the winding and connections for a 120-volt lap-wound armature.

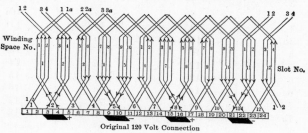

FIG. 169.—Duplex lap winding for a 120-volt armature.

Each coil consists of two parts, which will be called Section 1, and 1a, Section 2 and 2a, Section 3 and 3a, etc. The following is the winding table for Fig. 169.

TABLE FOR WINDING COILS IN SLOTS OF FIG. 169

Coil number	Coils are wound	
	In spaces number	In slots number
1–1a	1 and 6	1 and 3
2–2a	3 and 8	2 and 4
3–3a	5 and 10	3 and 5
4–4a	7 and 12	4 and 6
5–5a	9 and 14	5 and 7
6–6a	11 and 16	6 and 8
7–7a	13 and 18	7 and 9
8–8a	15 and 20	8 and 10
9–9a	17 and 22	9 and 11
10–10a	19 and 24	10 and 12
11–11a	21 and 2	11 and 1
12–12a	23 and 4	12 and 2

This 120-volt winding is to be changed so that it can be operated on a 240-volt circuit. As shown in Fig. 169 Section

TABLE FOR CONNECTING COILS TO THE COMMUTATOR OF FIG. 169

Start of coil number	To bar number	End of coil number	To bar number
1	3	1	5
1a	4	1a	6
2	5	2	7
2a	6	2a	8
3	7	3	9
3a	8	3a	10
4	9	4	11
4a	10	4a	12
5	11	5	13
5a	12	5a	14
6	13	6	15
6a	14	6a	16
7	15	7	17
7a	16	7a	18
8	17	8	19
8a	18	8a	20
9	19	9	21
9a	20	9a	22
10	21	10	23
10a	22	10a	24
11	23	11	1
11a	24	11a	2
12	1	12	3
12a	2	12a	4

1 and 1a of coil 1 are connected in parallel through the brush connections, and by changing the connections so that Sec-

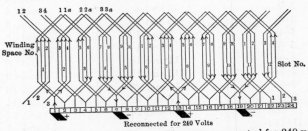

FIG. 170.—The 120-volt lap winding of Fig. 169 reconnected for 240 volts by connecting the turns of each coil in series and using smaller brushes.

tions 1 and 1a will be in series instead of in parallel, it will then be possible to operate the winding on a 240-volt circuit.   The winding table for Fig. 170 will be the same as for Fig. 169 but the connecting table will be as follows:

TABLE FOR CONNECTING COILS OF FIG. 170 TO COMMUTATOR

Start of coil number	To bar number	End of coil number	To bar number
1	1	1	2
1a	2	1	3
2	3	2	4
2a	4	2	5
3	5	3	6
3a	6	3a	7
4	7	4	8
4a	8	4a	9
5	9	5	10
5a	10	5a	11
6	11	6	12
6a	12	6a	13
7	13	7	14
7a	14	7a	15
8	15	8	16
8a	16	8a	17
9	17	9	18
9a	18	9a	19
10	19	10	20
10a	20	10a	21
11	21	11	22
11a	22	11a	23
12	23	12	24
12a	24	12a	1

The brushes used on Fig. 170 should only be as wide as one commutator bar. By tracing the current through the winding in Fig. 169 it will be seen that there are three coils in series in each of the paths or circuits from the positive brush to the negative brush. In Fig. 169 there are six coils in each path or circuit, or twice as many as before the reconnection.

If the winding in Fig. 169 had been connected to a 12-bar commutator instead of a 24-bar commutator, the reconnecting from 120 volts would have been somewhat different. In Fig. 169 the numerals from 1 to 12, which are placed above and between each two bars, will give an idea of how the connections would look. For instance, Sections 1 and 1a of coil No. 1 would be connected across bars Nos. 2 and 3, instead of Section 1 to bars 3 and 5, and 1a to bars 4 and 6.

Then to reconnect the winding from 120 volts to 240 volts when only 12 commutator bars are used, Sections 1 and 1a of Coil No. 1 would have to be connected in series, but not through commutator connections as in Fig. 170. By omitting the connections of commutator bars, No. 2, 4, 6, 8 and 10, etc., and simply splicing the end of Section 1 to the beginning of Section 1a of coil No. 1, the same results will be obtained by using only 12 commutator bars.

Fig. 171 is a "duplex wave" winding for operation on a 120-volt circuit. This winding consists of 13 coils wound with two strands of wire and connected to 26 commutators bars. This winding could also be connected to a 13-bar commutator. The winding table for Fig. 171 is as follows, each coil being considered as two Sections, 1 and 1a.

TABLE FOR WINDING COILS IN SLOTS FOR FIG. 171

Coil number	Coils are wound	
	In spaces number	In slots number
1 and 1a	1 and 6	1 and 3
2 and 2a	3 and 8	2 and 4
3 and 3a	5 and 10	3 and 5
4 and 4a	7 and 12	4 and 6
5 and 5a	9 and 14	5 and 7
6 and 6a	11 and 16	6 and 8
7 and 7a	13 and 18	7 and 9
8 and 8a	15 and 20	8 and 10
9 and 9a	17 and 22	9 and 11
10 and 10a	19 and 24	10 and 12
11 and 11a	21 and 26	11 and 13
12 and 12a	23 and 2	12 and 1
13 and 13a	25 and 4	13 and 2

The winding as it is now placed and connected will operate on a 120-volt circuit. It is desired to change it so that it will operate on a 240-volt circuit. There are two methods by which this can be accomplished. The first is shown in

TABLE FOR CONNECTING COILS OF FIG. 171 TO COMMUTATOR

Start of coil number	To bar number	End of coil number	To bar number
1	23	1	9
1a	24	1a	10
2	25	2	11
2a	26	2a	12
3	1	3	13
3a	2	3a	14
4	3	4	15
4a	4	4a	16
5	5	5	17
5a	6	5a	18
6	7	6	19
6a	8	6a	20
7	9	7	21
7a	10	7a	22
8	11	8	23
8a	12	8a	24
9	13	9	25
9a	14	9a	26
10	15	10	1
10a	16	10a	2
11	17	11	3
11a	18	11a	4
12	19	12	5
12a	20	12a	6
13	21	13	7
13a	22	13a	8

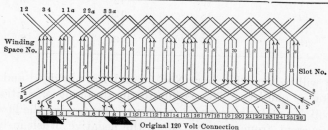

FIG. 171.—A duplex wave winding for a 120-volt armature.

Fig. 172. In this case it will be seen that Section 1 of coil 1 is dropped, that is, it is not connected to the commutator. This may be done so that a wave winding is possible. Instead of connecting the different sections of a coil in parallel

17

through the commutator and brush connections, they are now connected in series in the same way. The connecting table is as follows:

TABLE FOR CONNECTING COILS OF FIG. 172 TO COMMUTATOR

Start of coil number	To bar number	End of coil number	To bar number
1a	21	1a	9
2	22	2	10
2a	23	2a	11
3	24	3	12
3a	25	3a	13
4	1	4	14
4a	2	4a	15
5	3	5	16
5a	4	5a	17
6	5	6	18
6a	6	6a	19
7	7	7	20
7a	8	7a	21
8	9	8	22
8a	10	8a	23
9	11	9	24
9a	12	9a	25
10	13	10	1
10a	14	10a	2
11	15	11	3
11a	16	11a	4
12	17	12	5
12a	18	12a	6
13	19	13	7
13a	20	13a	8

It will be seen that bars Nos. 26 and 1 are bridged and are acting as one bar. This is due to the dropping of Section 1 in coil No. 1 for reasons given above. By tracing the flow of the current from the positive to the negative brush in both Figs. 171 and 172, is will be found that there are twice as many coils in series in Fig. 172 as there are in Fig. 171. It is, therefore, possible to operate Fig. 172 on a 240-volt circuit.

The other method of reconnecting Fig. 171 so as to operate

it on a 240-volt circuit is shown in Fig. 173. The coils in this case have been placed the same as in Figs. 171 and 172,

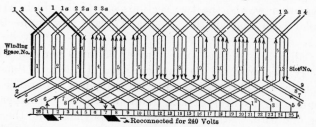

FIG. 172.—The duplex wave winding of Fig. 171 reconnected for 240 volts by connecting the coils in series through the commutator and the brushes.

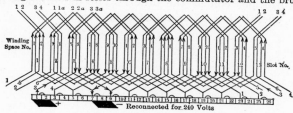

FIG. 173.—The duplex wave winding of Fig. 171 reconnected by connecting the turns of each coil in series and using one-half the number of commutator bars. In this case two adjacent bars must be connected together and brushes wide enough to cover two bars.

therefore the winding table will be the same. The connecting table is as follows:

TABLE FOR CONNECTING COILS OF FIG. 173 TO COMMUTATOR

Start of coil number	To bar number	End of coil number	To bar number
1	23	1a	9
2	25	2a	11
3	1	3a	13
4	3	4a	15
5	5	5a	17
6	7	6a	19
7	9	7a	21
8	11	8a	23
9	13	9a	25
10	15	10a	1
11	17	11a	3
12	19	12a	5
13	21	13a	7

From the above connecting table it will be seen that the end of Section 1 is connected to the beginning of Section 1a or, in other words, the two sections of a coil, which were in parallel with one another in Fig. 171 are now connected in series.

As already explained, the number of turns per coil will be directly proportional to the voltage. In Fig. 171 assume that there are 20 turns per coil with two wires in parallel. By reconnecting as in Fig. 173, there will be 40 turns per coil, using one wire. From this it will be seen that while there are 13 coils in each winding, Figs. 171 and 173, one has twice as many turns per coil as the other. This fact makes it possible to operate Fig. 173 on a 240-volt circuit.

CHAPTER XI

PRACTICAL WAYS FOR RE-CONNECTING INDUCTION MOTORS

There are certain changes in the windings of an induction motor that can be made by the repairman to adapt a motor to changed operating conditions. There are also certain changes that should not be attempted. Details of the most practical re-connections and their effects on motor operation have been carefully outlined accompanied by diagrams, in the *Electrical Journal* by A. M. Dudley. These details are summarized in what follows.

The changes that can be made in the connections of the induction motor may be divided into three classes. The first class includes those which leave the motor entirely normal and the performance in all essential respects the same as before re-connection. Such changes, for example, are represented by connecting the polar groups of a winding in series for 440 volts and in parallel for 220 volts. The second class of changes leaves the performance in some respects unchanged and alters it in others. These may be represented by operating a motor in star on 440 volts and in delta for 220 volts. In this case there is little change in efficiency or power factor; the starting and maximum torque, however, are only 75 per cent. of their original values. In such a case the advisability of the change depends upon the work that the motor must do. If the torque at the altered values is sufficient to start and carry the driven load easily, there is no objection to operating the motor indefinitely so reconnected, since the motor will not run any warmer than before and its efficiency and power factor may be better.

The third class of changes leaves the motor operative in the sense of producing torque enough to do the work required, but so alters its performance as to heating, or efficiency or power factor or insulation that it is undesirable to leave the

261

motor operating indefinitely in such condition. Such changes are represented by re-connecting a three-phase motor without changing the coils for two-phase operation. This is equivalent to operating the three-phase motor at 125 per cent. normal voltage. In addition, the coils which should have extra insulation where the phases change have only group insulation. The iron loss and heating may be increased to a dangerous degree and the power factor greatly decreased. Such changes should only be used in an emergency and the proper permanent changes made as soon as possible.

Points to Consider before Making Re-connections.—Before a repairman attempts to make a radical change in the connections of an induction-motor winding he should consider carefully the limitations of the design and the effects of the changes The following points will serve as a guide.

1. Changes in voltage alone are the easiest and can usually be made.

2. Changes in number of phases alone can rarely be made satisfactorily and are usually only makeshifts.

3. Changes in number of poles are limited, due to the mechanical form of the coils.

4. Changes of frequency alone or in combination with voltage or phase can sometimes be made if changes in speed are not objectionable.

5. Complicated changes should not be attempted except by persons of some experience and should be handled with caution.

6. If the peripheral speed of the rotor (which equals rotor diameter in feet $\times$ 3.14 $\times$ rpm.) exceeds 7000 feet per minute on any proposed change, the maker of the motor should be consulted before making the change.

7. In case of any doubt on any point, refer to the manufacturer of the machine.

Diagrams for Different Changes of Connections.—Two kinds of diagrams are most used to indicate the connections to be made in induction motors. These are shown in Figs. 174 and 175. The diagram of Fig. 174 is a three-phase, four-pole winding connected in star on a 36-slot core. It represents the coils as they would look if removed from the machine and laid on a table with the actual connections made. The diagram of Fig. 175 is a conventional sketch for the winding of Fig. 174 showing the polar groups. The latter diagram is much used.

In the winding illustrated, since there are three times four or 12 polar groups and 36 coils, there are three coils connected in series to form a polar-phase-group. It should be borne in

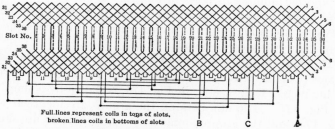

Fig. 174.—Complete winding diagram for a 3-phase, 4-pole motor having 36 slots, and connected in series-star.

mind that there are not actually 12 magnetic poles in the machine, for the reason that three consecutive polar-phase-groups unite to form one magnetic pole by virtue of the phase difference of the currents in the three phases. There are two magnetic north and two magnetic south poles formed by this winding at any instant, and these poles are equally spaced around the air-gap like four mechanically projecting pole pieces excited by four coils carrying direct current. Something of this conception is gained if one imagines the armature of a direct-current generator held stationary and the field poles rotated around it. At any given instant the magnetic field can be conceived to be the same as the field which is formed by the winding shown in Fig. 174. The coils in slots 3, 6, 9, 12, etc., are shown by heavy lines to indicate that the insulation on these coils is heavier to withstand the greater strain at the points where the winding crosses or lies adjacent to coils

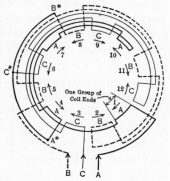

Fig. 175.—Circle diagram for the connections shown in Fig. 174.

differing greatly in potential. This is called "*phase insulation*," and may be put on the first coil in each group or it may be put on the first and last coil of each group where there are a large number of coils in the group. This is one of the reasons why a machine may not at times be reconnected for another number of poles or phases. If such reconnections were made the maximum differences in potential might occur between two adjacent coils unprotected by this extra insulation and a break-down result.

The conventional diagram of Fig. 175 represents the same connections as Fig. 174, except that each pole-phase-group as numbered 1, 2, 3, etc., in Fig. 174, is shown by a short arc in Fig. 175. The numbers on the groups are identical with Fig. 174, and the group connections. The arrows are shown simply to indicate a method of checking up to insure the proper phase relations. There is considerable danger, in a three-phase connection, of getting a 60-degree relation between the phases instead of a 120-degree relation or, as it might be expressed on the diagram, there is danger that the wrong end of the B phase, for example, may be connected to the star point. As a check against this, when the diagram is completed, the current is assumed as going in at all three leads toward the Y point. Arrows are put on each pole-phase-group as shown, and when all three phases are traced through, the winding is correct if the arrows on consecutive groups run alternately clockwise and counter-clockwise. It may be argued that this is an artificial assumption and that at no instant is the current flowing toward the star in all three phases. It may also be argued that in a correct winding, if the current be assumed as flowing toward the star in two phases and always from it in the third, the arrows will fall in successive sets of three in the same direction and then three in the reverse direction. These statements are true, but a little experimenting will show that an incorrectly connected or 60-degree winding can in this way be shown to give successive sets of three arrows and still be wrong. There is but one exception to the correctness of the check as shown in Fig. 175 where the current is assumed as flowing toward the star in all three phases and the arrows alternate in direction. This exception to the rule is the case where the winding forms consequent poles or passes through all the pole-phase-groups in a north direction instead of alternately north and south. Such connections are rarely used, and then usually on special motors wound for multi-speeds.

Diagrams for Three-phase Motors.—Fig. 176 gives a com-

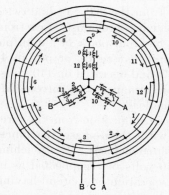

FIG. 176.—Diagram for a 3-phase, 4-pole winding with parallel-star end connections. Schematic equivalent in center.

FIG. 177.—Diagram for a 3-phase, 4-pole winding with 4-parallel-star end connections. Schematic equivalent in center.

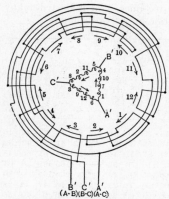

FIG. 178.—Diagram for a 3-phase, 4-pole winding with series-delta end connections. Schematic equivalent in center.

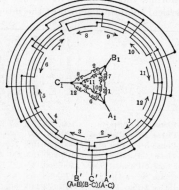

FIG. 179.—Connecting diagram for a 3-phase, 4-pole, parallel-delta winding. A schematic equivalent is shown in the center of the diagram.

bined conventional and schematic representation of a so-called **parallel star** diagram, where the two halves of each phase are in parallel. If a given machine were connected, as shown in Fig. 175, for a normal voltage of 440, it could readily be reconnected according to Fig. 176, and would then be suitable for operation on 220 volts having the same performance in all respects except that it would draw from the 220-volt line twice as many amperes under a given load as it previously drew from the 440-volt line. Similarly, if it had four poles, or a multiple of four poles, it could still be paralleled again, or put in 4-parallel star, as shown in Fig. 177, and operated on 110 volts, and would still have the same performance at a correspondingly increased current at the same load.

Fig. 178 represents a variation in connection from the foregoing, which is possible only with three-phase machines. This is the so-called **delta or mesh** connection. If a machine connected as in Fig. 174 for 440 volts be reconnected as in Fig. 178 it would be suitable for operation on a circuit having a voltage of 440 ÷ 1.73 or 254 volts.

COMPARISON OF MOTOR VOLTAGES WITH VARIOUS CONNECTIONS

If a motor connected originally as shown in any horizontal column had a normal voltage of 100 its voltage when reconnected as indicated in any vertical column is shown at the intersection of the two columns.

	3-Ph. Series Star	3-Ph. 2-Par. Star	3-Ph. 3-Par. Star	3-Ph. 4-Par. Star	3-Ph. 5-Par. Star	3-Ph. Series Delta	3-Ph. 2-Par. Delta	3-Ph. 3-Par. Delta	3-Ph. 4-Par. Delta	3-Ph. 5-Par. Delta	2-Ph. Series	2-Ph. 2-Par.	2-Ph. 3-Par.	2-Ph. 4-Par.	2-Ph. 5-Par.
3-Phase Series Star......	100	50	33	25	20	58	29	19	15	12	81	41	27	20	16
3-Phase 2-Parallel Star..	200	100	67	50	40	116	58	38	29	23	162	81	54	40	32
3-Phase 3-Parallel Star..	300	150	100	75	60	174	87	57	44	35	243	122	81	60	48
3-Phase 4-Parallel Star..	400	200	133	100	80	232	116	76	58	46	324	163	108	80	64
3-Phase 5-Parallel Star..	500	250	165	125	100	290	145	95	73	58	405	203	135	100	80
3-Phase Series Delta....	173	86	58	43	35	100	50	33	25	20	140	70	47	35	28
3-Phase 2-Par. Delta....	346	172	116	86	70	200	100	66	50	40	280	140	94	70	56
3-Phase 3-Par. Delta....	519	258	174	129	105	300	150	100	75	60	420	210	141	105	84
3-Phase 4-Par. Delta....	692	344	232	172	140	400	200	133	100	80	560	280	188	140	112
3-Phase 5-Par. Delta....	865	430	290	215	175	500	250	165	125	100	700	350	235	175	140
2-Phase Series..........	125	63	42	31	25	73	37	24	18	15	100	50	33	25	20
2-Phase 2-Parallels......	250	125	84	63	50	146	73	49	37	29	200	100	67	50	40
2-Phase 3-Parallels......	375	188	125	94	75	219	110	73	55	44	300	150	100	75	60
2-Phase 4-Parallels......	500	250	167	125	100	292	146	97	73	58	400	200	133	100	80
2-Phase 5-Parallels.....	625	313	208	156	125	365	183	122	91	73	500	250	167	125	100

Use of Table of Connections.—Different reconnections or conversions are shown in the Table on page 266 where the problem just shown may be worked out by selecting *Three-phase Series Star* in the horizontal column (first line) and reading across to the vertical column headed *Series Delta* where the figure 58 appears. This means that if 100 volts was normal on the series star connection and a change is made to series delta the corresponding voltage is 58. By multiplication, if 440 was the series star voltage, the series delta voltage would be 4.4 × 58 = 254, as noted above. Figs. 179 and 180 show a parallel and 4-parallel delta connection, respectively, and bear the same relation to Fig. 178 that Figs. 176 and 177 do to Fig. 175.

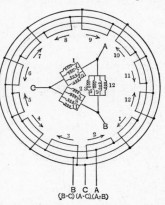

Fig. 180. — Connecting diagram for a 3-phase, 4-pole, 4-parallel-delta winding.

Two-phase Diagrams.—In Fig. 181 a development of a two-phase winding is shown similar to Fig. 174, except for the difference in the number of phases. An inspection of the coils represented in heavy lines and a comparison with the coils in

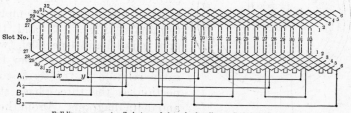

Full lines represent coils in tops of slots, broken lines coils in bottoms of slots

FIG. 181.—Complete winding diagram for a 2-phase, 4-pole motor series connected. The coils from *x* to *y* form one pole-phase-group.

Fig. 174 indicates at once what is meant by the "phase coils" or phase insulated coils being differently situated. This also explains one of the good reasons why two-phase motors should

not be reconnected for three-phase, or vice versa, without
changing the position of these "phase coils.

Fig. 182 gives the conventional and schematic equivalent of

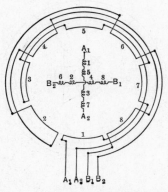

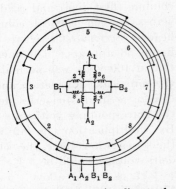

FIG. 182.—Connecting diagram for
a 2-phase, 4-pole winding with series
connections.

FIG. 183.—Connecting diagram for
a 2-phase, 4-pole winding with parallel
connections.

Fig. 181. The arrows shown in the three-phase diagrams are
omitted here, for the reason that the two phases are not interconnected, and the only effect
of reversing one phase is to
reverse the direction of rotation
of the motor. This is readily
corrected by reversing the two
leads of one phase at the motor
terminals. Figs. 183 and 184
give parallel and 4-parallel, two-
phase connections and bear the
same relation to the series connection as the three-phase star
and delta diagrams. From these
2-parallel and 4-parallel connections it may be readily seen that
where the number of poles is a

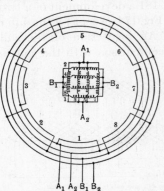

FIG. 184.—Connecting diagram
for a 2-phase, 4-pole winding with
4-parallel connections.

multiple of three, as 6, 12, 18, etc., there is a possible analogous
3-parallel connection; also where the number of poles is a
multiple of five, such as 10, 20, etc., there is a corresponding

possible 5-parallel diagram. These are the connections which are indicated in the Table on page 266 as "3-parallel" and "5-parallel."

Fig. 185 shows a possible three-phase connection which may be made from a two-phase winding by a method similar to the Scott transformer connection. It is a connection which should be used only as a temporary expedient until better arrangements can be made.

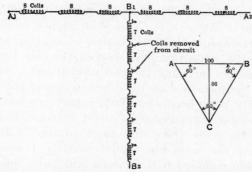

FIG. 185.—The T-connection by which a 2-phase motor may be operated on a 3-phase circuit.

Meaning of the Term Chord Factor.—It is well known that the span of the coil must in general be somewhere near the quotient of the bore periphery divided by the number of poles. It is not so generally understood that changing the span of the coil within limits has an effect similar to increasing or decreasing the number of wires in the coil. If the coil is exactly pitch, *i.e.*, spans exactly from the center of one pole to the center of the next, the turns of wire in that coil are producing their maximum effect upon the magnetic field. The coil is then considered to span 180 electrical degrees. It is customary to wind the coil in slots so that it spans something less than a full pole pitch. The effect of the turns in the coil is then somewhat less than the maximum. The effect of the turns in the coil varies as the sine of half of the angle in electrical degrees which the coil spans.

To illustrate, if there are 72 slots in an eight-pole machine, the coils would be exactly "pitch" if they lay in slots 1 and 10, or in other words, if there were eight slots between the two slots in which the two sides of any coil were located. Such a coil would span 180 electrical degrees. Half of 180 degrees is 90 degrees and the sine of 90 degrees is 1; therefore the effect of the turns in such a coil is one. Suppose instead the coil lies in slots 1 and 8. It would then span 140 degrees electrically, since $72 \div 8 = 9$ slots represents 180 degrees, and one slot therefore represents 20 degrees. The sine of half of 140 degrees, or 70 degrees, is 0.938. It follows that the effect of the turns in this coil is less than that of the full pitch coil by the ratio of 0.938 to 1. This is of interest in the present problem, because it is often possible in making changes to change at the same time the span of the coils by one slot, more or less, by springing the coil mechanically, and so improve the performance of the machine under the new conditions. The point becomes of vital importance, immediately, when changing the number of poles without changing the throw of the coils. Referring again to the 72-slot motor, assume that the coils are wound in slots 1 and 8. For an eight-pole connection these coils will have the effect of 0.938, as explained above. If the connections are changed for six poles the effect is entirely different. $72 \div 6 = 12$ and $180 \div 12 = 15$, or each slot represents 15 electrical degrees. A throw of 1 and 8 covers seven complete slots, or $7 \times 15 = 105$ degrees; the sine of half of 105 or 52.5 degrees $= 0.79$, which means that when connected for six poles the coils have an effect of only 0.79, as against 0.938 when connected for eight poles. It is possible to avoid using the sine of half the angle and secure a factor which is sufficiently accurate practically by using the expression,

$$\sqrt{\frac{\text{(Number of slots per pole)}^2 - 2\text{(Number of slots dropped)}^2}{\text{(Number of slots per pole)}^2}}$$

Using the same eight-pole example above, the number of slots per pole is $72 \div 8 = 9$ and the pole pitch is 1 and 10. When the coil is wound 1 and 8 it spans seven slots and there are $9 - 7 = 2$ slots dropped. The expression then becomes

$$\sqrt{\frac{(9)^2 - 2(2^2)}{(9)^2}} = \sqrt{\frac{73}{81}} = 0.948$$

and similarly for the six-pole,

$$\sqrt{\frac{(12)^2 - 2(5^2)}{12^2}} = \sqrt{\frac{94}{144}} = 0.807$$

which agrees roughly with the other method. A coil should in no case be chorded more than half of the pole pitch, as secondary disturbances of the magnetic field are occasioned by chording which become prohibitive at that point. The expression, "sine of half the angle spanned by the coil," is given the name **chord factor,** and it should be considered in the work of re-connecting. For example, if the poles are changed from 8 to 6, as in the example above, and the chord factor changes from 0.938 to 0.79, the new line voltage should be 0.79 ÷ 0.938 times the old, neglecting the effect of other changes which are being made. If nothing else was undergoing change and the normal voltage was 440 in the first place, it should be 370 after the change is made or, expressing it another way, if it was still operated at 440 volts after the change, the motor should be thought of as operating at about 18 per cent. over voltage.

Phase Insulation.—It is the practice of many manufacturers to put heavier insulation on the coils at the ends of the polar groups which are mechanically adjacent to one another and are also subjected to the voltage between phases, which may be the maximum voltage between supply lines. Such coils are illustrated at Nos. 3, 6, 9, 12, 15, etc., in Fig. 174. By comparing this diagram with Fig. 181 for two-phase connection, it appears at once that both the number and location of these so-called "phase coils" should be changed at the time the machine is re-connected from two- to three-phase, or *vice versa*, assuming that the voltage can be changed so that a phase change is permissible. Also in changing the number of poles, the number and location of the "phase coils" must also be changed. In fact, whatever re-connection is attempted the "phase coils" should be checked and re-arranged, since this is comparatively easy and adds considerably to the protection of the machine from breakdowns of insulation.

RE-CONNECTING MOTORS TO MEET NEW OPERATING CONDITIONS

Re-connections Frequently Made.—The following changes are made on account of changes in operating conditions or the service conditions on the circuits from which the motors are operated.

1. Changes to operate on a different voltage.
2. Change for operation on a different phased circuit, three- to two-phase, etc.
3. Changes to operate on a different frequency.
4. Change in number of poles of the motor.

In case of change No. 4, the re-connection may be independent of all other changes to secure a faster or slower speed or it may follow as a result of change No. 3 in order to keep the same speed on a driven machine when the motor is operated on the new frequency.

Procedure when Considering a Re-connection of Windings. The procedure in checking up a machine to see whether or not it can be re-connected is as follows: First, ascertain the existing connection and the throw of the coils in order to know what the possibilities are in the way of number of turns and throw. Second, if it is a phase or voltage change, find directly from the Table on page 266 what connections will give approximately the proper new voltage and new phase. If any one of these connections is possible with the number of poles in the machine, select it as the new connection and arrange the phase coils properly at the beginning or ending of the groups, or at each end of the groups if there are enough of them in the old winding. Since the speed has not changed, the horsepower should remain approximately the same, and the current in the coils themselves will remain somewhere near the original. If the frequency is to be changed either independently or in conjunction with a phase or a voltage change, the applied voltage should be changed in the same direction and by the same proportional amount as the frequency is changed, or if the voltage is to remain unchanged the number of turns in series in the coils should be changed in the opposite direction to the frequency and by the same amount. For example, if a 25-cycle motor is to be run on 30 cycles, it should have the voltage increased 20 per cent., or else have the groups re-connected so that there will be 20 per cent. less turns in series and run on the same voltage.

If the number of poles is to be changed, and consequently the speed, check first the effect of the coil throw or chording with the new number of poles. Then think of the motor winding as generating counter emf. and bear in mind that with a constant field a higher speed will generate more emf. and a slower speed less emf. Converted into voltage this means that with a higher speed a higher voltage should be applied in direct proportion and with a lower speed a lower voltage should be applied. If the voltage can not be changed try to change the diagram of group connections so as to vary the number of turns in series in the right way, that is, if the voltage should be increased, the same effect can be obtained by decreasing the number of turns a like amount. In all these cases it is the voltage per turn or per conductor which counts, just as in a transformer, and a careful consideration of the effect of different connections will show whether the desired change in voltage per conductor is being accomplished.

Practical Example for Reconnection.—Assume a 25-hp., four-pole motor operating on 40 cycles, two-phase, 220 volts. It is desired to know whether it can be re-connected to operate on 60 cycles, three-phase, 550 volts at the same speed and horsepower. An inspection of the machine shows that it has 72 slots and 72 coils and that any individual coil lies in slots 1 and 15, also that the groups are connected in parallel. Since there are 72 ÷ 4 = 18 slots per pole, each slot is 180 ÷ 18 = 10 electrical degrees and 14 slots = 140 electrical degrees. (The throw of 1 to 15 means spanning 14 slots.) The sine of one-half of 140 degrees or 70 degrees = 0.94 = chord factor, or figured by the formula without trigonometry, since there are 18 slots per pole and a throw of 1 to 15 means dropping four slots from exact pitch, the chord

$$\text{factor} = \sqrt{\frac{18^2 - 2 \times 4^2}{18^2}} = 0.948.$$ The synchronous speed of the motor on 40 cycles as it stands is 4800 ÷ 4 = 1200 rpm. To get this same speed on 60 cycles it is evident the motor will have to be connected for 7200 ÷ 1200 = six poles. If the throw of the coils be left 1 to 15 they will throw two slots

18

further than full pitch, since $72 \div 6 = 12$ slots per pole and 1 to 13 would be exact pitch. Throwing the coil over pitch has the same effect as throwing it under pitch so the new chord factor on six poles $= \sqrt{\dfrac{12^2 - 2 \times 2^2}{12^2}} = 0.97$, or sine of one-half of 150 degrees $= 0.98$. Taking into account the changes in phase, poles, frequency and chording, the new applied voltage per phase should be $\dfrac{880}{3} \times \dfrac{4}{6} \times \dfrac{60}{40} \times \dfrac{0.98}{0.94} = 305$ volts.

The explanation of this expression by terms is: The first term, $(880 \div 3)$ comes from the change in phase from 2 to 3. Since the original connection was in parallel and was for two-phase, the voltage across one phase in series would be $2 \times 220 = 440$, and the voltage across both phases in series would be $2 \times 440 = 880$ volts. If the winding is divided into three separate phases not interconnected, the applied voltage on each phase would be $(880 \div 3)$. The next term, $(4 \div 6)$ is due to the change in poles. A motor with six poles would run slower on the same frequency than a motor with four poles and would generate less counter emf. Consequently, the applied voltage should be decreased in the same proportion. This should not be confused with the fact that the frequency is being changed in this case and the speed kept the same because a separate factor is introduced to take care of the frequency. The pole change should be considered as an item separate from the frequency change. The next term, $(60 \div 40)$ is due to the change in frequency and is the application of the rule to change the applied voltage directly as the frequency is changed. The last term, $(0.98 \div 0.94)$ is due to the difference in chord factor. With a throw of 1 to 15, the coils are more effective to generate counter emf. on the six-pole than on the four-pole connection by the ratio of the chord factors 0.98 to 0.94, hence the applied voltage should be raised with the counter emf.

The value of 305 volts means that if the winding was divided into three separate phases not interconnected in any way, the voltage should be 305 volts across each phase. If the three phases are connected in series star, as in Fig. 175, the applied voltage should be $1.73 \times 305 = 530$ volts. Since this is only about 3.5 per cent. off from the 550 volts which is to be used, the motor will operate satisfactorily. This calculation for voltage so far neglects the difference in the so-called "distribution factor" between three-phase and two-phase, but this is immaterial. This factor acts the same way as the chord factor, and is about 0.955 for any normal three-phase windings and 0.905 for any normal two-phase winding, so that the applied voltage should really be $530 \times \left(\dfrac{0.955}{0.905}\right) = 560$ volts, which is almost exactly what is required. This motor could then have its phase coils re-arranged for six poles and be connected series star and would be satisfactory for the new conditions. The changes involved do not materially effect the slip, so that no change is required in the rotor winding. This example illustrates a rough calculation that can be made to see what the possibilities of re-connection are.

Changes in Voltage Only with all Other Conditions Remaining the Same.—This is the simplest change which can be made in an induction-motor winding and in principle is the same as that of a transformer coil in which the number of turns of wire in series must be varied in exact proportion to the voltage applied. Practically all commercial motors are arranged so that they can be connected for two voltages, say 110 and 220, or 220 and 440. This is accomplished by putting the polar groups in series, as in Figs. 175 and 182, for the higher voltage, and in parallel, as in Figs. 176 and 183, for the lower voltage.

Assume a case in which the motor as it stands is connected for 2200 volts and is connected in series star as in Fig. 175. It is desired to re-connect it for 440 volts for the same horsepower, phase, cycles and speed. Four hundred and forty volts is 20 per cent. of 2200. Refer to the Table on page 266 and use the horizontal column marked 3-*Phase, Series Star*. Since a re-connection is desired to give 20 per cent. of the original voltage, read along the horizontal line until the figure 20 occurs This is found first under the vertical column marked 3-*Phase*, 5-*Parallels*. This is obvious, of course, because if the number of poles in the machine is divisible by five, it could be re-connected in five parallels and operated on $2200 \div 5 = 440$ volts. But suppose the number of poles is not divisible by five. Look still further along the horizontal line and the figure 19 appears under the vertical column headed 3-*Phase*, 3-*Parallel Delta*. In other words, if the number of poles in the machine is divisible by three it can be put in *three-parallel delta* and operated on $2200 \div (3 \times 1.73) = 424$ volts, which is near enough to 440 to give perfectly satisfactory operation.

If the number of poles on the machine is not divisible by five or by three, it is evident from the table that it is not possible by any ordinary three-phase connection to approach closer than 550 volts with a four-parallel star connection, or 330 volts using a four-parallel delta connection. The relation between 550 volts and 330 volts as just given is not quite the theoretical 1.73 which would be expected, but this is due to the table being made up to the nearest integral figure without using fractions. The error in this instance is three per cent. which is immaterial.

A point which is brought out by the example just cited is that, so far as insulation is concerned, a motor may always be re-connected for a lower voltage—for instance, a 2200-volt motor may be re-connected for 440 volts—but, on the contrary, a motor originally designed for 440 volts may not be run on 2200, even if the re-connection is possible so far as number of turns is concerned, because the insulation will not stand the dielectric strain. It may be stated generally that practically all manufacturers use two classes of insulation up to 2500 volts, one class good up to 550 volts and the second good from 600 volts to 2500. This should be carefully considered and a motor never re-connected from the lower into the higher class, although the change from the higher to the lower is permissible from the insulation standpoint.

Change of Phase Only.—The most common problem which presents itself is the change from **two-** to **three-phase**, and *vice versa*. Theoretically, for the same voltage there should be about 25 per cent. more total turns in a two-phase winding than in a three-phase winding. Then, if a three-phase motor be re-connected for two-phase at the same voltage and with the same coils, it will exhibit all the symptoms of a motor operating at 25 per cent. over voltage and usually would overheat to a dangerous degree after a short period of operation. Conversely, a two-phase motor re-connected and run on three-phase at the same voltage with the same coils will show all the signs of a motor operating at 20 per cent. under voltage. In this case there are too many turns in the machine, One-fifth of the total coils might be dead-ended to secure the proper voltage on the remaining 80 per cent. The dead coils should be distributed as symmetrically as possible around the machine to balance the voltage as nearly as possible on all phases. Parallels in the winding should be avoided, as they give a chance for unbalanced, circulating local currents, which may cause excessive temperatures. Since the normal full-load current on a three-phase motor at any given voltage is about 12.5 per cent. greater than the two-phase full-load current at the same voltage, it follows that the three-phase horsepower will have to be cut down about 12.5 per cent. from the two-phase in order to keep the current density in the winding as it was on two-phase. Unless the current density is kept approximately the same greater heating will result. Another makeshift, shown in Fig. 185, is the so-called Scott or T connection for operating a two-phase motor on three-phase. By this scheme 14 per cent. of the coils in one phase of the two-phase machine are omitted as symmetrically as possible around the machine. One end, B_1 of this phase, is then connected to the middle of phase A_1–A_2. The resulting voltages between the points A_1–A_2–B_2 are practically in a balanced three-phase relation. This connection would give fairly good results if the coils between A_1 and B_1 were so situated on the machine that they would be acted upon by the magnetic field in exactly the same manner as the coils between B_1 and A_2. Practically, as motors are wound nowadays, this is rarely possible, and if the usual winding is connected in T there are practically always unbalanced currents in the three phases. The current in the high phase will be about 20 per cent. greater than the current in the low phase. This results in a poorer performance in torque, power-factor, efficiency and heating. The efficiency on the T connection is 1.6 per cent. lower, the power-factor 5.2 per cent. lower, the starting torque 38 per cent. lower, the maximum torque 4 per cent. lower and the temperatures from 8 to

13.5° higher than on the normal three-phase winding. This shows that changing from two-phase to three-phase, and *vice versa*, is at best very unsatisfactory. It is better to re-wind with normal three-phase coils and avoid the troubles which may follow.

One essential in any phase re-connection is to go over the winding and re-arrange the "phase coils," or coils having heavier insulation, so that they will come properly at the ends of the groups where the voltage is highest. This is illustrated in Figs. 174 and 181.

One case of voltage and phase change which works out very well is the change from three-phase 550 volts to two-phase 440 volts, or *vice versa*. This uses all the turns in the winding for either connection, since the two-phase voltage should be about 80 per cent. of the three-phase, and since the higher volt-age on the three-phase cuts down the current, which would otherwise be higher than the two-phase circuit. If the phase coils are re-arranged there is practically no objection to such a re-connection and the motor will give essentially the same per-formance on either connection.

The table on page 266 shows the possibilities of interphase connections, as well as the different voltage changes. For example, in the case just cited, follow the horizontal line marked 2-*Phase Series* to the first vertical column headed 3-*Phase Series*. The figure is 125. This means that a motor originally connected two-phase series, if re-connected three-phase series, should be operated on 125 per cent. of the original voltage. Or, if the two-phase voltage was 440 the three-phase would be $1.25 \times 440 = 550$ volts. The convenience of the table is demonstrated for phase changes, as well as voltage changes, or for combinations of both.

Changes in Frequency.—The occasion often arises for chang-ing 25-cycle motors to 60-cycle and 60 to 25. There is also some changing done from 60 cycles to 50 and 50 to 60. Occa-sionally 40-cycle motors are changed to 60, but these changes are infrequent.

In all cases of changed frequency the question that first arises is: How is the resulting change in speed to be taken care of? The synchronous speed of any motor (which is only a few per cent. higher than the full-load speed) is given by the general expression $\dfrac{\text{Alternations per Minute}}{\text{Number of Poles}}$. This would be $\dfrac{3000}{\text{Number of Poles}}$ for 25 cycles, $\dfrac{7200}{\text{Number of Poles}}$ for 60 cycles, etc. If then the frequency is changed and the number of poles left the same, the resulting rpm. will vary directly as the frequency. This immediately brings up two questions: First, is the mechanical design of the rotating part adequate to allow such a change in speed? Second, can the speed of the driven machine be adjusted to suit the new speed on the motor?

Consider first the case where the frequency is changed and the number of poles remain the same. The resulting change in speed in this case is taken care of either by applying the motor to a new load or by changing the pulleys on the old load so as to keep the same rpm. on the driven machine. The next thing that must be considered is the necessary change in the voltage applied to correspond to the change in frequency, or the other way about, if the new circuit at the new frequency has the same voltage as was used with the original frequency, how can the coils in the motor be re-connected so as to get the proper voltage on each coil?

The easiest rule to remember is to *vary the applied voltage on the motor in exactly the same way as the frequency is varied.* If this be done the magnetic field in the iron will remain the same and the current in the stator and rotor coils will remain the same, if the motor is working against the same torque. This is another way of saying that if the frequency and voltage are varied together, the motor will develop the same torque at all times and have flowing in it approximately the same current. If the torque remains the same, the horsepower developed will vary directly as the applied frequency. For example, a 60-cycle, 50-hp. motor operated on 25 cycles at 41.6 per cent. of its original voltage would develop the same normal full-load torque, which would be 20.8 hp.

Changing from 25 to 60 cycles.—A change from 25 cycles to 60 cycles, can often be made by impressing twice the voltage on the coils on 60 cycles as on 25 cycles. A 220-volt, 25-cycle motor operated on 440 volts, 60 cycles, will have about double the horsepower. Theoretically, this should be $60 \div 25 = 2.4$ times the voltage, instead of twice, and the resulting horsepower would be 2.4 times. In this case suppose the motor was connected in series star for 440 volts on 25 cycles and it is desired to run it on 440 volts, 60 cycles. It should then be connected in parallel star and run on 440 volts, which would have the same effect as impressing 880 volts on the original series connection. On 60 cycles the motor would then run 2.4 times as fast and develop about twice the horsepower.

Sixty-cycle Motors on 50-cycle Circuits.—Sixty-cycle motors are often run on 50 cycles without change. From the rule above, that the voltage must vary with the frequency to keep the same magnetic densities, it will be noted that the densities on 50 cycles at the same voltage will be six-fifths of the 60 cycles densities. The motor will then operate as if it had 120 per cent. of normal voltage impressed. This will result in increased iron losses, which makes the motor hotter, and the decreased speed on 50 cycles with the same number of poles also makes the ventilation poorer, so that the output of the motor in horsepower should be reduced to keep down the copper losses.

Another point that should be watched in changing frequency if the motor has a squirrel-cage rotor, is to make sure that the rotor winding has enough resistane to give the proper starting torque. As the frequency is raised the resistance of the short-circuiting rings at the ends of the rotor winding should be increased to keep the same relative value of starting torque to full-load torque. As long as the motor starts its load satisfactorily no change is necessary, but if trouble is experienced, the short-circuiting rings may have to be changed for ones of higher resistance. Conversely, when decreasing the frequency the resistance can be reduced to advantage, thereby cutting down the rotor copper loss and the heating.

Change in Frequency with Same Speed.—In this case the number of poles must be changed in the same ratio as the frequency, or as nearly so as possible. For example, if a motor has four poles and is operated on 25 cycles, it will have a synchronous speed of $3000 \div 4 = 750$ rpm. If the motor is to have the same speed on 60 cycles, the nearest possible pole number is 10 and the synchronous speed will be 7200 ÷ 10 = 720 rpm. It is apparent that in very few cases of this kind is it possible to re-connect the same winding. The main reason for this is in the throw or pitch of the coil. In the four-pole winding the individual coil spans approximate one-fourth of the stator bore, and in the 10-pole winding normal coils should span about one-tenth of the stator bore. In the paragraph on "chorded windings" (page 269) it was pointed out that the coil throw has an effect on the generated counter emf proportional to the sine of one-half the electrical angle spanned by the coil. This consideration makes hardly possible such a condition as connecting a winding for 10 poles when the individual coils have a four-pole throw. When reducing the frequency the number of poles should become smaller to keep the same speed. This introduces another difficulty in the magnetic circuit. In re-connecting the winding the object is to keep the total magnetic flux in the machine the same as it was originally. This keeps the magnetic density in the teeth constant. This total magnetic flux is divided up into as many equal parts or circuits as there are poles The iron in the stator core between the bottoms of the slots and the outside of the core has to carry the flux for each magnetic circuit. Consequently, if there are 10 poles and 10 magnetic circuits, the core iron below the slots has to carry at a given cross-section one-tenth of the total magnetic flux. With the same total magnetic flux, if there are only four poles and four magnetic circuits, the same cross-section of core has to carry one-fourth of the total magnetic flux, which it is probably unable to do. This is the reason why the rotor diameter and stator of a 25-cycle machine are smaller than those of a 60-cycle machine of the same horsepower and speed, although the outside diameter may be nearly the same. It is to get a larger cross-section behind the slots for the passage of the magnetic flux, since the total flux is divided into fewer parts, owing to the smaller number of poles. From this it follows that a machine may in general be re-wound or re-connected for a larger number of poles, but that great caution is required in re-connecting for a smaller number of poles.

It is easier to re-wind or re-connect 25-cycle machines for 60 cycles than it is to re-connect 60-cycle machines for 25 cycles. This follows logically from the physical fact that there is more copper and more iron in 25-cycle machines for the same horse-power, voltage and rpm. than in 60-cycle machines. It is always easier to make changes where there is a larger supply of material available. Another condition that is against changing the number of poles on a squirrel-cage motor is the current in the short-circuiting rings of the rotor winding. These rings are in nearly the same relation as regards current that the primary core is as regards magnetic flux. That is, the total secondary amperes, which remain nearly the same if the re-connection is done properly, are divided into as many circuits as there are poles, and it follows at once that the smaller the number of poles the larger must be the cross-section of the short-circuiting rings, although the total secondary amperes remain nearly the same. Altogether, the possibility of re-connecting for different numbers of poles when changing frequency is usually a matter for the designing engineer to investigate.

Changes in the Number of Poles, all Other Conditions Remaining the Same.—The need for such changes comes from the desire to speed up or slow down the driven machine to meet new requirements. It might be broadly stated that there are many cases where a change of two poles is permissible, as for example, changing from four poles to six, or from ten to eight and the like. The changes would consist in re-arranging the phase coils to agree with the new grouping and checking the chord factor, to note its effect on the voltage. It is often possible to get a fair operating half speed by connecting for twice the number of poles. Practically all re-connections involving pole changes give only a fair operating performance.

Testing a Re-connected Motor.—After a motor has been re-connected or after any change is made in the winding, it should be started up slowly and the load gradually thrown on, observing carefully to see if there are any signs of distress, such as sudden heating, noise or mechanical vibration. If the motor seems to operate normally read the amperes in each phase and the voltage across each phase to see that they are balanced and are reasonable in amount. The full-load current for three-phase 550 volts is somewhere near one ampere per horsepower for normal motors of moderate speeds between five and 200 horsepower. At other voltages this will be inversely as the voltage, that is at 440 volts, three-phase, about 1.25 amperes per horsepower. On two-phase the current per phase is about 87 per cent. of the corresponding three-phase value. If the readings as above look reasonable a thermometer should be placed on the stator iron and another on the stator coils and read at 15-minute intervals for an hour, and at half-hour intervals thereafter, until the temperature is constant. The speed should be checked at intervals. If the rpm. shows a tendency to decrease rapidly or fall below 90 per cent. of synchronous speed, it may be suspected that the rotor has too much resistance and is getting hot. By making all these checks, reasonable assurance may be had that the reconnection is satisfactory.

Effects of High and Low Voltage on Motor Operation.— All changes in alternating-current motors whether of phase, voltage, poles or frequency, may be considered as voltage changes and reduced to such terms. In making such calculations and comparing the results, it is advisable not to apply a voltage that differs from the rated voltage by more than plus or minus 10 per cent. The general effect of high and low voltage may be expressed briefly as follows:

Effect of High Voltage:
 a. Increases magnetic density.
 b. Increases magnetizing current.
 c. Decreases "leakage current" (leakage reactive component).
 d. Increases starting torque and maximum torque.
 e. Decreases slip or change in speed from no load to full load.
 f. Decreases secondary copper loss.
 g. Increases iron loss.
 h. Usually decreases power-factor.
 i. May increase or decrease efficiency and heating, depending upon the proportions of primary copper loss and iron loss in the normal machine and also the degree of saturation in the iron.

Effect of Low Voltage:
 a. Decreases magnetic density.
 b. Decreases magnetizing current.

   c. Increases leakage current.
   d. Decreases starting and maximum torque.
   e. Increases slip.
   f. Increases secondary copper loss.
   g. Decreases iron loss.
   h. Usually increases power-factor.
   i. May increase or decrease efficiency and heating, depending upon the proportions of primary copper loss and iron loss in the normal machine and also the degree of saturation in the iron.

Operating Standard Alternating-current Motors on Different Voltages and Frequencies.—When a motor is to be operated on a different voltage or frequency than the motor was designed for, there should be a corresponding change made in circuit to which the motor will be connected. That is, if there is to be an increase in frequency or voltage, an equal decrease in voltage or frequency of the circuit will bring about normal results. Present-day designs of motors can be used in most cases without excessive heating when the variation either up or down of frequency or voltage is not more than 10 per cent.

For an induction motor the following conditions result with a change of frequency or voltage:

1. Pull-out torque and starting torque vary as the square of the voltage and inversely as the square of the frequency.

2. The copper loss in the primary varies as the square of the current. The current varies inversely as the voltage, but is not affected by a change in frequency, except to the slight extent produced by changes in magnetizing current. The secondary copper loss and slip tend to vary inversely as the square of the voltage, but this tendency is modified by the changes in primary *IR* drop and magnetic leakage. The secondary copper loss and slip remain constant with change in frequency.

3. The iron loss is composed of hysteresis and eddy current losses. The hysteresis loss varies as the 1.6 power of the flux; the eddy current loss varies with the square of the flux; and the flux varies directly as the voltage and inversely with the frequency. The magnetizing current varies directly with the flux except for modifications produced by saturation of the magnetic circuit.

4. The power-factor is usually decreased by an increase in

voltage or a decrease in frequency and vice versa, but the total change is small.

5. The efficiency is not materially altered by a change in either frequency or voltage.

The accompanying curve, Fig. 186 shows the operating voltage on which a standard motor can be used when con-

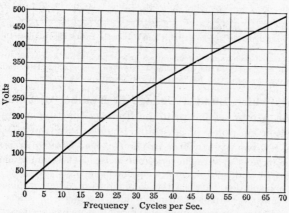

FIG. 186.—Standard motor frequency and voltage curve.

This curve indicates the voltage which, if employed in connection with the respective corresponding frequencies, will result in the operation of apparatus at approximately uniform core densities. By adherence to the relations betweeen frequency and voltage indicated, the range of application of standard apparatus can be broadened and the required number of different designs minimized. Allowance is made for the use of somewhat reduced densities at the higher frequencies, as indicated by the drooping character of the curve (R. E. Hellmund, *Electric Journal*, September, 1910, page 691).

nected to a circuit of a different frequency from that for which it was designed. The accompanying table also shows the effect on speed and horse-power rating when a motor is used on a different voltage and frequency.

The voltage and frequency of a motor should never be varied in opposite directions at the same time. In general any change from normal frequency should be accompanied by a change in voltage proportional to the square root of the frequency. In the case of 400-volt, 60-cycle motor operated on a 66⅔ cycle circuit, the voltage should be 422. That is $\sqrt{(66\frac{2}{3} \div 60)} \times 400 = 422$. In case of decreased frequency, the motor should be operated on less than normal voltage on account of the increased current and temperature.

Rating of motor	Voltage and fre- quency of circuit	Speed	Hp. rating
220 volts, 25 cycles	250 volts, 33 cycles	Increased 33 to 25	Increased 33 to 25
440 volts, 25 cycles	500 volts, 33 cycles	Increased 33 to 25	Increased 33 to 25
(a) 440 volts, 60 cycles	220 volts, 25 cycles	Reduced 60 to 25	Reduced 60 to 25
440 volts, 60 cycles	220 volts, 33 cycles	Reduced 60 to 33	Reduced 60 to 33
(b) 220 volts, 60 cycles	220 volts, 50 cycles	Reduced 60 to 50	Reduced 60 to 50

(a) Where good power-factors are essential it may be advisable to use 550-volt, 60-cycle motor or a 220-volt, 25-cycle circuit and reduce the rating according to the heating between 35 to 45 per cent. of the rating at 60 cycles.

(b) Standard 60-cycle motors of liberal rating can be used on a 50-cycle circuit with the same rating. Best results are secured however, when 220-, 440-, and 550-volt motors are operated on 200-, 400- and 500-volt circuits at 50 cycles.

Factors which Limit a Change in Number of Poles of an Induction Motor.

—The principal factors limiting a change in the number of poles of a squirrel-cage induction motor are given as follows by a writer in the *General Electric Review:*

(a) The number of turns in series per phase. These must remain the same since the applied voltage is to be unchanged.

(b) The insulation between the conductors of different phases. Of this there must be sufficient to not reduce the factor of safety against breakdowns after the regrouping of the conductors has been carried out.

(c) The saturation of the iron. It is often inadvisable to use a magnetic density much higher than normal.

Because the designs of induction motors vary widely with different manufacturers and also in the product of each maker (for the purpose of supplying motors for various types of service), it will be impossible to make other than very general statements regarding the expected change in characteristics of the motor when running at the higher speed. Furthermore, the following statements must not be expected to hold true when the number of poles has been decreased sufficiently to raise the normal speed more than say 25 per cent.

After the reconnection,

(a) The normal speed will be equal to approximately the original normal speed times the original number of poles divided by the new number of poles.

(b) There will be a somewhat higher torque per pole exerted, due to the slightly increased flux per pole that arises from the shortened pole pitch, so that the total motor torque might be expected to be decreased but little by the change.

(c) The running-light current will be slightly lowered.

(d) The starting torque will probably be slightly decreased.

(e) The power-factor might be expected to be somewhat higher.

(f) When the power-factor is higher the rating of the motor can be increased about in proportion to the square root of the increase in speed with the same heating.

(g) The efficiency will be practically the same as before the change.

Single-circuit Delta and Double-circuit Star Connections.

The use of a one-circuit delta and a double or two-circuit star winding for a three-phase motor, as pointed out by Henry Scheril (*Electrical Record*, March, 1919) depends upon operating conditions or design to meet certain requirements. One of the best illustrations is offered in the winding of a phase-wound rotor of the induction motor. Suppose that the rotor has been wound with a two-circuit star winding and the voltage between rings on open circuit is 220 volts. Let us assume that the full-load current in the rotor is 200 amperes. Since the winding has a double circuit, each circuit will take care of 100 amperes. The voltage per phase will be 127 volts.

Manufacturers, in general, standardize the brush rigging used in connection with machines, using a certain number of brushes per ring. If it is found, for instance, that 200 amperes, as in this example, brings the current density in the brush to too high a value, it would mean that the number of brushes per ring must be increased. Since this is not practical nor economical, a change in the connections of the winding may bring about the desired results, that is, reduce the current density in the brush to within the allowable value.

If the winding were then reconnected from two-circuit star to single-circuit delta, then the voltage between terminals will be increased from 220 volts to 254 volts and the current per ring would be reduced from 200 amperes to 173 amperes, or a reduction of 13.5 per cent. This reduction may just be sufficient to decrease the brush density to the desired value. Since controllers used in the rotor circuit are made to take care of voltages of reasonable variations, an increase in voltage from 220 volts to 254 volts will not require a change in the controller and therefore the 220 volts controller can be used on the 254-volt circuit.

Cutting out Coils of an Induction Motor.—In case coils burn out in an induction motor, they can be cut out and the motor operated for a time or until it can be repaired. It is advisable to cut the entire coil and tape up the two ends so that they can not come together. There is a limit to the number of coils that can be cut out as this is equivalent to raising the voltage on the motor which will cause heating. Where more than two coils must be cut out the motor should be repaired at once or the same number of coils in each phase cut out, evenly distributed around the stator.

PROCEDURE WHEN CONNECTING THE COILS OF AN INDUCTION-MOTOR WINDING

At the end of this chapter typical diagrams for connecting the windings of polyphase alternating-current motors are shown as prepared by A. M. Dudley.[1] When an armature winder or repairman knows the number of poles and phases for the winding, and has been supplied with the necessary coils of the proper throw, the problem of inserting the coils and then connecting them up can be easily understood for each of the diagrams referred to if the fundamental procedure for any one is understood. This procedure is explained by the author of the diagrams as follows:

The diagrams are not dependent on the total number of slots in the machine nor upon the number of coils per group, nor upon the throw or pitch of the coils, but are general for all machines of the same number of phases and poles. Each one of the small arcs in each diagram represents the ends of the coils in a single pole-phase-group in the winding. This is illustrated in Figs. 187 and 188 showing a stator in three stages of being connected. In Fig. 187 (*A*) a machine is shown in which the coils have simply been placed in the slots by the

[1] The diagrams shown have been selected from a series of eighty-one devised by A. M. Dudley, Engineer industrial division of the Westinghouse Electric & Mfg. Co., to be incorporated in an excellent book by him on "Connecting Induction Motors." (McGraw-Hill Book Co., New York.) Mr. Dudley's diagrams begin with two-pole windings and give practically all possible combinations for two- and three-phase, star and delta and series-parallel connections.

winder and no connections have been made. The wires
which are the beginnings and endings of the coils are sticking

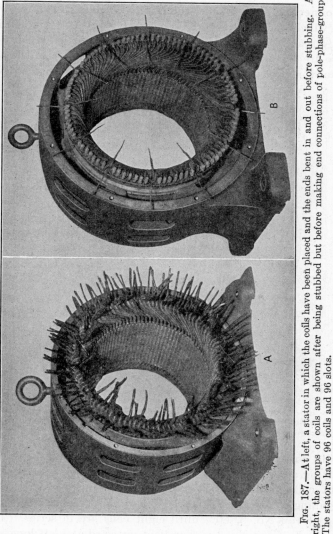

FIG. 187.—At left, a stator in which the coils have been placed and the ends bent in and out before stubbing. At right, the groups of coils are shown after being stubbed but before making end connections of pole–phase–groups. The stators have 96 coils and 96 slots.

out at random. In Fig. 187 (*B*) the coils have been connected
into several distinct groups and the remaining wires, which

19

protrude radially toward and away from the center of the machine, form the beginning and the end of each pole-phase-group.

Connecting Pole-phase-groups of a Winding.—The operation which has been performed between Fig. 187 (*A*) and Fig. 187 (*B*) can be described in this way: Suppose, for example, that there are 96 total coils in the winding and that it is to be connected for three phases and four poles.   There will then be 3 ×

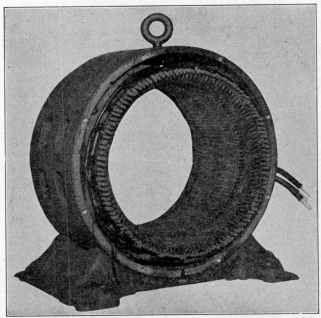

Fig. 188.—Stator of a 100-hp., 3-phase, 8-pole, 220-volt, 60-cycle, 120-coil, 120-slot, induction motor completely wound with pole-phase-groups properly cross connected.

4 = 12 pole-phase-groups, and 96 ÷ 12 = 8 coils in each group. Starting at any arbitrary point, the winder connects the first eight coils in series by connecting the end of coil No. 1 to the beginning of coil No. 2, and the end of coil No. 2 to the beginning of coil No. 3, etc., until eight coils are in series.   The beginning of coil No. 1 is then bent outward and left long and the end of coil No. 8 is bent inward and left long.   Between

these two are seven short "stubs" or coil-to-coil connections, which are shown taped up in Fig. 187 (*B*). The winder then proceeds to connect coils No. 9 to No. 16 in series in the same manner to form pole-phase-group No. 2, and so on around the machine until he has completed 12 pole-phase-groups and used all the coils. The winding then looks as shown in Fig. 187 (*B*).

In case the winding has certain coils provided with heavier insulation on the end turns to take the strain of the full voltage

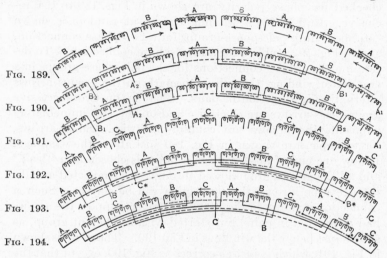

Fig. 189.
Fig. 190.
Fig. 191.
Fig. 192.
Fig. 193.
Fig. 194.

Fig. 189.—Thirty-two coils connected into 8 pole-phase-groups for a 2-phase winding.

Fig. 190.—Same as Fig. 189 with pole-phase-groups connected according to direction of arrows.

Fig. 191.—Same as Fig. 190 with B-phase reversed.

Fig. 192.—Forty-eight coils connected into 12 pole-phase-groups for a 3-phase winding.

Fig. 193.—Same as Fig. 192 with pole-phase-groups connected according to direction of arrows.

Fig. 194.—Same as Fig. 193 except leads are brought out from different groups.

of the machine where different phases are adjacent, the operation is slightly different. In this case the number of coils per pole-phase-group must be determined before the coils are inserted in the slots, and the specially insulated **phase coils** placed on both ends of each group. In this case the location of the pole-phase-groups is definitely determined by the winder before he starts connecting the coils together.

The next step is to mark the pole-phase-groups $A-B-C-A-B-C$, etc., around the machine and then to connect all the groups together in the proper manner to form a three-phase winding as indicated by the diagram of connections. The completed winding will then appear as shown in Fig. 188.

General Theory on which Connection Diagrams are Constructed.—Simple methods by which any winding may be checked for phase polarity are shown in Figs. 189 to 194, inclusive. In Fig. 189 a winding chosen at random is shown "stubbed" into pole-phase-groups for a two-phase connection, and in Fig. 192 stubbed for a three-phase connection. To determine the proper connections for the pole-phase-groups in a two-phase winding, the rule is to mark on the groups arrows alternating in direction in pairs. That is, on two successive groups the arrows are clockwise and on the two immediately adjacent, the arrows are counter-clockwise. Such arrows, for example, are shown in Fig. 189 just above the windings. If now one end of any group in a phase is chosen as a "lead" and all the groups are followed through and connected as indicated by the arrows, the connection will be correct. Such a connection is shown in Fig. 190. However, suppose the arrows had alternated in pairs, but started with a different group, as shown just below the windings in Fig. 190. The result is shown in Fig. 191, which is just as correct as Fig. 190, except that the motor would run with the opposite direction of rotation. Since the rotation can be changed by reversing the two leads of either phase outside of the motor, it is evident that the rule using the arrows alternating in pairs is correct in all cases. It should also be noted that it makes no difference from what group the lead is taken, provided all the groups are followed through with the arrows.

In the three-phase machine the method is even more simple. The rule in that case is to put arrows on the groups alternating in direction from group to group, as shown in Fig. 192. Any group may then be chosen as a "lead" group or a "star" group so long as the arrows are followed in passing from the lead to the star in each phase. Figure 193 shows one arrangement and Fig. 194 another equally correct, and there might be an indefinite number more, simply by choosing the lead from another group and following the arrows through to the star in each phase. Although shown for a developed four-pole winding only, these diagrams may be considered as strictly general, as additional groups may be added to make six, eight, or any other number of poles, and the current passed through them in any order, so long as the phases are kept in the correct rotation and the current in the right direction as indicated by the arrows.

In case of a delta connection instead of a star, check the connections through as for a star and then connect the *A* star

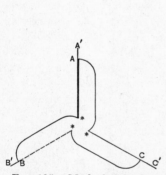

FIG. 195.—Method of checking a delta connection from a star connection.

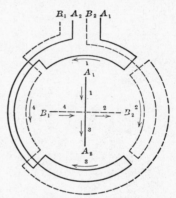

FIG. 196.—Winding diagram for 2-pole, 2-phase motor with series connections of coils.

to the *B* lead, the *B* star to the *C* lead, and the *C* star to the *A* lead, as shown in Fig. 195; or connect the *A* lead to the *B* neutral, the *B* lead to the *C* neutral, and the *C* lead to the *A* neutral. The three motor leads will be taken from the corners of the delta so formed.

Determining Number of Poles from Slot Throw of Coils.— As an example assume a 96-slot stator whose coils span 12 slots. Then number of slots ÷ span of coil = number of poles, or 96 ÷ 12 = 8 poles. Suppose however, the coils span 10 slots. The quotient is then 9.6 which is an impossible number of poles. This indicates a chorded winding and the correct number of poles is probably the next lower even number which will again be 8. This is not an invariably correct rule. A further check is as follows: Divide the number of slots by the number of phases. If this number is divisible by the number of poles obtained as above, it may be safely assumed that the correct number of poles has been determined.

Typical Circle Diagrams for Connecting Induction Motors. On the following pages, 295 to 300 typical winding diagrams are shown by which induction motors may be connected for a variety of operating conditions.

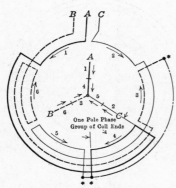

Fig. 197.—Winding diagram for 2-pole, 3-phase motor with series-star connection of coils.

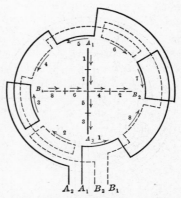

Fig. 198.—Winding diagram for 4-pole, 2-phase motor with series connections of coils.

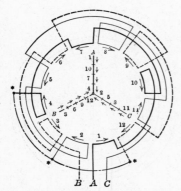

Fig. 199.—Winding diagram for 4-pole, 3-phase motor with series-star connections of coils.

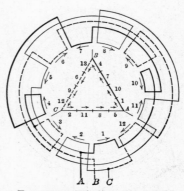

Fig. 200.—Winding diagram for 4-pole, 3-phase motor with series-delta connections of coils.

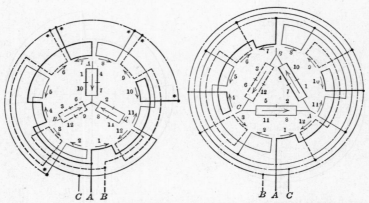

FIG. 201.—Winding diagram for 4-pole, 3-phase motor with 2-parallel star connections of coils.

FIG. 202.—Winding diagram for 4-pole, 3-phase motor with 2-parallel delta connections of coils.

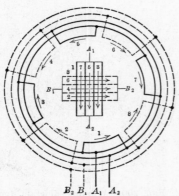

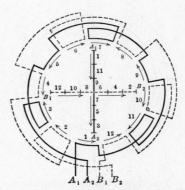

FIG. 203.—Winding diagram for 4-pole, 2-phase motor with 4-parallel connections of coils.

FIG. 204.—Winding diagram for 6-pole, 2-phase motor with series connections of coils.

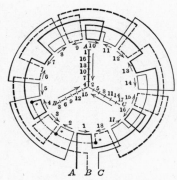

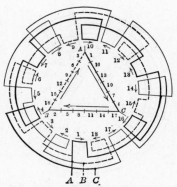

Fig. 205.—Winding diagram for 6-pole, 3-phase motor with series-star connections of coils.

Fig. 206.—Winding diagram for 6-pole, 3-phase motor with series-delta connections of coils.

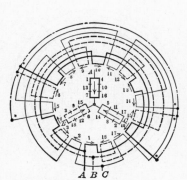

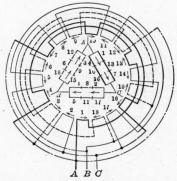

Fig. 207.—Winding diagram for 6-pole, 3-phase motor with 2-parallel star connections of coils.

Fig. 208.—Winding diagram for 6-pole, 3-phase motor with 2-parallel delta connections of coils.

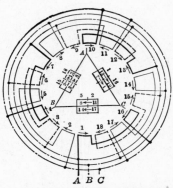

Fig. 209.—Winding diagram for 6-pole, 3-phase motor with 3-parallel delta connections of coils.

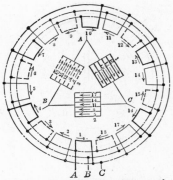

Fig. 210.—Winding diagram for 6-pole, 3-phase motor with 6-parallel delta connections of coils.

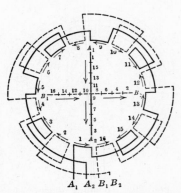

Fig. 211.—Winding diagram for 8-pole, 2-phase motor with series connections of coils.

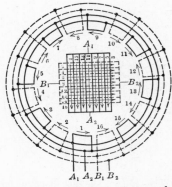

Fig. 212.—Winding diagram for 8-pole, 2-phase motor with 8-parallel connections of coils.

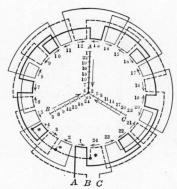

FIG. 213.—Winding diagram for 8-pole, 3-phase motor with series-star connections of coils.

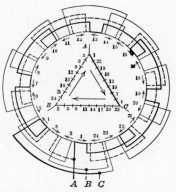

FIG. 214.—Winding diagram for 8-pole, 3-phase motor with series-delta connections of coils.

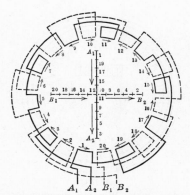

FIG. 215.—Winding diagram for 10-pole, 2-phase motor with series connections of coils.

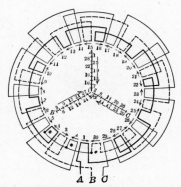

FIG. 216.—Winding diagram for 10-pole, 3-phase motor with series-star connections of coils.

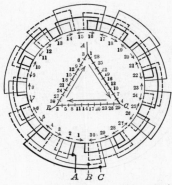

Fig. 217.—Winding diagram for 10-pole, 3-phase motor with series-delta connections of coils.

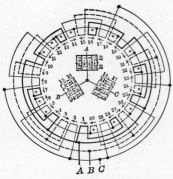

Fig. 218.—Winding diagram for 10-pole, 3-phase motor with 5-parallel star connections of coils.

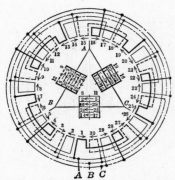

Fig. 219.—Winding diagram for 10-pole, 3-phase motor with 5-parallel delta connections of coils.

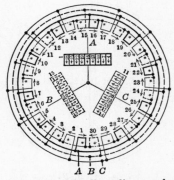

Fig. 220.—Winding diagram for 10-pole, 3-phase motor with 10-parallel star connections of coils.

CHAPTER XII

COMMUTATOR REPAIRS

Commutator troubles are more easily located than faults in an armature, but a repair job on an old style motor, many of which are still in use, is sometimes a trying and tedious operation.

Causes of Commutator Troubles.—Sparking at the brushes is generally the first symptom of commutator trouble. One of the most frequent causes of sparking is a rough or pitted commutator. This may be due to many irregularities, such as overload; brushes out of line; not set at neutral points in regard to load; poor contacts; current density per square inch of brush contact too great; open circuit; weak magnetic fields; commutator out of round; high or low bars or high mica. The most common cause of sparking is high mica which causes the brushes to chatter and to make poor contact. This condition results in a rapid blackening and burning of the bars, sometimes to the extent that the copper is eaten away leaving the mica segments standing out above the surface of the commutator. Some motors seem to be particularly subject to this trouble, due to the fact that the mica is too hard a grade, or the copper too soft. When there is no time to turn down the commutator the high mica can be removed by grinding down with a piece of sandstone, and using fine sandpaper for smoothing.

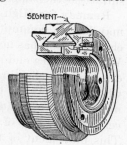

Fig. 221.—Section of a small commutator showing construction of bars and how they are held by the clamping rings.

Troubles Resulting from High Mica.—High mica, while it may seem a small matter at first, is often the cause of more serious complications. The commutator may become so hot from the poor brush contact afforded, that the solder will be melted and thrown out, resulting in short-circuits between bars and open-circuits due to the armature leads becoming disconnected. About the only permanent relief for sparking at brushes due to high mica is undercutting the mica. This remedy is recommended when it is reasonably certain that the high mica is caused by the natural condition of the copper or mica. If it is not, then the real cause must be found, otherwise, undercutting the mica would probably improve the running condition somewhat, but would fail to remove the cause.

The mica should not be cut too deeply, a depth of $\frac{1}{32}$ to $\frac{1}{16}$ inch below the surface of the copper being sufficient. Care must be exercised to remove the mica the full width of the segment, for any thin slivers left flush with the surface will often defeat the purpose of the undercutting. (For details for undercutting mica, see page 320.) This method has corrected some stubborn cases of sparking and if the job is properly done, all that will be necessary to preserve sparkless commutation is to keep the slots clean and well below the surface of the copper.

Remedy for High or Low Bars.—A new or repaired motor may have a commutator that is not "settled." That is, the clamping ring has not been drawn up as tightly as it should be. When the mica end rings are cut they are only slightly flexible due to the shellac in them and cannot be made to fit perfectly when cold. When the commutator is hot, the shellac in the mica will soften and allow it to move under the strain of the centrifugal force of the bars when the machine is running. This movement of the mica allows the bars to move and is frequently the cause of high or low bars. To remedy this trouble, the machine should be run until its normal operating temperature is attained and then shut down. The clamping ring can then be tightened. This process may be necessary several times, or until the commutator is perfectly solid. Care must be taken not to tighten the bolts too much while the commutator is warm.

In the case of a high bar, it should be tapped down until it rests firmly against the mica end rings. It can then be filed even with the rest of the bars. A low bar can be raised by prying up, and inserting a narrow strip of mica beneath it, but in the majority of cases this makes a poor job. Usually the only alternative is to turn the commutator down to the level of the low bar.

Burn-out Between Bars.—Probably the most frequent commutator trouble is a burn-out between bars. It occurs often on the corner of the bars, and is not infrequently caused by

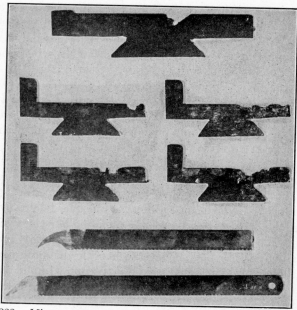

Fig. 222.—Mica segments taken from damaged motors showing the effects of short circuits in the commutator. Two tools are also shown made from hack saw blades for use in plugging a commutator.

oil working along the shaft from the bearing and up onto the commutator. This oil collects dust and dirt and finally causes current to leak from one bar to the other. The mica then becomes carbonized, and a short-circuit results. This is one of the causes of burned-out armature coils. Sometimes the short-circuit will burn itself clear, and no harm will be caused except to burn a hole in the mica. However, it may continue to arc across and burn a good sized hole in the bars also.

Plugging a Commutator.—When mica segments are burned but not too deep, the holes can be cleaned with a thin knife blade and plugged with some kind of filling. If a good filling compound is used, and the commutator kept free from oil, it will hold for a year or possibly longer. It is always advisable to save the wearing surface in this manner whenever it can be done, for every time a commutator is turned down in a lathe on an average of three years of its useful life is lost.

A good filling compound for commutators can be made as follows: Two parts plaster-of-paris; one part powdered mica; and enough glue to make a thick paste. This, when applied, will dry quickly, and assume about the same degree of hardness as the mica segments.

When a segment becomes burned deep down into the commutator, a new one must be inserted. Before attempting to do this, the armature should be thoroughly blown out with compressed air in order to remove all dust that may have accumulated. This is essential, for it is an easy matter for small particles of foreign matter to work in under the back end between the bars and the sleeve when the commutator is loose. Determine just which mica segments must be taken out, and number the bars at each burn-out, since the bars may have to be removed also in order to get the mica segments out. If the segments were not shellaced when the commutator was built, the chances are they can be lifted out without disturbing the bars. Otherwise the bars will have to be taken out with the segments.

Removing Bars and Mica Segments for Repairs.—Remove the bolts that hold the clamping ring in place. Mark the ring so that it may be put back just as it was taken off. Tap the end of the ring lightly with a hammer. If the mica ring does not loosen from the commutator, it will have to be heated, as the ring is probably stuck fast with shellac. Heat the commutator with a torch to an even temperature all around. This will expand the copper and cause it to bulge out from the end ring. Tap the ring again lightly, and it will be found to work loose. Then it can be pulled out.

Pry the bars apart slightly at one of the burned places to see if the mica segments are stuck to the bars. If they are not, it is a simple matter to remove them from the commutator. If they are held fast, the leads from one bar adjoining

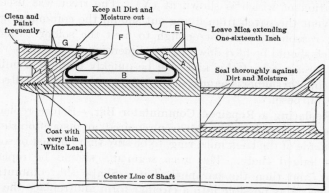

Fig. 223.—Section of an assembled commutator of a railway motor.

the burned segment should be unsoldered and the bar lifted out. Proceed in the same way with the remaining bad places. New segments can be marked off by using one of the old bars as a guide. The bars should be scraped and filed clean, and all rough corners rounded off.

Repairing a Burned Commutator Bar.—Frequently it happens that there is a good-sized hole burned in the commu-

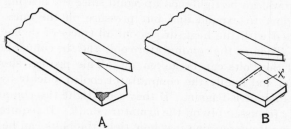

A   B

Fig. 224.—Repair of a burned place on a commutator bar.

tator bar. This should be repaired before it is used again. As there is usually no stock of exactly the proper size on hand in a small repair shop out of which to make a new bar, a good repair is the next best thing. In Fig. 224 (*A*) shows the end of

20

a bar with a burned place and (B) the method of repair. In this case the bar was cut down enough to remove the burn, and a piece of copper strip carefully squared and soldered in the cut. It was then riveted with a small copper rivet, the location of which is shown at (X). The rivet was used to prevent the patch from flying out should the commutator for any reason become hot enough to melt the solder. Such a patch should be filed down to the dimensions of the bar. The cut for a patch of this kind can be quickly made if a milling machine or shaper is handy, otherwise a good sharp file will serve the purpose.

Replacing a Repaired Commutator Bar.—Before replacing a commutator bar that has been repaired, an inspection should be made of the back mica ring, to be sure that no dust or solder has lodged there. The mica segments should be replaced first, and then the bar pushed in. Shape the commutator as nearly as possible into a circular form and replace the end ring. Tighten the clamping nuts as much as possible while the commutator is cold. It is a good plan to paint the end of the commutator with shellac, in order to fill up any cracks that may exist between the bars and the ring.

Tightening up a Repaired Commutator.—When a commutator has been taken down in a repair shop and assembled again, all lock nuts and screws should be first set up hard and the commutator baked in an oven. Then the lock nuts and screws can be tightened up again since the heating causes the copper to expand and put pressure on the mica which, combined with the heat, drives out all traces of shellac in the mica. Then as the commutator cools and the copper becomes normal the bolts can be taken up. This process should be repeated and finally the commutator cooled quickly by a fan, and the nuts tried again. If they seem tight the commutator is ready for assembly on the armature shaft. It requires some experience to determine just how tight the bolts can be drawn on a commutator without injuring the mica end rings. The one precaution is not to draw up the bolts finally until the commutator has cooled. The commutator surface can now be turned down in a lathe. After doing this a short-circuit test should be made with a test lamp from bar to bar. Failure.

FIG. 225.—At the left, mounting an assembled commutator on an armature shaft. At right, assembling bars and mica of a 1000 kw. commutator.

of the lamp to light indicates that the commutator is free from short-circuits. See also Chapter V, pages 123, 126 and 135. A test for grounds should also be made at this time (see pages 131 and 175).

Baking Commutator with Electric Heat.—In those cases where an oven is not available for baking a rebuilt commutator and it is too large to heat with a torch, the electrical method shown in Fig. 226 has been successfully used (Albert Krause, *Electrical World*, July 26, 1919, page 190)   A satisfactory heating element can be made up by using a layer of $\frac{1}{16}$-in. asbestos paper around the commutator and winding over this about

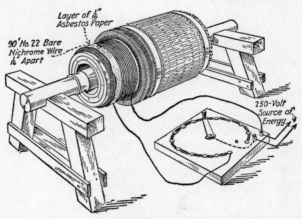

Fig. 226.—Uniform temperature produced by heating element wound around commutator.

90 ft. of No. 22 Nichrome resistance wire. By applying 250 volts to the terminals of this resistance wire a uniform heat in the commutator can be produced to permit evening up the insulating segments and clamping the end rings. Ordinarily it would be advisable to have a variable resistance in series with the heating element so its temperature can be kept at a desirable value. By covering the armature after the commutator is heated in this manner varnish may be applied thereto and baked in by the heat conducted to the armature through the leads from the commutator.

Removing and Repairing Grounds in a Commutator.—The

ground frequently occurs between the sleeve ring and the end of the bars. A small hole is generally burned through the mica ring or taper cone. Some times the mica ring on the rear end is punctured. In that event a number of bars in the neighborhood of the ground will have to be taken out. The burned mica should be cut out and a patch put on. When the trouble occurs on the front end of the commutator, remove the ring and cut out the bad mica. The patch can be made as shown in Fig. 227. This new mica must be a trifle thicker than the original mica removed, for it will squeeze together somewhat when the ring is drawn up tight and the commutator heated.

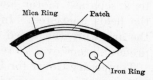

Fig. 227.—Patch on a mica end ring of a commutator.

After the repair, test the commutator for grounds with a proper voltage (see page 175). Place one terminal on the shaft, and move the other completely around the surface of the commutator. Freedom from grounds will be indicated by no sparking at the terminal moved over the surface. A lower test voltage should be used on low-voltage commutators and a higher voltage for those of high voltage machines.

On some of the old-style motors, the sleeve nut is on the back of the commutator. When this happens, the armature leads will have to be disconnected and bent back out of the way in order to work on the commutator. The best procedure in such a case, if there is time, is to remove the commutator and reverse the sleeve, as both ends are usually bored to the same diameter. By reversing the sleeve in this manner in order to get the nut where it can be easily reached, much time and work will be saved when future repairs must be made.

Turning Down a Commutator without Removing Armature from Machine.—The method sometimes used in turning down a commutator on a repair job where the armature is too large to remove, is to leave one or two pairs of brush arms on and run the machine from these at as low a speed as the field regulation will permit or possibly with a water rheostat in the armature circuit. This method will do where no other means of turning the commutator is available. There is always bad sparking and burning at the point of the cutting tool due to its short-circuiting the bars when it crosses the mica. The tool has to be sharpened frequently and a job is seldom good even where the greatest care is exercised.

For these reasons it is always preferable to belt the machine to a separate motor and turn down the commutator with the fields unexcited. In connecting up a motor for driving the armature the speed should be made as low as possible, preferably not over 75 revolutions per minute.

Temporary Cover for Use When Turning Down a Commutator.—In cases where it is necessary to turn down the commutator of a direct-current machine without removing it from

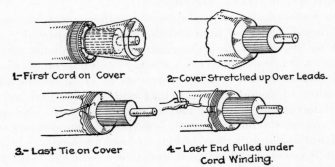

1.—First Cord on Cover   2.—Cover Stretched up Over Leads.

3.—Last Tie on Cover   4.—Last End Pulled under Cord Winding.

Fig. 228.—Steps in applying a cotton cover over the end of an armature before turning down the commutator to prevent copper chips falling behind the bars to cause short circuits.

the frame, H. S. Rich has made use of a muslin cover (*Electrical Record*, December, 1918) tied over the open leads so that copper chips cannot find a way down behind the bars to cause a short-circuit. This cover is made and applied as follows: Cut a strip of muslin wide enough to reach across the commutator and well past the leads, and long enough to go around one and one-half times. Tie this very securely with fine strong cord, with the muslin laid over the bars as shown in Fig. 228.

Draw the covering and stretch a little at a time all around and up over the open leads far enough back to allow of at least two separate cords to be tightly wound around and very securely tied on the core body. Turn the armature slowly to see that the covering does not interfere with any brush holder. If so, the holder should be shifted. The surplus edging, all loose strings and threads should now be trimmed off all around.

By turning back the muslin over the leads the first cord tied around the bars is covered neatly. The cords wound around the core body can be secured without knots by winding over the first end a few turns, and then by winding over a short extra loop, the last end can be jerked under all the turns and cut short so that a knot is not needed. For a permanent armature covering, shellac should be applied all over it which seals the cords and stiffens the muslin.

Refilling a Commutator.—When a commutator is to be refilled, disconnect the armature leads and remove the commutator. A simple device for accomplishing this is shown in Fig. 229. Two long bolt rods are screwed into holes tapped into the sleeve ring, and a bar of heavy iron placed across the end of the shaft, with bolt rods coming through, as shown. By tightening the nuts evenly, the commutator can be pulled off. Next count the number of bars carefully, and enter this in a note book for future reference. Remove the sleeve and if possible save the mica rings. If these are in good condition they can be used again. Carefully caliper the diameter of these rings and enter this in the note book also, as the new commutator will have to be bored to fit these rings.

With a micrometer caliper, measure the thick and thin edges of one of the bars in thousands of an inch; also the thickness of the mica segment.

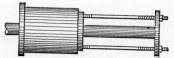

Fig. 229.—Device for removing a commutator from an armature shaft.

It is advisable to order the bars and mica segments from the motor manufacturer sawed to the proper size, as in all probability this can be done cheaper than in an ordinary repair shop not equipped for this work. When ordering new bars a detailed drawing should be sent, giving all necessary dimensions of the old bar for boring and turning purposes. Hard drawn copper is usually used as it wears at about the same rate as the mica segments (see page 319).

Use of a Commutator Clamp.—When assembling the commutator, a clamp will be necessary to hold the bars together while boring.   Several makeshift methods are available, but it will pay any repair shop to have suitable cast-iron clamps, such as shown in Fig. 230.   The clamp should be smaller than the diameter of the commutator, so that when it is drawn tight, there will be a space of about ⅛ inch between the sections.   When using this clamp as shown in Fig. 230 at the right, wooden blocks (*C*) can be employed to hold the clamp about midway of the commutator.   *D* is an iron face plate.   The clamp (*B*) should first be placed on the plate as shown, and the bars and mica segments stacked in a circular form within it.   Care must be exercised to make sure that a

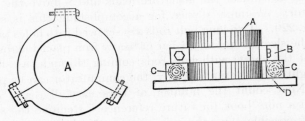

Fig. 230.—At the left, a clamp for holding commutator bars together when being assembled.   At the right, the use of this clamp is shown.

mica segment is placed between each copper bar. Count the bars carefully, so that their number corresponds with the number of bars in the original commutator.

Take several pieces of copper wire (about No. 9 B. & S. gauge) and remove the insulation. Place these around the commutator near the top and lower ends to act as band wires, and twist them tight. The clamp may then be removed, and the commutator straightened. Bring out the mica segments even with the surface of the bars by holding the fingers against the inside edge of the segments and tapping the bars on the outside with a small mallet. Place a square or steel scale on the face plate and tap the bars on the outside with a small mallet. Place the square or steel scale on the face plate and see that the bars line up perpendicularly with one edge of the square. If they do not, a gentle pressure one way or the other on the top end of the commutator with the palm of the hand will bring them in line. See that each bar and segment is down flat against the surface of the plate, since that end will be fastened to the face plate on the lathe when facing off the ends of the bars. Tap each bar and segment down solid with a square ended punch, a little narrower than the thickness of the bar. When this has been done, the band wires can be drawn a little tighter, and the surface of the commutator, where the clamp will fit, should be filed to remove any protruding mica, and present a smooth surface for the clamp.

Replace each section of the clamp about the commutator again using the wooden blocks mentioned before. Draw the clamp tight, being sure to leave the same amount of space between each clamp section. A small gas burner, or some other source of heat should be handy, and the commutator placed over it and heated. When it is good and hot to the hand, tighten the clamp, allow it to cool, and again tighten.

Boring out the End of a Commutator.—The next thing to do is to bolt the commutator to the face plate of the lathe and center it. The same wooden blocks can be used again for supporting the clamp. Face off the end of the bars, and then groove out the end for the taper rings to the same diameter as the mica rings on the sleeve. Take one of the old bars, and with a bevel protractor determine exactly the taper used on the old commutator. The usual taper employed is shown in Fig. 231. A small groove (shown at *A*) should be cut below the intersection of the two tapers to allow room for the edge of the mica ring. The other end should be treated in the same manner.

When the boring has been completed, a close inspection must be made of all turned surfaces, to make certain that no copper has been dragged over the mica to form a short-circuit. The corner of the groove *A* (Fig. 231) should be carefully gone over, as it is here that drag-overs most frequently occur. Scrape and wipe the mica rings on the sleeve clean; also wipe out the inside of the commutator with a soft rag. Place the sleeve in the commutator again, and draw

up on the end nut. On a refilling job, when the old mica
rings are used again, cracks may be found between the band
ring and the commutator copper due to the irregularity of
the mica ring caused by the shape of the old commutator.
These cracks can be filled by pushing in thin sheets of mica.
Shellac should be used liberally on the ends.

Bake the commutator in an oven for about one hour until
it becomes thoroughly hot, and tighten the nuts. Reduce
the heat somewhat, and bake at a low heat until the shellac

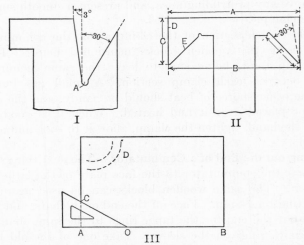

Fig. 231.—I shows taper of commutator bars. II is a template for laying
out mica end rings. III shows a scheme for laying out the taper *E*, of the
template shown in II.

becomes hard. Tighten the nuts again and allow the commutator to cool. When cold give the nuts a final setting up.
The clamp can now be removed.

In order to finish the commutator, use a mandrel to fit
the bore of the sleeve, and take the final finishing cuts. After
finishing, a bar to bar test with the test lamp outfit should
be made to be sure there are no short-circuits between bars.
A test for grounds should also be made by holding one wire
of the test lamp on the iron sleeve and passing the other from
bar to bar around the commutator. A high-voltage test for
grounds should be made also later.

The slots for taking the armature leads must next be cut. It is well to cut them a little wider than the diameter of the lead wires. These slots should be made in a milling machine if one is at hand, otherwise a hack saw can be used. Sometimes two blades fastened together will give the required width of slot. The commutator can now be placed on the armature shaft.

Mica Used in Commutators.—The selection of mica for the insulation of commutator bars and for V-rings is usually based upon the type of motor being repaired, but built-up mica has been found to be the most satisfactory. India mica is generally too hard and domestic mica too brittle for use between

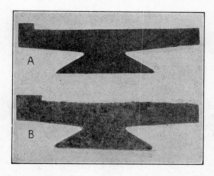

Fig. 232.—Mica segment (*B*) cut from sheet using bar (*A*) as pattern. Such a segment is cut large at top and at ends so as to turn down evenly with copper bars when commutator is finally surfaced.

bars. Domestic mica also has cracks and fissures which fill up with dirt and cause short circuits. Amber mica gives good service but it comes in such odd sizes that it is too wasteful for the average repair job. Hard-baked built-up mica is found best to be used between bars and the unbaked best for building up the V-rings. The unbaked mica is usually obtained in sheets 0.025 inch and 0.030 inch thick. Heavier mica would be difficult to bend and to cut in shape. The same sizes of hard-baked mica with the addition of 0.02 inch and 0.035 inch have been found sufficient stock to fill almost any size of commutator. In cutting up the unbaked mica for the V-ring insulation it is safer first to fit a piece of paper around the ring and then use this as a template.

Shaping Mica End Rings.—When it is impossible to save the old mica end rings, new ones must be made. These can be made of flexible mica usually 0.030 inch thick. It is best to make the rings in three pieces to the layer on small commutators; three layers constituting a ring. When heated slightly, this mica can be bent around the sleeve to the desired shape. Trim the edges square on each piece and fit them tightly in the bore of the commutator. The taper rings should be fitted in the same manner with a slight space being left between abutting ends.

Templet for Making Mica End Rings.—A good shop method for making a template to lay off mica end rings is as follows:

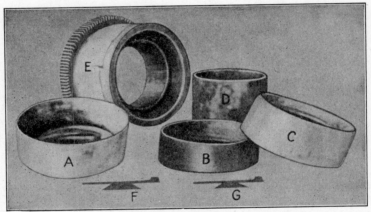

FIG. 233.—Parts of a medium sized commutator.

(*a*) and (*c*) Mica end rings. (*b*) Iron clamping V-ring. (*d*) Mica bushing sleeve for inside of commutator. (*e*) Commutator bars and mica segments assembled. Sample bars and mica segments are shown at (*f*) and (*g*).

Mark off on a piece of cardboard an arc of a circle, the radius of which is equal to the diameter *A* in Fig. 231. Strike another arc from the same center with the radius of the dividers made smaller by the distance *C*. This will give a templet for the band *D*.

A templet for the taper *E* can be prepared as illustrated in the following example: Assume the diameter *B* to equal seven inches. Then in Fig. 231 lay off one-half this diameter, or $3\frac{1}{2}$ inches from *A* on the edge *AB* as shown at *O*. If the taper is 30 degrees, take a 30- by 60-degree triangle and square its lower edge with the line AB, having its apex, or point touching the point at O. Draw the line OC, which will be the radius of the arc of a circle D, shown dotted. Strike another arc from the same center with the radius made smaller by the distance F, Fig. 231. This will give a templet for the taper E.

Micanite as a Commutator Insulation.—For use in insulating commutators, the Mica Insulator Company, New York City, has developed a mica laying machine which successfully constructs large sheets of micanite from thin mica laminæ with cement uniformly applied between the layers. These sheets are finished by drying and baking under high pressure after which the sheets are packed through milling machine and finished to accurate thickness. The company gives the following directions for using micanite as a commutator insulation.

If micanite segments for insulation between copper bars of a commutator are to be cut from full size sheets of micanite plate, a fine tooth band saw with moderate set should be used. Bookbinders' shears or foot power cutters are poor tools to use as the edge of the micanite is likely to be bruised and this may result in dragging of the copper over the micanite when the commutator is turned in a lathe. Short circuits, or near short-circuits, are often caused in this manner. It is not necessary to coat the surface of either the copper bars or the micanite segments with shellac before assembling the commutator. After turning the V's for the end rings carefully examine all surfaces and scrape clear any places where the lathe tool has dragged the copper. Before placing micanite rings, carefully remove all dust from both commutator and rings. Short-circuits are sometimes caused by overlooking these details. After the commutator is assembled on the shells, with the rings in place it should receive a baking at a temperature of about 150°C. (302°F.). This baking is for the purpose of embedding the end of the segments and setting the cement in the rings.

Precautions when Tightening a Commutator.—It is essential on account of the expansion of the copper, that the commutator is not screwed up too tight before it is baked. The best results are obtained by tightening up the commutator gradually after baking as it cools, giving a final tightening when nearly cold. Many of the troubles met with in commutators is due to excessive tightening. In arch-bound commutators, it is important that the assembled segments are not tightened too hard in the arch before the V parts are turned, as the resulting stresses from the expanding copper, distort the parts and often are the main cause of high bars. Similar care should be taken not to exert more pressure than necessary on the end rings and whenever possible means should be provided to measure the pressure. Cases have been known where the angles of the clamp rings in small commutators have been changed by excessive pressure. Approximately 1500 lb. per sq. in. on the projected area of the inside cone or taper rings is a satisfactory medium pressure.

Making Micanite End Rings.—It is often necessary for the commutator builder, particularly the repair man, to make up his own rings. For that purpose a different kind of plate known as No. 1 micanite or moulding plate is furnished by the Mica Insulator Company. This plate is made from white mica selected with same care as for micanite commutator segment plate and contains the proper proportion of cement to produce satisfactory moulding characteristics. Micanite is not ductile and will not stretch uniformly like sheet metal. It is, therefore, necessary to cut the pattern for micanite commutator rings into the exact development of the ring before moulding. The pattern should be long enough to allow for a tapered splice at the ends. For cementing the splice, use a high grade shellac of about 2 lb. to the gallon of solvent. When the No. 1 micanite is placed on a steam table or metal plate heated to about 140°C. (284°F.), it becomes plastic and can be moulded readily into the desired shape. The micanite should not remain on the hot plate any longer than necessary as the cement might set, making it less pliable. It is advisable to turn the micanite over so as to heat uniformly from both sides. After placing the micanite in the mould or in the commutator, it should be under pressure while cooling.

Causes of Excessive Commutator Wear.—Warren C. Kalb has pointed out (*Power*, March 18, 1919) that commutator wear may be caused by the use of abrasive brushes. It may also result from the same mechanical or electrical causes that produce brush wear. Mechanical conditions of this nature are: Rough commutator due to poorly prepared surface; rough commutator caused by burning; vibration from any source such as the pound of a direct-connected engine, belt lacing, improper mounting, loose bearings or commutator out of true; high peripheral speed, causing brushes to chatter or creating an excessive temperature at the brush faces due to friction; type of brush-holder or angle of operation, resulting in the chattering of the brushes.

Copper Used to Make Commutator Bars.—The bars for commutators can be made from drop forged, cold rolled, hard drawn or cast copper bars. The drop forged copper is usually considered the best and cast copper the worst for bars. Probably most commutators are made of cold rolled or hard drawn copper. Cast copper is poor on account of the many pin holes and larger that are liable to be in the structure of the bar. These show up at every turning and require filling to prevent carbon dust from accumulating. If they are near the edge of the bars the carbon is liable to bridge the mica between the bars and cause a short-circuit and burn a hole in two bars. This calls for a patching of the bars and the insulation which adds a weak spot to the commutator and simply hastens the time when it must be rebuilt. A good grade of copper for bars is economical from points of service and reduction of repair costs.

However, when hard-rolled, or drop-forged copper is not available for the repair man, cast copper makes a good substitute. If the castings are soft they have a minimum conductivity of 60 per cent. and are more free from blow holes; also, they wear from 75 per cent. to 90 per cent. as long as the hard-drawn or drop-forged copper bars. The castings are soft but tough, and the low conductivity is due to the fluxes used in melting the copper. A reduction in the amount of flux used increases the conductivity of the copper, but it also tends to make the metal more brittle, more porous and liable to have blow holes below the surface. The 60 per cent. soft-copper castings do not need filling or machining on the sides. They can be easily straightened and any projection flattened out on a surface plate by the aid of a steel flattener and a hammer.

Test for Oil-saturated Mica in a Commutator.—When the mica between commutator bars appears to be saturated with oil the following test can be applied. Wet a rag or piece of waste with gasoline and wipe the surface of the commutator dry. Then with a torch heat the commutator at the point where the mica appears to be saturated. If oil has worked down between the mica and the bar it will ooze out in small bubbles. In such a case new mica segments must be inserted.

Blackening of a Commutator at Equally Spaced Points.— This is usually caused by an open circuit in the armature winding. The open circuit may be at the commutator necks or at the rear-end connections of the winding when two-piece coils are used. ' When these spots are noticed on a commutator it should be tested out for open circuits at once before further commutator troubles develop.

UNDERCUTTING MICA OF COMMUTATORS

The object of undercutting the mica of commutators is to clean out the mica between the copper segments to a depth of about $\frac{1}{32}$ to $\frac{3}{32}$ inch so that the copper bars will wear evenly free from the poor commutation that often results when the mica is hard and does not wear down evenly with the copper segments. The undercutting operation should be done after the armature has been rewound, soldered and banded. The commutator should also be trued up and all excess solder removed from the neck and face.

Tools for Undercutting Mica.—Special motor-driven or belt-driven saws are available for doing this work which can be

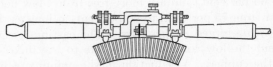

Fig. 234.—Hand tool for undercutting mica that can be connected to a small motor by a flexible shaft.

used when the armature is centered in a lathe. The saws are usually clamped on an arbor which is mounted on a head that moves on slide rails. By means of a hand-operated lever or foot pedal controlled by the operator, the revolving saw is carried over the face of the commutator. A shaper equipped with a special tool can also be used. Frequently a milling machine will be found convenient for undercutting the smaller sizes of armatures. A less expensive device consists of a motor-driven circular saw which is mounted in such a way that the saw can be guided over the commutator face by hand. Two such motor driven tools are shown in Figs. 234 and 235.

Size of Circular Saw Required.—For the cutting tool a circular saw or miller about ¾ to 1¼ inch in diameter

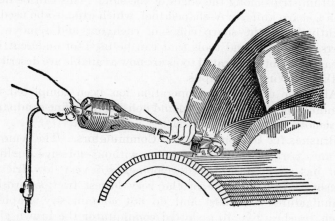

Fig. 235.—Motor operated hand tool that can be connected to a lighting circuit for undercutting the mica of a commutator.

with from 15 to 30 teeth seems to give the best results. A small diameter saw must be used in order to cut the slot to the proper depth and at the same time not cut into the neck of the commutator. The saw should be driven at approximately 1500 rpm. and be about 0.005 inch thicker than the mica in order to remove the mica completely. If the commutators are of large diameter, one or two spacers of the same thickness as the bars may be used between the saws and two or three slots cut at the same time. The cutting edge of the saw should revolve in a direction toward the operator while cutting the mica. When the hand-operated motor-driven

21

tools are used they should be drawn toward the operator, in order to properly guide the tool.

It is advisable to have a jet of compressed air or a fan so located that the particles of mica and copper will be blown away from the armature to prevent this material falling in behind the commutator and at the same time make it easy for the operator to see the slot when the saw is throwing the particles toward him on the face of the commutator.

Finishing Slots and Commutator Surface after Undercutting.—After the slots are sawed it is advisable to go over them with a sharp hand tool to remove remaining particles of mica and thin strips along the edges of the slot. This can be done with a sharp knife, or V-shaped tool, which can also be used to slightly bevel the sharp edges of each bar and remove all burrs. Several hand tools that can be used for undercutting mica when motor operated tools are now available are described in the following paragraphs.

After the undercutting operation has been completed the commutator should be stoned and polished with fine sandpaper to remove all burrs of copper.

Brushes for Use on Undercut Commutators.—The removal of mica permits the use of brushes without abrasive qualities and has resulted in the development of very low friction brushes. In fact some of the very lowest friction brushes manufactured are hard and do not contain any graphite. Such brushes give to a slotted commutator the brown gloss that shows perfect operation. The life of a hard non-abrasive brush is several times that of a graphite brush. Some criticism has been made of slotted commutators which has been traced to the fact that the brushes used were not suitable. Often when the same brushes are used on an undercut commutator that were used before, the commutator will be ridged and worn rapidly and the slots filled with copper dust with short-circuits and burned out coils the result. The fault in such cases is in the brush not in the undercutting process.

It should also be remembered that the brush tension on an undercut commutator can often be much lower than before. Brush authorities recommend 1½ to 2½ pounds per square inch of cross-section on stationary motors, from 3 to 5 pounds per square inch for crane motors and from 4 to 8 pounds per square inch on railway motors when the commutators are undercut.

Another factor in good operation of undercut commutators is cleaning at regular intervals.   If the motor is operated in a place where the accumulated dust and dirt is dry, it can be removed with a blast of compressed air.   Even in such cases the slots should be scraped occasionally.   A lubricant should never be used on an undercut commutator nor any other when operating conditions are correct.

Hand Tools for Undercutting Mica of Commutators.—An easily made hand tool for undercutting the mica of com-

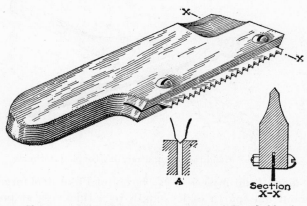

Fig. 236.—Short saw blade clamped in a vulcanized fiber holder for use in undercutting mica.

mutators is shown in Fig. 236 as devised by William H. Watson (*Power*, Oct. 1, 1918).   The slot in the holder is made as deep or deeper than the width of the hacksaw blade, with small bolts to clamp the blades at each end.   Any depth of cut desired can be made by adjusting the blade in the holder, but there seldom is occasion to move the blade.   The handle part is cut away just enough to allow the fingers to pass over the commutator without rubbing.   In undercutting commutators care must be taken that no rough edges are left after the mica is cut, but it is sometimes hard to avoid this, especially if it is an old commutator.   These rough corners can be smoothed, after the mica has been undercut, with a V-shaped tool made of hardwood or vulcanized fiber, run between the segments as shown at *A*, and it does not spoil the bar.   The front corner of the undercutter, which is made of fiber, can be used to smooth these raw edges.

Another hand tool recommended by T. M. Sterling (*Power*, Nov. 5, 1918) for undercutting mica and as useful in other ways by the repairman, is illustrated in Fig. 237.   In the illustration *A* represents a steel straight-edge about ¼ inch thick and slightly longer than the length of the commutator segments and square at one end to butt up against the head of the commutator.   *B* is the undercutting tool, about 12 inches

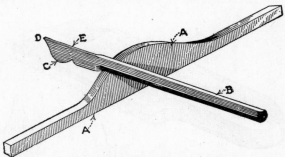

Fig. 237.—Hand tool for undercutting commutator mica.

long, made from a piece of ⁵⁄₁₆ hexagonal tool steel forged flat for about one-fourth of its length to a thickness at point *D* equal to the thickness of the mica between the segments.   The "half-heart" shaped lobe *C* affords a bearing place for the fingers in using the tool.

When using this tool lay the straight-edge on the commutator with its edge in line with the mica between the segments and the square end against the head of the commutator. Hold it firmly with the left hand.   Then, holding tool B in the right hand, draw the point *D* along the mica the same as drawing a pencil along a ruler in ruling paper.   This operation will start a nice groove in the mica without burring the edges of the copper on either side.   After one or two passes the tool can be turned endwise with point *D* down and the mica taken to any desired depth or a saw blade may be used to finish the groove. The disadvantage of the saw blade is that the set of the teeth burr the copper more or less, while with this tool all chance of a burr is eliminated.

The tool will also be found handy in raising coil leads out of the slots in the head of a commutator when unsoldering them preparatory to removing the commutator or making coil repairs. After heating the ends of the coils until the solder starts to melt, drive the point of the tool into the slot under the ends of the wires, with lobe C down, for a fulcrum, on the bottom of the slot. The ends of the coils can then be easily raised by a downward pressure of the hand. Square edge E can be used as a scraper for taking the surplus hot solder off the ends of the wires as they are raised.

CHAPTER XIII

ADJUSTING BRUSHES AND CORRECTING BRUSH TROUBLES

Many of the troubles which are charged to brushes of motors and generators can be traced to improper application and adjustment or to other defects of the machine that show up in sparking at the commutator. A careful selection of brushes is important but no more so than carefulness in adjustment and frequent inspection in operation, for proper care of brushes and brush rigging results in good commutation and prolonged life of both brushes and commutator. The repairman should, therefore, give due consideration to brush adjustment when overhauling a machine.

Fitting or Grinding-in Brushes (*Instruction Book*, Westinghouse Electric & Mfg. Co.).—When it becomes necessary to install a new set of brushes, sand paper or garnet paper may be used that is long enough to go around the commutator. It should have a lap of several inches and be so mounted on the commutator as to preclude the lapped end butting against the brushes when the machine is rotated for grinding. With many commutators the friction between the commutator bars and sandpaper (if the paper is taut) will suffice to keep the paper from slipping, especially if, when starting, the paper is given a pull in the direction of rotation by the operator. If the paper persists in slipping use a little glue to stick the under end of the paper at the lap to the commutator. All traces of the glue must be removed from the bars before putting the machine into service.

A second method is to remove the middle brush on each arm and bind the paper to the commutator by running tape or string entirely around the periphery. If necessary, also bind the paper at the inner and outer ends of the commutator. After the paper is anchored the commutator may be rotated by hand, or in any convenient way. Great care must be exercised in "grinding in" brushes in this way, as the cutting is very rapid, especially with soft brushes, and much of the life of the brush may be ground away in a very few revolutions. If after the brushes have been surfaced in the above manner,

FIG. 238.—Grinding-in brushes of a direct-current generator with a strip of sandpaper.

the trailing edge shows a poor seat on account of having had to mount the ridge due to the lap in the paper, a final surfacing should be done with very fine sandpaper by hand. The foregoing method is particularly desirable when a machine has very hard brushes, or a large number of soft brushes.

328 *ARMATURE WINDING AND MOTOR REPAIR*

It is a great time-saver after the knack of applying and anchoring the paper is understood.

With slip rings, if carbon or graphite brushes are used, the same general scheme is applicable, but if metal graphite brushes are used, emery cloth, or its equivalent, is preferable.

There are those who advocate and those who practice pulling the grinding paper in the direction of rotation in order to more accurately surface the brush. This seems logical enough on first thought, but inasmuch as the commutator is not in motion when the brushes are surfaced in this manner there is no assurance that the brush will bear the same relation to its holder (and therefore to the commutator) when the commutator is rotating and, consequently, no assurance that the contact will remain fixed. This perhaps explains why brushes frequently show perfect contact when idle, but poor contact when in service. This method of fitting the brushes, therefore, is not necessarily more dependable than other methods, though in some instances it can be recommended.

After the brushes have been fitted all dust should be carefully blown out of the commutator by compressed air. The pressure should be about, 50 to 80 pounds per square inch used with a ⅛-inch nozzle. A higher pressure may injure insulation and is not necessary.

It is important that the brushholders, whether for direct or alternating-current use, be neither too close to nor too far from the commutator or slip rings. A suitable distance is from three-sixteenths to one-quarter of an inch.

If the brushes are copper-coated, the coating should be not allowed to come in contact with the commutator or slip rings. This means that as the brushes wear the copper coating should be scraped back and not allowed to extend below the brushholder box. With proper shunts there should be no need for copper coating from an electrical standpoint, although for mechanical reasons it may be desirable as a protection for soft or structurally weak brushes.

If the toe of the brush is very sharp it is good practice to "nose off" the knife edge. This reduces breakage and militates against gouging into the commutator.

Adjustment of Brushholders (*Instruction Book*, Westinghouse Electric & Mfg. Co.).—If the commutator or slip-ring speed is low, a holder having a sluggish spring and slow action will give entirely satisfactory results but such a holder on a high-speed machine may fail miserably. High speeds require quickness of action on the part of the brush. This means a sensitive quick-acting spring and a holder designed to aid the spring. A high-speed holder, therefore, may give excellent results on low-speed machines, but a low-speed holder is not likely to approach even fair results on high-speed machines. This is a point a repairman must bear in mind when changing the speeds of direct-current machines.

The box, or part holding the brush, should be as nearly a full box as possible. Whether the rotation is against the toe or against the heel, both the toe and heel sides of the holders should have approximately equal areas for the support of the brushes. It is obvious that the shorter the box, the greater will be the shifting movement of the brush on the commutator due to looseness in the holder; and the deeper the box, the less will be the shifting. From this it follows that the boxes should not be too short, nor should the brushes be too loose in the boxes.

It is an established fact that with even very slight play in the holder the changing brush friction due to load, temperatures, etc., will result in a changing relation between the brush and the commutator, and thereby cause changing and misleading brush drops from day to day. This accounts for the difficulty in verifying, on different days, brush drops, although the loads may be identical. The neutral does not change, but the relation of brush contact to commutator does change, and the brush drops vary accordingly. Another explanation for the changes that take place in brush drops is that when brushes have been freshly "sand-papered" or "ground in" the surfaces have unglazed or soft faces, the brush drops being influenced by the porous condition of the faces, and the lubricating values of the particles liberated during the time the brush face is seating itself to the commutator. During this period the commutation, with certain kinds of graphitized brushes, may be much better than after the glaze or permanent surface forms on the brush.   Drops taken during this time may not be the same as drops taken after the brush is "faced up" and may prove seriously misleading.   Definite or reasonably permanent drop values are, as a rule, to be had only after the brush faces have reached a fixed condition.

From the foregoing it is obvious that brushes should fit snugly, but not tightly, in the holders; also that there are certain relative dimensions which are preferable between the brushes and holders and which must not be ignored if the best results are to be obtained.   For instance, the side of the holder in the direction of rotation should not have less area than the lagging side.   In fact, the side against which the brush presses should have preferably a greater area than the opposite side—certainly not less area.   With a limited area to oppose the brush, movement of the brush in the holder due to looseness, oscillation and imperfect relations between the brush and commutator, accentuates the change in the angle of contact, and results in poor commutation, as well as in mechanical and electrical damage to that part of the brush in contact with the holder.

If a brush is thin, its length and holder contact should be greater than if it is thick, for the reason that the thinner the contact area on the commutator, the less stable will be the brush on the commutator, and the greater will be the need of support from its holder.   To illustrate:—If the brush contact is a knife edge, serious chattering may result and there may be a maximum of instability, but if the knife edge be gradually removed the brush will become increasingly stable as the thickness of the brush contact increases, and if the brush angle is correct the maximum stability will be reached when the brush has its greatest thickness in contact with the commutator.   It stands to reason, therefore, that the greater the area due to thickness, the more stable will be the brush on the commutator, regardless of the holder, and that as a consequence a holder for a thick brush might not prove at all suitable for a thin brush, the speeds being equal.   If, however, there is the same amount of lost motion in the holders for a given length of thin brush and thick brush, and the brush angle is such that the thick brush moves its maximum in the holder, then the thick brush will show a greater change in its relation to the commutator than the thin brush. The thick brush, however, will not be so likely to shift its maximum on account of its bearing surface being greater than the bearing surface of the thin brush. In other words, it rests on a greater area.

Causes of Rapid Brush Wear.—Warren C. Kalb (*Power*, March 18, 1918) has found that the following electrical conditions cause rapid brush wear: Sparking, from any cause whatever; glowing of brushes; pitting of brush faces.

Glowing results from excessive current density and may be local or may cover the entire contact end of the brush. Common causes are unequal collection of current by different brushes of the same polarity and very heavy short-circuit currents in the coils undergoing commutation, which, added to the load current, bring the temperature of the carbon at the face of the brush up to the glowing point.

Pitting may result from glowing in small spots on the brush face. It is also caused at times by particles of copper becoming attached to the brush face. This causes a heavy current to localize in a small area, disintegrating the carbon and forming a small crater in which the copper embeds itself.

The increased brush wear caused by increase in current density is due to the higher temperature so created at the brush face and the consequent more rapid disintegration of the carbon at that point. Any factor tending to further increase the temperature at the brush face will add to the rapidity of wear. Some of the things having this effect are: High coefficient of friction; higher contact drop than is needed for commutation, especially on machines of low voltage and high current capacity; contact drop too low for sparking voltage, permitting heavy currents to flow in the short-circuited coil; lack of carrying capacity or very high current density.

Higher current densities are permissible where there is no sparking voltage than where there is. This is because the heating effect of commutation current is absent and higher load currents can be applied before the same temperature rise is attained.

Average volts per commutator segment may be as high as 15 to 20 volts without difficulty being encountered. Or the reactance voltage may be that high and still be neutralized by interpole flux or fringing field within sufficiently close limits to secure good commutation. But the sparking voltage—that is, the resultant between the reactance voltage and the other electromotive forces generated within the coil undergoing commutation—should be less than the contact drop of positive plus negative brush to attain perfect commutation. Inasmuch as 3 volts is about the highest brush-contact drop obtainable, it will be seen that the sparking voltages mentioned would not be neutralized within 12 to 17 volts. Such a voltage would set up excessive currents in the short-circuited coils and result in rapid burning away of the brush faces even with no-load current whatever carried by the machine.

Methods for Locating the Electrical Neutral in Setting Brushes.—The following methods have been suggested by

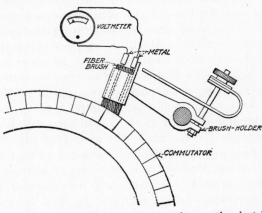

Fig. 239.—Pilot-brush method of locating brushes on the electrical neutral.

T. F. Barton (*Power*, July 16, 1918) for setting brushes on the electrical neutral in direct-current machines.

With the machine running at no load, normal speed and voltage, shift the brushes until a low-reading voltmeter shows no deflection when connected to points just inside the heel and toe of a pilot brush. The pilot brush must be the full size of the brushes used on the machine and can be made of fiber or wood with holes drilled through it to allow contact on the commutator at the desired point, which should be at the center of two adjacent commutator bars as indicated in Fig. 239.

Operate the machine as a shunt-wound commutating-pole motor, checking the speed in both directions of rotation, holding the same value of armature voltage and shunt-field current in each case. The brushes are on neutral when the speed is the same in each direction of rotation.

It is preferable to locate the brushes on the electrical neutral and make the adjustments on the commutating- and series-field windings to give the desired results. Brush shift can be used, provided the final brush position is in a satisfactory commutating zone. The capacity of a machine is not reduced by shifting the brushes if the rated voltage and current can be successfully obtained.

Angle at which Brush is Set.—When machines are not subject to reversals, the proper angle for the brush will depend upon whether the rotation is against the toe of the brush or against the heel. It also depends upon the friction coefficient of the brush. If set against the toe, the angle should approximate 35 degrees. Above 35 degrees the toe becomes very sharp and mechanically weak. If set against the heel, the angle may be from 12 degrees to 25 degrees. In instances where the brush touches more bars than required, the sharp toe can be beveled off thereby reducing the brush contact and the short-circuiting current under the brush. This also increases the mechanical strength of the brush. Whether running against toe or heel, it is good practice to round off the sharp or knife edge of the toe. This reduces the possibility of the knife-like edges digging into the commutator in case the brushes jam or become tight in their holders and at the same time protects against brush breakage.

The friction coefficient of a brush is a variable one, influenced by the characteristics of the brush, by the glazing of the contact face of the brush, the varying brush temperature due to load and spring pressure and the condition of the commutator, whether it is smooth or undercut, hot or cold, in good or poor mechanical condition. The poor mechanical condition of the commutator can be eliminated by proper attention. The other influences are permanent except as they may be modified by finding the most suitable brush angle.

Checking Brush Setting.—To check the spacing of brushes, place a strip of paper completely around the commutator under the brushes and mark the position of each set. The strip can then be removed and the distance between marks measured. If the distance varies the brush holders should be moved into the proper position. The degree of accuracy with which brushes should be set depend upon the type of machine. With interpole machines, the spacing should be more accurate than with other types of machines. The brushes on any given stud should be staggered with respect to those on adjacent studs so that the entire commutator will be covered by the brushes except a slight space at each end. This prevents grooves wearing in the commutator.

Brush Pressure.—This depends upon the character of the brush, the commutator speed in feet per minute, and the mechanical condition of the commutator. It varies from two to five pounds per square inch, the pressures generally used being from 2.5 to 3.5 pounds on commutators and from three to five pounds on slip rings. If there is a tendency for the commutator to burn, this can at times be corrected by increasing the pressure, and thereby increasing the abrasive effect of the brush sufficiently to scour out the burning and maintain a polished surface. When the mica is not undercut the brush should have sufficient abrasive effect not only to scour out possible burning of the commutator bars but also to wear and keep the mica flush with the commutator bars.

Common Brush Terms.—The following terms are frequently used in describing brush characteristics and their performance.

Contact Drop.—This refers to the drop in voltage between the brush and the commutator. It differs with different materials, different brush pressures and different loads, being between one and two volts. For a given material and given load the contact drop decreases with increased pressure and increases with the load. It varies little with changes in speed above 2500 feet per minute and but little with temperature changes under normal conditions.

Brush Friction.—The coefficient of friction depends upon the brush material, brush angle and commutator speed. With a given material and brush angle, the coefficient of friction increases with load and brush pressure and in general decreases with increased commutator speed. Increased temperatures, in actual practice, justify the conclusion that the friction coefficient increases with increased temperatures.

Specific Resistance.—The ohmic resistance of a cube having one-inch sides.

Current Density or Carrying Capacity.—This is based on the maximum continuous current capacity per square inch, without glowing, honeycombing, undue heating or sparking.

Glowing.—A brush is said to "glow" when it becomes red or incandescent in spots in proximity to the commutator. This is due to the short-circuiting current under the brush, or to the short-circuiting current in combination with the working or load current. It may also be due to a lack of homogeneity of the brush (hard or soft spots of the same or different materials having characteristics foreign to the material in the body of the brush); to incorrect brush position; to improper brush selection; to selective commutation; to the brush covering too many bars; to high mica; to the machine having inherently poor commutating characteristics due to improperly shaped or spaced main poles or commutating poles; to bad commutating pole adjustments, or to a poor distribution of the armature windings. In the event the glowing can not be stopped by correcting such of the brush or mechanical troubles as may exist; or by shifting the brushes, or readjusting the commutating poles, or both; a brush having higher current density values and less susceptible to the effects of high voltages between the commutator bars should be installed. If a suitable brush can not be had, the design of the machine itself may be subject to modification.

Honeycombing.—When brushes gradually burn away, forming small craters in their faces, they are said to "honeycomb." This is due to continuous sparking of a more or less hidden nature and may be of either a slow or rapid nature. If the growth is slow it is sometimes possible to correct it by increasing the brush pressure, thereby decreasing the contact drop and the contact arcing, and at the same time increasing the abrasive effect of the brush and grinding away the minute craters as they form. Honeycombing is due to the same causes, on a reduced scale, as glowing, and at times both may take place simultaneously on the same machine. Honeycombing has been traced directly to high mica, in combination with loose commutators; also to improperly spaced main poles; and unequal air gaps; and in non-commutating-pole machines, to an abnormal shifting or distorting of the magnetic flux. The trouble is most frequently corrected by substituting a more highly refractory brush possessing abrasive characteristics.

Hardness.—Brushes have widely varying physical densities —some being very hard, others very soft. Very hard brushes usually carry a large amount of abrasive and have a low current density or carrying capacity. The softer brushes are more highly graphite, carry abrasive to a limited extent only and have a high current density. The hardness or scleroscope reading is, therefore, indicative to a limited degree of the character of the brush.

Brush Inertia.—This has to do with the weight of the brush. The lighter the brush, the more readily will it follow the irregularities of the rotating element, and the more promptly will it respond to a given spring pressure. Again, the wearing of the commutator may not prove so great. If a light and a heavy brush prove equally satisfactory electrically on a machine, the lighter brush is preferable. If the materials from which brushes are made are heavy, it is advisable to have an increased number of small brushes, rather than a limited number of large brushes; also the spring pressure should be in excess of the pressure on lighter brushes having the same dimensions, and used for the same service.

Refractory.—Any material which resists the ordinary methods of reduction is said to be refractory. A brush, therefore, which resists wholly, or to a marked degree, high temperatures, such as the heat generated by an electric arc, is said to be highly refractory.

Peripheral Speed.—This is the speed in feet per minute of the commutator or slip ring. Peripheral speeds which vary greatly require brushes having different characteristics. Generally speaking, carbon brushes are not as suitable for high peripheral speeds as graphite brushes.

Procedure for Locating Causes of Brush Trouble.—Sparking at the brushes of a motor or generator can usually be traced to one or more of the following causes.

1. Too low brush pressure.
2. Incorrect spacing of brushes.
3. Unequal air-gaps or defective fields.
4. Brushes not operating on electrical neutral.
5. Incorrect thickness of brushes.
6. Using brushes of wrong characteristics.

The above causes are given in the order in which they should be checked up in the machine. All but two of these defects may cause abnormal short-circuit currents under the face of each brush or between two or more studs of the same polarity. This point should be kept in mind when searching out the trouble. The procedure for investigating each of the causes has been outlined by E. H. Martindale of the National Carbon Company as follows:

Before starting an investigation, eliminate the question of high mica. If the commutator runs nearly true, stone it enough to grind the mica even with the bars. If, however, the commutator is not true, or there are flat bars, turn or grind the commutator before looking further for the seat of the trouble.

Too Low Brush Pressure.—Low pressure will cause poor contact between the brushes and the commutator, and force the current to pass from one to the other through a small arc. This will burn both the brushes and commutator and produce high mica. The heat of the arcs between brushes and commutator will also increase the temperature rise. Further, poor pressure produces a high contact drop, which will also heat the commutator and brushes. This high contact drop and arcing caused by too low pressure frequently heats the brushes to a red heat, or, as we say, "to the glowing point," which is always accompanied by pitting or disintegration of the faces of the brushes. This again reduces the available contact area

22

and increases the current density through the balance of the brush.   The bad effects of too low brush pressure are greatly aggravated when the commutator is slightly elliptical or runs unbalanced.

Whether the pressure is high or low, care should be exercised to get all the brushes on one machine at a uniform pressure.   If the pressure is unequal, the brushes with the highest pressure will carry the highest current.   In many cases some brushes on a machine may carry three or four times as much current as other brushes, due to this variation in pressure. This excessive current may be enough to burn off the pigtails, overheat the brushes, and cause glowing and pitting of the brush faces.   The best value of brush pressure should be determined for any machine by trial, as it is influenced greatly by local conditions.   A pressure of from 1.75 to 3 pounds per square inch of contact surface may be used for motors and generators, and from four to seven pounds per square inch for such machines as crane motors and railway motors where vibration is comparatively severe.   However, these values are given only as an indication of best average practice, and are not always the best to use.   See table on page 342, paragraph 6 of heading No. I.

Incorrect Spacing of Brushes.—By spacing of brushes, is meant the distance between brushes on adjacent studs measured around the commutator.   Thus, in a four-pole machine the brushes on each stud should be at a distance exactly one-fourth the circumference from the brushes on the adjacent studs.   This may be checked up by counting the total number of commutator bars, then dividing by the number of poles, and setting the brushes that number of bars apart.   A better way, however, is to obtain a piece of wrapping paper of the same length as the circumference of the commutator and of the same width as the commutator.   Measure off the correct brush spacings and draw lines across the width of the paper. Replace this on the commutator, and with one set of brushes set so as to toe one mark, set the brushes on all the other studs exactly on their respective marks.   If, then, the sparking can not be entirely eliminated by shifting the brush yoke either forward or backward, examine the field coils and air gaps.

Defective Fields.—The field coils on the machine are usually connected in series so that a part of one coil may become short-circuited without becoming apparent except by test. Obtain a voltmeter with a suitable scale and test the voltage drop across each coil. The drop should be the same for each field. If one coil has higher drop than the others, the coil has been incorrectly wound. If one coil is lower than the other, the coil is either incorrectly wound or a portion of it has become short-circuited. Either case will require a new coil.

Another more common defect in compound machines is a reversal of one of the series field poles. For this test use a compass and check the shunt as well as the series coil. First pass current through the shunt coils. Next, bring the compass near one coil; mark it either South or North, depending on which end of the needle is attracted to the field pole. If the bearings of the compass are not perfectly free, use care not to bring the needle suddenly too close to the pole, as it is easy to reverse the magnetism in the needles of moderate-priced compasses. After marking one pole, proceed around the machine and test in the same way each pole. The needle should reverse direction at each pole. If two adjacent poles are found to attract the same end of the needle, one coil is reversed.

Field coils can also be tested for polarity by two ordinary iron nails as described on page 136.

After all the shunt fields have been tested, current from some source should be passed through the series fields only, care being taken to see that this current flows in the same direction as when the machine is in operation. Nearly all compound machines are cumulative compound, in which case each series field should attract the same end of the needle as the shunt field attracts. The differential compound winding is used only when it is desired to have a rise of speed with an increase of load, and is not in extensive use. In such machines, however, the series fields produce poles of opposite polarity to those produced by the shunt fields.

Unequal Air Gaps.—Unequal air gaps may be the cause of serious trouble, particularly in "lap" or "parallel wound" machines. Poor centering of the armature when the machine was assembled, may be the cause or it may result later from worn bearings. The wear may be either at the bottom of the bearings, due to the weight of the armature, or on a belt-connected machine, at the side of the machine, due to the pull of the belt. This may be checked mechanically by measurement with thin sheets of metal or fiber. For lap wound machines a more accurate method, however, is to disconnect the bus bars or leads which connect the studs of the same polarity. Then, without any load on the machine, each stud will be independent, and with a low-reading volt-meter any difference between the voltage generated under the various poles can be detected. This is valuable on a lap wound machine, but on a wave wound machine the variations are equalized and the mechanical method is more reliable.

After having correctly spaced the brushes, checked the drop across the field coils, the polarity of the field poles and the uniformity of the air gaps, it should be possible to shift the brushes to a point where no sparking will appear with a steady load on the machine. If the sparking reappears with a variation in load, either the brushes are of incorrect thickness or the neutral field—that is, the distance between adjacent pole tips—is too small.

Incorrect Thickness of Brushes.—The best way to investigate this sparking is with a voltmeter reading about 5 volts. Take two ordinary lead pencils and trim down one side of each pencil as much as possible without exposing the lead. Near the top of each pencil cut a groove deep enough to expose the lead and attach a piece of lamp cord or other flexible wire to each pencil. Remove one brush and hold the pencils in the brushholder with the points on the commutator and the flat side of one pencil against the front edge of the brushholder and the flat side of the other pencil against the back edge of the holder. This will give the voltage generated across the brush, or, in other words, the "commutation voltage." Now shift the brushes to a point where they do not spark and read the "commutation voltage." Increase the load until the brushes spark and again read the "commutation voltage." If it has decreased, the brushes are too narrow—that is, the period of commutation is too brief.

The remedy is to use thicker brushes or to shift the brushes with each change of load. This condition, however, seldom obtains.

An increase in the commutation voltage indicates that the brushes are too thick—that is, they span too many bars or the neutral field is too small. This thickness of the brushes may easily be changed by cutting down the face of the brush with a hack saw or file, leaving the body of the brush the proper size to fit the brushholders. This will help the trouble, and if the sparking does not entirely cease, it may be necessary to widen the neutral field by increasing the distance between adjacent pole pieces. This can be done by filing the edges of the pole faces.

Brushes of Wrong Characteristics.—If none of above remedies cure the sparking, the machine is being operated with brushes not adapted to the service. The next step should be to give a manufacturer full details regarding the machine and ask for recommendation of a brush best adapted to the machine and service, since carbon brush manufacturers maintain an engineering department capable to give valuable advice along this line.

As a guide in the location of other brush troubles, the accompanying table will be found useful.

Possible Causes of Brush Troubles on Motors and Generators and Their Remedies Compiled by E. H. Martindale of the National Carbon Company

I. CAUSES AND REMEDIES FOR SPARKING AT BRUSHES

1. *Brushes off electrical neutral.* Shift to neutral by trial, or set on neutral by means of voltmeter.

2. *Brushes spanning too many bars.* Trim down faces of brushes for short distance back from end or, if holders are clamp type, order thinner brushes.

3. *Brush studs not parallel with the commutator bars.* Bend the brush studs or grind or shim under the bolts which fasten the studs to the yoke.

4. *Incorrect brush spacing.* Check the spacing by counting the number of bars between studs or by placing a strip of paper around the commutator with divisions marked off equal to the number of studs, and correct the spacing by rotating the brush studs or the brushholders on the studs.

5. *Brushes tight in brush holders.*   Clean the holders with gasoline and if brushes are still tight, sandpaper them down or file out the holders carefully.

6. *Brush pressure too low.*   Pressure should be $1\frac{3}{4}$ to $2\frac{1}{4}$ lb. per square inch cross-section for stationary motors and generators, $2\frac{1}{2}$ to 4 lb. for elevator and mill motors, 3 to 5 lb. for crane motors, 4 to 7 lb. for rail way motors.

7. *Too low contact drop of brush.*   Consult a brush manufacturer.

8. *Insufficient abrasive action of brushes.*   Use a commutator stone or more abrasive brushes.

9. *High mica.*   Use abrasive brushes, a commutator stone or undercut the mica.

10. *Chattering.*   See heading No. VII for remedies.

11. *Poor adjustment of interpoles.*   Consult the manufacturer of the machine.

12. *Overloads.*   Undercut the mica, use low-friction brushes and check up all causes for short-circuit currents (see heading No. IV) to reduce temperatures as much as possible.

13. *Open circuit in armature coil.*   Rewind that part of the armature.

14. *Loose end connection.*   Scrape and resolder all defective connections.

15. *Worn bearings.*   Shim or renew the bearings.

16. *Unequal air gaps.*   Shim the short poles or grind off the faces of the long poles, or if from worn bearings, see paragraph above.

17. *Short-circuit currents be'ween brush studs caused by unbalanced armature winding.*   Consult the manufacturer of the machine.

18. *Eccentric commutator on high-speed machine.*   Turn or grind.

19. *Poor belt lacing.*   Re-lace or still better use a continuous belt.

20. *Pound of reciprocating engine driving the machine.*

21. *Unstable foundation.*

22. *Cross currents between generators operated in parallel driven by reciprocating engines due to variation in angular speed of engines.*   Use heavier flywheel.

II. CAUSES AND REMEDIES OF FLAT SPOTS ON COMMUTATOR

1. *Any form of sparking.*   See heading No. 1.

2. *High bar.*   Tighten the commutator bolts and turn or grind the commutator.

3. *Low bar.*   Use commutator stone or turn or grind the commutator.

4. *Eccentric commutator on high-speed machine causing the brush to jump from the commutator at the high spots.*   Turn or grind the commutator.

5. *Surges of load current due to short-circuit on the line or an instantaneous high peak load.*

6. *Mechanically unbalanced armature.*   Place on balancing ways and add weight at lightest point.

7. *Difference in hardness of commutator bars.* Undercut the mica and use non-abrasive brushes.

8. *Difference in hardness of mica.* Undercut the mica and use non-abrasive brushes.

III. CAUSES AND REMEDIES FOR BLACKENING OF COMMUTATOR

1. *Sparking.* See heading No. I for causes and remedies.
2. *Too much lubricant.* Clean commutator with gasoline.

IV. CAUSES OF HEATING IN A MOTOR OR GENERATOR WITH REMEDIES

1. *Severe sparking.* See heading No. I.
2. *Short-circuit currents.*
   (*a*) Brushes off neutral.
   (*b*) Faulty brush spacing.
   (*c*) Too thick brushes.
   (*d*) Unequal air gaps.
   (*e*) Crooked brush studs.
   (*f*) Too low contract drop of brushes.
   (*g*) Unbalanced armature.
For remedies of items *a* to *g* see same causes under heading No. 1.
3. *Too high or too low brush pressure.* See paragraph 6 under heading No. I.
4. *High-friction brushes.* Undercut mica and use low friction brush.
5. *Commutator too small.* Consult manufacturer of machine.
6. *Too high a ratio of brush area to commutator surface.* Use fewer brushes of higher carrying capacity and lower friction.
7 *Overloads.* See paragraph 12 under heading No. I.
8. *Chattering of brushes.* See heading No. VII.

V. CAUSES AND REMEDIES FOR HONEY-COMBING OF BRUSH FACES

1. *Short-circuit currents.* See paragraph 2 under heading No. IV.
2. *Too low brush pressure.* See paragraph 6 under heading No. I.
3. *Brushes of insufficient carrying capacity.* Consult a brush manufacturer.

VI. CAUSES AND REMEDIES FOR BRUSHES PICKING UP COPPER

1. *Heavy short-circuit currents.* See paragraph 2 under heading No. IV.
2. *Sand under the brush faces.* Wipe brush face carefully after sandpapering either brushes or commutator.
3. *Commutator not thoroughly cleaned after turning.* Finish the surface with a commutator stone after turning.

4. *Collection of copper dust by lubricant in abrasive brushes.*   Undercut the mica and use non-abrasive brushes.

5. *Electrolytic action.*   Change the grade of brush; better consult a brush manufacturer.

VII. CAUSES AND REMEDIES FOR BRUSHES CHATTERING

1. *High-friction brushes.*   Change the grade or pressure.
2. *Rough commutator.*   Use a commutator stone.
3. *Dirty commutator.*   Clean with gasoline.
4. *High mica.*   Use a commutator stone or undercut the mica.
5. *Wide slots with thin brushes.*   Fill the slots with commutator cement.
6. *High bars.*   Tighten the commutator bolts and turn or grind the commutator.
7. *Flat spots.*   Use commutator stone unless the flat spots are too large for stoning, in which case turn or grind the commutator.
8. *Brush operating at the wrong bevel, frequently found where brushes are operating in a stubbing position with angles of less than 20 degrees.*   Change the grade of brush or angle of operation.   Better consult a brush manufacturer or the manufacturer of the machine.

VIII. CAUSES AND REMEDIES FOR LOOSENING OF BRUSH SHUNTS

1. *Poor workmanship in attaching shunts.*
2. *Insufficient carrying capacity.*   Consult a brush manufacturer.
3. *Heating.*   See heading No. IV.
4. *Vibration.*   See heading No. VII.
5. *Combination of heating and vibration.*
6. *Loose terminal screws causing unequal distribution of load.*
7. *Unequal brush pressure causing unequal distribution of load.*   See that all brush pressures are uniform and conform to recommendations given in paragraph 6 under heading No. I.
8. *Heavy short-circuit currents between different brushes.*   See *b, d, e, g,* of paragraph 2, under heading No. IV.

CHAPTER XIV

INSPECTION AND REPAIR OF MOTOR STARTERS, MOTORS AND GENERATORS

On account of the variety of troubles that may be corrected in a simple way at one time but require more extensive repairs at others, it is a very difficult matter to lay down hard and fast rules that will always work out on every repair job when followed to the letter. The ability to know when temporary repairs will suffice and when a permanent job must be done at once, comes largely from experience. The term repairman has been used throughout this book as a title that a good engineer can bear with pride when he measures up to all the qualifications of the man who in the majority of cases knows what to do and just how to do it and seldom guesses without a good percentage of the probabilities of being right in his favor. The main difference between the designer and the repairman is that the former must know *what* to do while the latter must know *how* to do it. A capable repairman combines both qualifications through years of experience. One of the best ways of saving time for the young engineer entering the repair field, is to serve as an apprentice with a large electrical manufacturing company. In this way through association with those who design and those who build and test, a great deal of information is absorbed that only years of experience from one job at a time will make possible. This fund of information is essential in an intelligent discussion of any repair job or the presentation of rules or suggestions for looking for the trouble and then actually making the repair.

In the accompanying pages there are presented suggestions for the repairman in the inspection and repair of motors and generators prepared by H. S. Rich, at the suggestion of the author and published in the *Electrical Record*, October, 1918 to April, 1919. These suggestions are accompanied with exploded views of the device discussed, so that the repairman can form a mental picture of the work described which will approximate as closely as possible the impression that would be secured by actually doing the work.

Cost of Repairs for Polyphase Motors.—For the purpose of furnishing estimates for repairing polyphase motors that will guide the repairman who has had a limited experience of repairwork, George A. Schneider has compiled the accompanying table (*Journal of Electricity*, May 1, 1917) from costs of actual repair jobs which he has handled. The table as presented has been revised to take into consideration the cost of materials entering into repairs for the year 1917. The data refers particularly to 60-cycle, two and three-phase, squirrel-cage motors wound for the standard voltages of 110 to 550.

For most of the sizes listed the costs were arrived at by taking the average cost of repairs for a given frame and then applying this cost to the various ratings built in that frame. This will be apparent by comparing the costs for the different ratings. Take for example, frame G. The cost of rewinding the stator is $34.75. This figure has been applied to the following ratings all of which are built in that frame: 1 horsepower, 900 revolutions per minute; 1.5 horsepower, 1200 revolutions per minute, and 3 horsepower, 1800 revolutions per minute. The frame sizes specified do not apply to any particular line of motors, but were arbitrarily chosen for the purpose of this table. However, the relative output of a given frame at the different speeds will be found to agree quite closely with several lines of induction motors on the market.

These estimates may also be used equally well for motors of other frequencies by taking the figures applying to a 60-cycle rating built in the same frame. This comparison can be easily made by referring to the manufacturer's rating and dimension sheets for that particular line of motors. The tables may be further applied to slip-ring or phase-wound motors, since the cost of rewinding the rotor of such a machine will not differ materially from the cost of rewinding its stator. On this basis the cost of completely rewinding a 10 horsepower, 1800 revolutions per minute slip-ring motor built in frame J will be $119, or $59.50 for the rotor or stator separately.

Cost of Repairs for 60-cycle Polyphase Motors Based on a Large Number of Repair Jobs

Horse-power	Synchronous speed in rpm.	Frame size	Rewinding stator	Re-soldering rotor	Bearing linings, per set of two	Painting	Re-crating
0.50	1200	C	$26.25	$2.50	$1.35	$1.00	$1.00
0.50	1800	A	24.25	2.25	1.35	1.00	1.00
0.75	1200	E	28.00	3.00	1.85	1.00	1.00
0.75	1800	B	24.25	2.25	1.35	1.00	1.00
1.00	900	G	34.75	4.00	3.10	1.50	1.50
1.00	1200	F	28.50	3.00	1.85	1.25	1.00
1.00	1800	C	26.25	2.50	1.35	1.00	1.00
1.50	1200	G	34.75	4.00	3.10	1.50	1.50
1.50	1800	E	28.00	3.00	1.85	1.00	1.00
2.00	1200	G	34.75	4.00	3.10	1.50	1.50
2.00	1800	F	28.50	3.00	1.85	1.25	1.00
3.00	900	I	53.50	6.50	5.25	1.50	1.50
3.00	1200	H	48.50	6.75	3.55	1.50	1.50
3.00	1800	G	34.75	4.00	3.10	1.50	1.50
5.00	900	K	73.75	8.75	8.05	1.75	2.00
5.00	1200	I	53.50	6.50	5.25	1.50	1.50
5.00	1800	H	48.50	4.75	3.55	1.50	1.50
7.50	900	L	70.75	12.00	7.85	2.00	2.50
7.50	1200	J	59.50	7.00	6.60	1.75	2.00
7.50	1800	I	53.50	6.50	5.25	1.50	1.50
10.00	900	M	75.00	13.25	7.85	2.00	2.50
10.00	1200	L	70.75	12.00	7.85	2.00	2.50
10.00	480	J	59.50	7.00	6.60	1.75	2.00
15.00	720	P	93.75	15.50	10.25	3.00	4.00
15.00	900	N	71.25	14.25	10.25	3.00	4.00
15.00	1200	M	75.00	13.25	7.85	2.00	2.50
15.00	1800	K	73.75	8.75	8.05	1.75	2.00
20.00	600	S	156.25	19.00	12.10	3.25	6.00
20.00	900	P	93.75	15.50	10.25	3.00	4.00
20.00	1200	N	71.25	14.25	10.25	3.00	4.00
20.00	1800	M	75.00	13.25	7.85	2.00	2.50
25.00	600	S	156.25	19.00	12.10	3.25	6.00
25.00	720	S	156.25	19.00	12.10	3.25	6.00
25.00	900	R	143.75	17.75	12.00	3.25	6.00
25.00	1200	P	93.75	15.50	10.25	3.00	4.00
35.00	600	T	187.50	20.50	19.95	3.50	6.25
35.00	720	S	156.25	19.00	12.10	3.25	6.00
35.00	900	S	156.25	19.00	12.10	3.25	6.00
35.00	1200	R	143.75	17.75	12.00	3.25	6.00
50.00	600	V	218.75	21.75	30.85	3.50	6.25
50.00	720	V	218.75	21.75	30.85	3.50	6.25
50.00	900	T	187.50	20.50	19.95	3.50	6.25
50.00	1200	S	156.25	19.00	12.10	3.25	6.00

Points to Consider when Estimating Cost of a Motor Repair Job.—The estimates for rewinding the stator or resoldering the rotor given in the accompanying table do not include any preliminary work required to put the stator structure in fit condition to receive the new winding or work required on the rotor before the actual resoldering can be started. In other words, the figures cover only the actual rewinding or resoldering, as the case may be. However, this preliminary work is frequently necessary and must always be considered in making up estimates. It is due to a number of causes.

For example, the motor bearing linings may have worn down sufficiently to allow the rotor to rub against the stator. If the motor has operated very long in this condition the laminations of either or both stator and rotor will probably be damaged, which may require considerable work to put them into their original condition. Again, a defective or broken bearing may injure the shaft. Sometimes this damage will be serious enough to require a new shaft. New bearing linings will probably be required in either case. Burned-out windings may also be accompanied by fusing of parts of the stator laminations. These fused portions must necessarily be removed before actual replacement of the coils can be commenced.

In a rotor which has been badly overheated, allowing the melted solder to be thrown out, arcing is frequently set up between the rotor bars and the end rings causing serious burning. When this occurs, new end rings are often needed either for one or both ends of the rotor or perhaps part of the bars will have to be replaced. With bolted end ring construction there is also liability of trouble. The expansion of the end rings caused by the excessive heat, tends to snap the bolts between the rotor bars and the rings, producing the most favorable conditions for arcing. Burnouts of this kind, for either soldered or bolted construction, are quite common in connection with motors which have been started from time to time under loads which have required heavy starting torque with long periods of acceleration. Two- or three-phase motors allowed to operate single-phase for a considerable length of time may also develop troubles of this kind. Very often the rotor will be badly damaged while the stator has only been only slightly overheated. Conversely, in some cases the stator will be burned out while the rotor is uninjured.

From these points it will be clear that estimates for repairing motors should not be made until after the motor has been given a careful inspection for otherwise there is liable to be a wide discrepancy between the estimated and the actual cost of making the repair. In furnishing an estimate under conditions where a detailed inspection is not possible, details of what the estimate covers should be given with a notation of additional repairs that may be necessary after an inspection. The data of the table on page 347, is based on a large number of repair jobs and is conservative for labor and material conditions in 1917.

I. INSPECTION AND OVERHAULING OF DIRECT-CURRENT MOTOR STARTERS

The following points to be considered by the repairman when inspecting and repairing a motor starter are given by T. H. Reardon (*Electrical Review*, May 25, 1918).

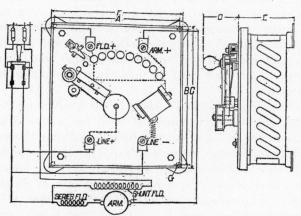

Fig. 240.—A starting rheostat with no voltage release for use with shunt and compound direct-current motors.

In direct-current motor service the ordinary rheostat in which an arm moves over contacts arranged on the arc of a circle is the most convenient starting device. All such rheostats are provided with an electromagnet which holds the arm in place after it has been brought up to the last notch or full running position. This magnet loses its power if the current goes off the line and the arm flies back to the starting position. The arm is returned to the starting position by a spring, which is always acting in opposition to the pull of the magnet that tends to keep the arm in last-notch position as long as the magnet is energized. If the pull of the spring is too great, which somtimes occurs when an inexperienced man makes certain changes in the way of correcting things, the pull of the magnet will not be sufficient to hold the arm in place when it is brought up and the arm will fly back. Conversely, if the strength of the spring becomes reduced, which often happens when motors are placed in damp places, or worse still, where dampness and certain bleaching agents (such as chlorine and oxides of chlorine) act jointly in bringing about metallic deterioration in apparatus, steel springs will be found corroded to such an extent that they do not possess their original strength and elasticity. As a preventive measure, springs as well as all other metal parts exposed to corrosive action should receive a drop or two of a mineral oil or be slightly smeared with vaseline occasionally to prevent such deterioration. The pull of the spring and the pull of the magnet are balanced against each other, but there are other conditions that must be taken into account in making adjustments.

After the current ceases to flow in the low-voltage release-magnet coils, which will not be until the motor comes to rest (the motor acting as a generator will maintain this current until the motor stops), the magnet will still exert a considerable pull on its armature due to the relatively large amount of residual magnetism that remains in the core of an electromagnet after the current has ceased to circulate and before the armature is pulled away from the magnet poles. An arm that will not fly back to starting point when the motor stops, if moved back by hand and then brought up again, will not stick. In certain cases, however, it may stick and when it does do so it is not due to any pull exerted by the magnet but it will probably be found that the sliding contact on the bottom of the arm bears so hard against the contacts that the strength of the spring is not sufficient to overcome this braking effect due to the friction of the shoe moving over the contacts.

Sometimes this friction effect may exist only on one contact, one contact standing higher than the rest, and if this particular contact happens to be next to the magnet, the movement of the arm will be retarded before the arm has a chance to acquire any momentum that would carry it back provided it once got started.

If the magnet pull due to residual magnetism after current circulation ceases should be responsible for the arm sticking after the motor stops (this will very rarely be the case, however), the keeper can be lightly tinned over with a soldering iron, thus placing a certain amount of reluctance in the magnetic circuit of the magnet and its keeper. A drop of oil occasionally on the stud on which the arm is pivoted will help in securing free movement.

II. INSPECTION AND OVERHAULING OF AUTO-STARTERS FOR A.-C. MOTORS

When examining and testing an auto-starter to locate troubles, T. H. Readron (*Electrical Review*, May 25, 1918) mentions the following points as possible causes of the troubles:

Auto-starters are generally used for starting alternating-current motors of the induction type when the motors are above five horsepower. Small motors are usually thrown directly on the line without any starting device and, although the starting current is four or five times greater than the normal current, the fluctuation, as a rule, is not serious enough to necessitate the use of an auto-starter. Usual practice is as follows: Polyphase induction motors up to 5 hp. are thrown directly on the line. Motors of 7.5 to 30 hp. are started by means of a star-delta switch which is not an induction starter but simply a switch operating in oil and changing the connections of the motor from star on starting to delta on running. The motor in that case is provided with six terminals to accommodate the change. Auto-starters or auto-transformers are mostly used for squirrel-cage induction motors of considerable size or over 30 hp.

The auto-starter being adapted for alternating-current work, differs from the rheostat in that it possesses not only some resistance but considerable reactance in damping current flow, while the rheostat possesses resistance only. Moreover, the rheostat is a step-by-step starting device; its arm is to be moved slowly over the contacts, while the auto-starter has but one step from starting to running and the handle should always be thrown promptly from one position to the other position.

FIG. 241.—An auto-starter or compensator for use with alternating-current squirrel cage induction motors.

The accompanying diagram (Fig. 242) shows the plan of the auto-starter as usually constructed. Six wires are brought to the rocker cylinder of the switch, which is moved by the switch handle. One wire is a feed or line wire, the wire next goes to the motor, the next wire is line and the next one motor again, etc. When the switch is thrown to the starting position, the six contacts on the switch cylinder meet six contacts on the starting block and the current from a line contact on the switch cylinder passes to the contact on the starting block through one coil of the reactance and back to the next contact on the switch cylinder, and thence to the motor.

When the handle is thrown to the running position, only three contacts on the switch cylinder make contact— these are the motor contacts on the switch cylinder and they meet three contacts on the running block, which contacts are directly connected to the line wires either through fuses or overload relays.

The line contacts on the switch cylinder, when the cylinder is thrown to running position, do not connect with anything— they stand clear or dead-ended. These contacts on the switch cylinder can be identified by using a lamp bank and making contact with them, the switch handle being in off position. A light will be obtained between line and line.

The first trouble to look for is burned or imperfect contacts.

After taking the oil pan off the switch contacts can be inspected without any trouble.

If the contacts are burned or rough, they should be taken off and filed smooth or replaced with new ones. The same applies to the fingers that meet the contacts. The handle should be thrown to one position and then the fingers should be tried to see that they press firmly and evenly against the contacts on the switch cylinder. If they do not, throw the switch handle to off position and they can easily be bent inward sufficiently to make a firm contact. It will be well not to bend them too much at once, for if this is done, they will not slide over the switch cylinder contacts properly.

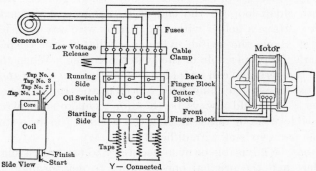

FIG. 242.—Connections for a common form of auto-starter for alternating-current motors.

In regard to broken wires, the wires that are attached to the switch cylinder, six in number, are bent slightly every time that the switch handle is moved. These wires now and then break off. The other six wires that enter the auto-starter go to fixed immovable contacts and rarely cause trouble. To save labor, test everything out as far as possible with the lamp bank or some other way equally good, depending upon what kind of testing apparatus there is at hand.

It will be well to bear in mind that a ring obtained with a magneto or a light obtained with a lamp bank is not always conclusive. Instances are quite common where a wire or cable breaks inside of the insulation and there afterward remains a sheath of metallic oxide or smudge that will pass cur-

23

rent enough to give a dull light on a lamp bank or a feeble ring on the magneto.   When it is decided that a certain wire is broken, take out the two screws that hold that particular contact to the switch cylinder and pull down the terminal with a pair of pliers.

If the wire is intact, it will resist a strong pull.   If the wire is broken and is held by the insulation, it will easily pull apart.   If it pulls down through the switch cylinder sufficiently, attach a piece of new wire or cable to it and use it for a snake to draw the new wire into place, pulling at the top where the wires enter the auto-starter.   If this does not work, draw the broken wire out at the top at all events and get a piece of stiff brass or steel wire, about No. 14 gauge.   Bend a smooth small loop on the end of it and pass it down from above.   Have a helper with a small hook wire watch for it and hook it above the switch cylinder so that it can be passed through the proper hole in the switch cylinder.   When this is done, the terminal can be soldered on at the lower wire and the terminal drawn back and wire spliced at the stop of the auto-starter.   It should always be the aim to make such a repair if possible without disassembling the parts of the auto-starter as such parts go back with difficulty.

It may be advisable or even necessary to use a wire slightly smaller than the original one in order to get through tight places.   There will be no decided objection to doing this as the cross-section of copper is always sufficiently ample to justify a slight reduction when such a reduction in size is really necessary.

The following method of insulating leads on auto-starters will prevent siphoning of oil:

(a) Remove insulation from each lead just above the highest oil level for a distance of two inches.

(b) Sweat the strands of the cable thoroughly together so as to close up all spaces between the conductors for a distance of one inch.

(c) Insulate the lead with treated cloth tape, wrapping the tape tightly around the conductor and brushing each layer with insulating varnish while wrapping.

(d) Extend the wrapping to tape with three overlapping layers at least one inch on the insulation at each end of the bare section.

III. INSPECTION AND OVERHAULING OF DRUM TYPE CONTROLLERS

The drum type controller is used with variable speed shop motors, on trolley cars, elevated, subway and railway trains, on cranes, and on some types of elevators. This controller may be mounted in any position so as to permit handy control. On trolley and railway cars, it is placed vertically with the lever on top. For shop use it is sometimes mounted on a machine or on the wall upside down, being well out of the way and yet having its lever within reach. On some elevators it is

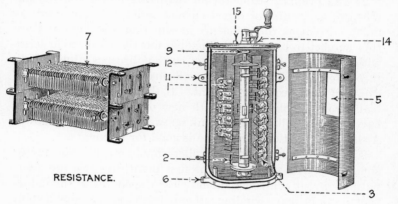

RESISTANCE.

CONTROLLER.

Fig. 243.—Gridiron resistance used with drum type controller shown at the right for variable speed motors. (Figures refer to numbers of paragraphs of text.)

installed horizontally and operated with a steel cable running over a grooved sheave wheel. Some drum type controllers have only a single arrangement of segments with the reversing connections operated by a separate lever, while others have duplicate segments, half of which are arranged to operate on reverse.

1*. The hard usage to which a controller is subjected usually will loosen some of its screws or connections, so these should be looked over often and kept tight. The line connections

* The following paragraph numbers refer to the parts in Figs. 243 and 244.

to the fingers and the segments themselves require the most attention.. A finger generally carries a copper block of various bevelled shapes, riveted to a stiff phosphor bronze strip which provides the necessary tension and is regulated by an adjusting screw. The fingers should be provided with flexible stranded copper pig-tails which carry the current. If the spring carries the current, it is liable to heat and loose its tension. Set the fingers so that they can not be jammed under a segment instead of riding upon it. If any are badly worn renew them, likewise overheated springs and defective pig-tails.

2. The primary segments for induction motor control and the field segments for direct-current motors do not carry as much current as the armature or slip ring segments and are thus subject to less wear. The ones mostly worn are in series with the slip rings or the direct-current brushes, thus if contacts are very poor the motor will not operate or it may run slowly if on alternating current. If the copper segments are badly worn, replace them with new ones having the proper curvature and with counter sunk screws tightly fastened down. A slight lubrication of vaseline is good for segments.

3. The direct-current controller should supply the motor shunt field with current on the first point, likewise the alternating-current controller should close the circuit to the induction motor primary winding either before or at the same instant that the armature receives current. If these contacts are not properly made at the first point, fuses are liable to blow as the result of no field.

4. Insulating partitions are often provided between the segments to prevent arcing over. If these are badly burned, renew them.

5. Controller diagram connections which are generally pasted inside of the cover are worth saving. If constant arcing is liable to deface the diagram, either provide a duplicate for reserve or remove the one from the cover and mark on it the controller number, etc., for identification.

6. Test with a magneto on a dead controller, or with a test lamp on a live one for any possible stray ground to the casing. It should test free, as a ground would likely bother the operator.

7. The controller resistance is usually of the gridiron type

which allows any speed continuously. This resistance has no connection with the primary winding or line segments. See that no grids are broken, as they are quite frail. A few extras in stock are handy. Test the resistance for a ground to its own frame. A perforated sheet iron hood should be used for its protection.

8. The conductors from the controller may be carried in conduit to the motor, and the motor, conduit and controller

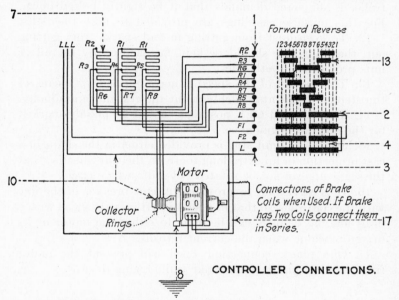

FIG. 244.—Wiring connections for a drum type controller.

should be well connected to a good ground pipe to protect the operator against sneak currents.

9. The different points or stops on the controller are determined by a notched star wheel just underneath the top cover. If its spring is broken or very weak, provide the good tension needed for positive operation, as placing the drum between contacts will cause trouble.

10. If the motor fails to run when the controller is on the second or third point, shut it off and test for current at the line contacts with a test lamp. Further testing of the motor

primary connections at the controller contacts may reveal an open circuit. If the motor still refuses to run, test the resistance for open circuit and look carefully over the slip-ring brushes for poor contacts. Exposed wiring between the motor, resistance and controller may get broken and thus stop its operation One open slip ring connection will cause slow speed.

11. The sudden and repeated operations to which a controller is subjected demands that it be tightly bolted down. For this purpose cast lugs are provided to take the bolts.

12. To keep dust from getting in and sparks from getting out, the front case should be kept fastened on by the finger nuts provided on both sides.

13. The control of the speed is accomplished by means of the stepped segments which cut out the resistance gradually.

14. The ON and OFF positions should be plainly marked for the operator's guidance.

15. See that a limit stop is provided either in the shape of a cast projection or an extra long tooth on the star wheel, so that the segments can not be rotated beyond a whole circle.

16. It is advisable to provide a circuit breaker in the line with the controller so that in case it is left on part speed with a dead line, no damage can be done to either the motor or its driven machine when the current returns.

17. One phase connection open will prevent the motor from starting, and it may smoke while trying to start.

IV. OVERHAULING A LARGE COMPOUND D.-C. MOTOR

All motors should be inspected and given a general overhauling at least once a year. Large sizes should not be slighted in any detail just because they look rugged and appear to stand everlasting work. Close observation of all parts and connections will often reveal some surprising defects. However small, they should not be allowed to go unattended.

When repairing a motor, it is advisable to remove all fuses and put them into the tool kit or your pocket so that by no chance current can be switched onto the motor when not expected.

In case of a belt drive, shift the motor, slip off the belt and tie the latter up to something near by.   If direct-connected, open the coupling by removing all the bolts.   Replace the nuts on them and tie the whole bunch together to save losing them.

If the motor is suspended, it would be well to lower it with two chain tackles and disassemble it on the floor, as its parts are too heavy to carry down a ladder and rather large to step over on a scaffold.   If on a shelf or platform, slinging it to the floor is often not very difficult.

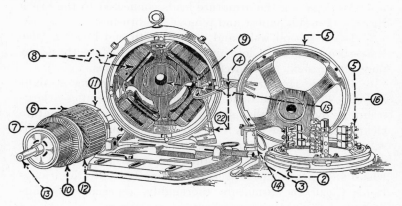

Fig. 245.—Essential parts of a compound direct-current motor.   (Figures refer to number of paragraphs of text.)

1*.   Remove the key and pulley, first marking or measuring the latter's location, which will help in replacing it.   If direct-connected, remove the commutator end shield to allow the armature shaft to draw open the coupling.   Mark location of the coupling on the shaft.   If the key is very tight, remove the set screws and pour kerosene into the holes, which will work around the key, then some motor oil may be dropped in to lubricate the key-way.   By lightly tapping proper shaped drifts, the key can often be started in a few minutes without a lot of battering and damage.   When the key is removed if the pulley is tight on the shaft, more kerosene will help. Also by using an 18-inch monkey wrench on the rim, it

* The following paragraph numbers refer to the parts shown in Fig. 245.

can often be started. Do not hammer on the rim, it may crack. If made of paper it will flatten. Strike a hard wood block butted against the hub or drive thin wedges behind. Tie the key and set screws to the pulley when removed for security.

2. Before removing commutator end shield, mark the position of the rocker arm which may get shifted.

3. With the pulley removed, try to lift the shaft a trifle in the bearing lining to learn if it is worn out of true. A year's wear may cause the armature to strike the lower pole shoe. It is well to observe this before disassembling.

4. Mark or tag the armature leads connected to the brush rigging, then disconnect and remove the brushes.

5. Drain the oil wells and remove both end housings also the brush rigging. Close up the oil wells before the screw plugs get mislaid. Be careful of the glass gauges.

6. Remove the armature to a pile of blocking straight ahead. This can be done with one lift by slipping a large iron pipe over the pulley shaft, which will carry the armature clear through and two feet beyond without dropping it. A suspended motor can be disassembled to best advantage on the floor. Set the armature on some burlap and not where any metal clips will imbed themselves into the insulation. Clean the armature thoroughly, especially the air-ducts.

7. If the commutator has enough stock left and is rough or grooved, turn it down in a lathe, taking only very fine cuts with a diamond pointed tool. Then polish with oil and No. 00 sandpaper, but not emery. If the commutator is badly worn down, a new one should be on hand and replaced, having the same number of segments.

8. Blow the dust out of the field frame and from around the field coils, or scrape with a stick but use no metal bar or knife. Wipe out clean with waste and some benzine. Examine the insulation of the field coils, shunt and series field leads, and if any abrasion is found use tape, thick armature varnish or shellac for insulation. If the field coils are loose, tighten the bolts usually found outside the frame. If a coil is burned out, remove and re-wind Weigh the wire that is stripped off and replace the same size and weight carefully wound on and

well insulated. In replacing a field coil, its shunt or series polarity are liable to be uncertain. To determine this, properly connect to the field windings three or four cells of dry battery and with a magnetic compass explore the polarity of each pole, marking it with chalk for reference. For both the series and the shunt windings, the two markings should be similar on any one pole, then the fields coincide. The newly wound coil should have an opposite sign to the coil on either side; if not, change its connections and test repeatedly to *make sure*, for the operation of the motor depends on the field polarities. Use armature varnish or shellac on all coils and leads.

9. Do not paint the inner surface of pole shoes.

10. If the commutator leads are loose solder solidly and neatly, being careful not to let hot solder drop down behind the commutator as it is liable to cause a short circuit.

11. If the armature has been striking the pole shoes, the banding wires will likely be polished in spots and partly worn through. Even if they are only loose, repair them now by slipping under plenty of shellaced mica.

12. If any armature coil is burned out, slip in a new one and thus put it in good shape with full power.

13. Caliper the armature shaft at both ends. If badly worn or cut a new one should be fitted in so that new bearing linings will fit perfectly.

14. If the bearing linings are worn enough to allow loose play of the shaft, put new ones in the end shields. Extra linings should be kept in stock the year round as it will save hours delay when one wears out suddenly from poor oil feed. Remove the set screw and strike against a hard wood block on the outer end of the lining but avoid damaging the oil rings. Usually each end has a different sized lining so that the proper pair are needed. If the oil rings get damaged true them at once. Try the linings on the shaft to see if they fit the bore. If linings are split they are easily removed. Fit the new ones exactly into place under their set screws no matter how long it takes, for if a lining ever turns over out of place it will run hot and be ruined. If the old linings are re-babbitted on the premises, have oil grooves and channels

cut in for lubrication and scrape the insides for a perfectly snug fit.

15. Flush out the oil wells with gasoline or benzine and wipe them out dry with cheese cloth, as waste is liable to leave threads to entangle the oil rings.

16. Clean the brush rigging especially around the insulators on the holder bars. Renew short brushes and bevel them as near as possible. Renew broken or weak tension springs. See that the holder bars are bolted tightly or they may turn. Clean out the brush holders and allow the brushes free movement, with the pig-tails fastened tightly for good current connection.

17. Now replace the brush rigging, put in the armature and put on both end shields. Connect the leads to the brushes. Set the rocker arm in its original neutral position and oil the bearings enough to allow the shaft to be rotated by hand. If it binds, look for the cause at once, as it should turn easily with the oil rings in their grooves. Turn the armature by using a monkey wrench on the shaft pushing against the key covered with tape to avoid marring.

18. Set the brush holders one-eighth inch above the commutator. Bevel all new and old brushes by drawing under them strips of No. 1 sandpaper until a good and full contact surface is assured. Have the tension on all springs similar, but not too strong. Smear the commutator with a little vaseline; it will not carbonize like oil. Replace the pulley and key and then rotate the armature and see that no pig-tails interfere.

19. Replace the motor and bolt it down firmly. Oil the bearings fully and run the armature with current for a few minutes with the belt off. Look sharply for trouble especially see that the oil rings are lubricated properly.

20. Slip on the belt, tighten it up, and run motor under some load. If direct-connected have the coupling well insulated and securely bolted. Look especially for sparking as the brushes may have imperfect contact, too light spring tension or be off neutral. Watch the motor for a few hours underload. Motor brushes should be set back of neutral point, or given a "lag" as it is termed.

21. If a compound motor persists in sparking badly under nearly a full load, it may be that during the repairing process the shunt and series fields were connected opposed to each other, whereas their polarities should be similar at each pole. Opposed fields really cause a still weaker field at increased loads and will result in sparking and flashing, but with the series and shunt fields magnetized in harmony there should be no sparking at the brushes if they have good full contacts and are neutrally placed.

22. If the direction of the armature is wrong, reverse the brush leads.

V. OVERHAULING A 50-HORSEPOWER INDUCTION MOTOR

Although an induction motor does not frequently call for a complete overhauling, the details given in what follows cover such a case in order to bring out the point which should be considered when the motor is completely taken apart and then reassembled after repairs.

1*. Remove all fuses and kill the line.

2. Slip off the belt and try turning the rotor by hand. If it will not turn, then one trouble has been located.

3. Remove the key and pulley by driving wedges behind the latter.

4. Drain the oil wells and remove both end shields which in this size of motor are probably in half sections.

5. Remove the rotor straight out ahead onto a pile of blocking. Slip a pipe over the short shaft so that the rotor may be carried through with one lift. If it seems to be polished on its periphery, this is evidence that at least one bearing lining is worn badly and has allowed the rotor to drop. Clean the rotor of all dust and dirt.

6. Clean the primary winding with waste and benzine and then look for any possible abrasion on the winding. If necessary apply some thick shellac. Coat all the winding with armature varnish, which will dry in a short time.

7. Remove both bearing linings if they are worn enough to allow loose play on the shaft. If they are split they may be

* The following paragraph numbers refer to the parts shown in Fig. 246.

re-babbitted on the premises, but must fit snugly and have oil channels properly cut in them.

8. Clean out both oil wells as dirt is liable to settle and stop the rings.

9. Replace the rotor and oil the bearings. Try to turn the former by hand, and see that the oil rings turn freely.

10. If the motor seems to be in good shape put on the pulley and key it securely.

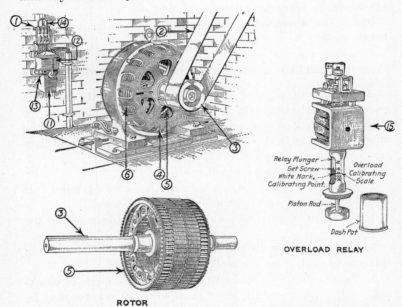

ROTOR

Fig. 246.—Squirrel cage induction motor installation showing arrangement of starter and type of relay that can be used instead of fuses. (Figures refer to numbers of paragraphs of text.)

11. Open the compensator case and look for trouble. Most compensator cases after being unbolted should be let down carefully as they contain oil in which the contacts are submerged.

12. Pull the operating handle over to the starting side and see that the contact fingers are making good connections. If any are burned short renew them. If their cables or leads are not all tight, one or more may be found which has the conductor broken inside of the insulation. These must be re-

connected solidly. Now throw the operating handle sharply to the running side and examine the other contact fingers and their connections. After all repairs are made to the fingers and contacts replace the oil case and put in the fuses for a trial spin of the motor. It ought to run nicely now.

13. Try the no-voltage release by opening the switch. If it fails to work instantly see if the solenoid core is free to move. If dirt is obstructing it or if the rod is bent, remedy it and adjust the stop nut for a certain distance. See that the solenoid leads are properly connected to one phase of the motor line behind the compensator. This circuit energizes the no-voltage release coil.

14. See that the fuses fit snugly in the clips, as a loose fit is liable to disconnect one phase. See that the line wires are tightly connected to the cutout and switch. Loose connections on a 50-hp. line are liable to heat very quickly. The fuses for a 50-hp. compensating starter ought to be not over 150-amp. size with knife-blade clips. This allows for about 20 per cent. overload at starting. If there is much load on the motor when being started, the fuses may be increased to 175 amp., but if they are too large there is no overload protection afforded to the motor.

15. For a motor of this size, it is worth the expense of installing overload relays in place of fuses, as they can be time-set for overloads of dangerous duration. The small spring contact on top of each relay is connected in series with the no-voltage release at the side of the compensator and also in series with one phase from the motor. Thus an overload on the motor raises the relay plunger which opens one or both of the top contacts, which in turn kills the no-voltage release solenoid and by its gravity drop the controlling handle is tripped to dead center thus cutting off the power. The coil of each overload relay is connected in series with each phase of the motor so that both are protected. The oil dash pot needs to be filled with relay oil and screwed up tightly. The plunger may be set at any amperage and locked with a set screw. In the piston cup is a plate having a few holes through which the oil is forced when the plunger raises. This plate may be set for any time, either slow or fast. It is well not

to have the plunger work too quickly as an induction motor may be called upon to carry a heavy load for about a minute, when it would be bothersome to have the relays kick. But more than a minute allows a large current to heat up the motor. These relays are trustworthy, and when encased in a steel box they work silently and promptly just when conditions demand their action. When they kick out and the power goes off, the relays will reset themselves, but they will act again at the very next overload.

After all the operations outlined in items 1 to 15 have been carefully completed, the job may be considered finished and the motor ready to run.

VI. OVERHAULING A 25-HORSEPOWER SLIP-RING MOTOR

A machine like a bull-dozer in a forging shop, a crane or a dredge is likely to have a motor of the slip-ring type with an external resistance control. Such a motor draws current from the line with no heavy rushes and will start with not more than one and one-quarter times its normal full load demand. This is a good feature as it is easy on the generator, fuses and line voltage. Otherwise there might be the annoyance of stopping and starting every few minutes. These motors, however, need repairing at times like all other motors and the following procedure is given for such repair:

1*. Assume a case that upon removing the belt and trying to turn the rotor by power, it is found that it runs very slowly, suddenly blowing a fuse or the overload release opens the line and the motor stops.

2. Remove all fuses, drain the oil wells and remove both end shields.

3. Remove the bearing linings from the end shields and try them on the shaft. If they are worn loose renew or re-babbitt them to fit snugly, and cut in oil grooves.

4. Remove the armature and rest the shaft on some blocking. Examine the slip rings and if they are worn down thin or rough, either renew them or turn them down very smoothly in a lathe. They are liable to roughen from poor brush

---

* The following paragraph numbers refer to the parts shown in Fig. 247.

contact. If renewed see that they are properly insulated from each other with one-quarter-inch fiber board, and tightly bolted up.

5. See that the band wires are tight on the armature. If they are worn thin renew and solder them all around.

6. Coat all the armature winding with a special black varnish, avoiding the core disks, for magnetic conduction.

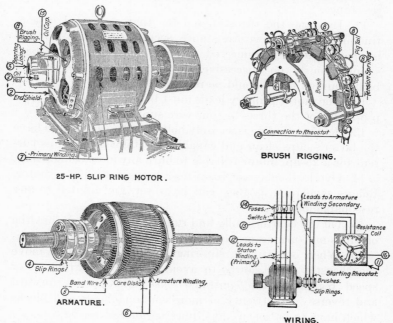

25-HP. SLIP RING MOTOR.

BRUSH RIGGING.

ARMATURE.

WIRING.

FIG. 247.—Parts and external resistance control for a slip ring alternating-current motor. (Figures refer to numbers of paragraphs of text.)

7. Clean all the dust and dirt from out of the primary winding, but use no sharp metal as the insulation is easily damaged. Wash with benzine, and coat with armature varnish.

8. Clean the brush rigging of all metal dust and gummed oil. Renew the short brushes and the broken and weak tension springs. All brushes should have good sized pig-tails to carry the current. The brush contacts should be perfect on the ring surfaces.

9. Replace the armature, brush rigging and both end shields. Smear vaseline on the slip rings and adjust the tension springs fairly strong.

10. See that the leads to the brushes are not loose or disconnected as the armature will turn very slowly and heat badly if only one conductor is open. It makes no difference to which ring any lead is connected coming from the external resistance.

11. Examine the rheostat and see that each lead is continuous from its own resistance section and that no coil is open or loosely connected. The sliding arms must bear simultaneously on successive buttons. If any are worn or badly burned they should be renewed.

12. The motor primary leads must be connected each to the proper leg of the three- or four-wire supply line.

13. See that the line is securely bolted to the switch, and have the latter's clips clean and capable of a tight contact, as current for a 25-hp. motor is liable to burn any loose connections.

14. Overload relays or fuses may be used with this motor. Relays save time as they can be re-set, and limited to any reasonable load.

15. Oil the bearings fully and run the motor. See that the oil rings are turning properly.

16. When operating a slip-ring motor be careful to move the rheostat lever slowly to avoid a rush of current. For speed regulation the controller has many speeds forward and reverse, with twenty or more contact fingers and blocks which have to be renewed at times because of arcing.

17. If a non-reversing motor runs the wrong way, merely exchange the leads of one phase of its line. Changing the slip-ring connections has no effect.

18. A slip-ring motor should have its brushes and rings protected from dust and dirt, and the wear on the bearings watched just as closely as those of an ordinary induction motor.

VII. OVERHAULING A SINGLE-PHASE COMMUTATOR MOTOR

On account of the rather special construction of the single-phase commutator motor, there are certain points to which the repairman should pay especial attention when it becomes necessary to overhaul such a motor or make repairs to it. These points are outlined in detail in the following paragraphs which refer to numbers of Fig. 248.

1.* Laminated field frame of the motor.

2. Main field winding which produces the main flux. The auxiliary field regulates the power factor and is connected permanently to one auxiliary brush, having a switch contact

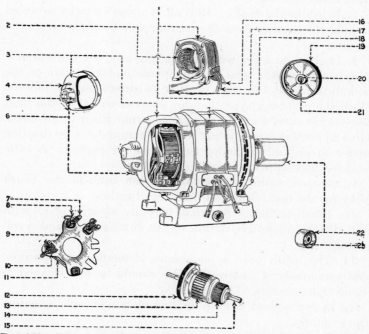

FIG. 248.—Essential parts of a single-phase commutator motor. (Figures refer to numbers of paragraphs of text.)

for the other auxiliary brush. Both of these windings should be coated with black armature varnish to improve their insulation.

3. Commutator end shield.

4. Oil-well cover. If this cover is missing, a new one should

* The following paragraph numbers refer to the parts shown in Fig. 248.

24

be fitted to keep dust from settling where it may cause the oil ring to stop.

5. Oil gauge.   When overhauling a motor take apart and clean out the gauges as any obstruction may produce a false oil level.   The bearings should also be drained and flushed with gasoline.

6. Oil plugs.   See that they are tight or the oil may drip from them and waste.

7. Brush-holder studs.   Bolt all of these up tight to avoid tipping the brushes from the commutator by their accidental turning.

8. Carbon brushes with copper pig-tails, in the variable speed compensated type of single-phase motor, remain on the commutator all the time, similar to direct-current motors. With the repulsion type they are short-circuited at the start but are removed by a centrifugal governor when up to speed. Give all brushes good contact with the commutator by drawing under them No. 00 sandpaper against the carbon.   A little vaseline will stop the squeak of brushes.

9. Short-circuiting connection on the back of the brush yoke for the main brush set or energy brushes.

10. Brush holders.   See that they are cleaned of all gum and dirt to allow free action of the brushes.   Renew weak springs.

11. The brush yoke is sometimes of moulded composition and sometimes of cast iron.   This should be well cleaned to avoid short circuits.

12. A fan is used to keep up a circulation of cool air against the windings.

13. Laminated armature with slot windings.   The squirrel-cage winding is usually placed in the bottom of the slots, and the compensating winding near the surface, and between the two windings a steel bar separator.   All coils should be well insulated to be moisture proof.   See that band wires are tightly soldered, with plenty of mica under them.   If the bearing linings are worn, the surface of the armature will show polished places.

14. Commutator.   To it are connected the leads of the commutated type of armature winding.   In the repulsion

type the commutator bars are all connected at full speed and the armature runs like an induction rotor. See that all commutator leads are well soldered in. If commutator is rough, turn it down in a lathe, but ever so little at a time with a diamond-point tool. Polish with No. 00 sandpaper and oil. Never use emery cloth.

15. Shaft. In some makes if it becomes worn or damaged it can be easily withdrawn and a new one replaced. If its bearing surfaces are cut they should be turned down smoothly before new bearing linings are fitted on.

16 and 17. Motor terminals to the line. Some designs allow for 110-volt operation by connecting the terminals in parallel, and 220-volt operation with them in series.

18. Terminals from the auxiliary or compensating field winding.

19. Pulley end shield.

20. Bearing linings. If they are worn enough to allow loose play of the shaft, new ones should be put in or the old ones re-babbitted with oil channels cut in from end to end.

21. Oil rings. See that they are not bent out of shape and when re-assembling be careful to get them into the slots. This is very important and a light might better be used than to guess at their location. Also turn the armature by hand and see that the rings turn also. Oil well before running.

22. Pulley should be tightly keyed on and fastened with a set screw. Only a balanced motor pulley should be used.

23. Set screw for motor pulley.

NOTE.—No rheostat is needed, although speed controllers are used. To reverse the armature rotation, interchange the leads to the compensating or auxiliary brushes.

VIII. OVERHAULING A DIRECT-CURRENT ENGINE TYPE GENERATOR

At least once a year the generators of any manufacturing plant should be thoroughly overhauled, cleaned, painted, and minor repairs made, even though not badly out of order. Such an inspection does no harm and often reveals a weak part that may later cause a break-down at a busy time.

A good job can be done in two or three days by two good repairmen on machines up to 150 kilowatts.

1.* If belt driven mark the position of the sliding base before setting back with the belt screw.

2. On both belt-driven and direct-connected machines, mark the position of the rocker arm, assuring the return of the brushes to the neutral point.

3. Avoid if possible, disturbing the brush holders.

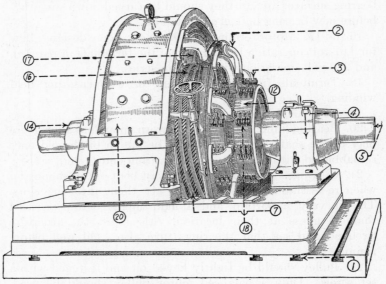

Fig. 249.—Parts of an engine type direct-current generator that should be regularly inspected.   (Figures refer to paragraphs of the text.)

4. With a traveling crane or a tripod rigging, remove the outboard bearing and pedestal, then the whole brush rigging "en masse." Be careful to mark the armature leads for proper re-connection.

5. The armature shaft should be blocked up level to its bearing before the latter is removed, otherwise the poles will have to support the weight and the other bearing sleeve may crack.

* The following paragraph numbers refer to the parts shown in Fig. 249.

6. Remove either the pulley or the coupling key from the other end of the shaft, and by properly slinging the armature it can be withdrawn far enough out past the poles to allow any small work to be done. No hitch or sling should be made around the commutator, even if it is covered with burlap. Support all weight by the shaft only.

7. Blocking under the armature core should be ready to support all of the weight when withdrawn, and so arranged as to prevent its rolling sideways.

8. Now with either an air hose, hand bellows or brush remove all dust, dirt, and lint from around the poles, in the air ducts, and from inside the frame, first covering the engine crank, if direct connected. The armature winding should be blown out neatly, and where any dirt is inclined to adhere use a narrow flat *stick* to avoid damaging the insulation.

9. After a good dusting all around a washing with gasoline will remove any remaining gummy dirt or oil.

10. Black armature varnish may be applied to all windings and leads, but not to the pole shoes, or armature core disks, because the distance between such parts is usually small and too much varnish may "freeze" the armature tight against the lower poles after a shut-down.

11. The armature winding and leads may be painted up to the commutator bars but not beyond. Plenty of it between the commutator open leads helps to insulate them. The band winding at the outer end of the commutator and its bolted end plate may also be painted.

12. If the commutator is very rough or badly cut it should be turned down either in a lathe or by a turning tool attached to the generator frame. After turning off ever so little copper No. 00 sandpaper should be applied with oil for a polish, but *use no emery*. If the commutator is badly worn down and beyond repair, a new one should be on hand, having been ordered weeks in advance, giving the manufacturer all the specifications possible from the name plate. Furthermore, when the commutator arrives examine the bore, diameter length and number of segments, otherwise somebody's mistake may not be discovered till the machine is taken apart. Do not pound on the commutator bars as they may sink.

13. If the shaft shows any marks of cutting have its surface trued before any bearing sleeve is repaired.

14. If the bearing sleeves are worn decidedly, have them re-babbitted to fit snugly but not too tightly, and grooved for oiling.

15. Be careful not to damage the oil rings, especially when replacing the bearings. Also see that all sediment is removed from the oil wells, and the glass gauges cleaned out.

16. If the armature band wires or mica insulation are loose, slip under some sheets of mica and re-solder the bands securely.

17. See that no field coils are loose on the poles; if so apply more wedging of wood strips.

18. If the brushes are dirty remove them, one set at a time, to avoid any mix up and clean the holders with gasoline, allowing the brushes to move freely. Replace short brushes with new ones; renew weak springs; tighten the pig-tails; or if of copper gauze they may be set ahead. Give each brush the proper and same tension, not too loose and not so tight as to cause cutting. Allow about one-eighth inch under the holders, and tip brushes at proper angles. Get the proper bevel on each brush to fit the commutator arc by drawing No. 0 or No. 1 sandpaper under it, cutting the carbon away while it rests on the commutator. Vaseline applied lightly to the commutator will help the lubrication of the brush contacts and prevent cutting and sparking.

19. Connect the main leads to their proper bolts tightly, and if belt driven slip on the pulley with its key and set screw, and with plenty of oil in the bearings turn the armature by hand a number of times and watch all parts for interference. Especially see that the oil rings are turning.

20. A timely warning—do not coat the generator with aluminum paint just for looks, as it is a metallic conductor. Leaky voltage and shorts may result. White enamel radiates heat the best, although it is some trouble to keep clean. Dark green is the usual color.

A. All these operations take some time when properly done, but what a pretty running machine one has when they are honestly completed.

B. If any insulation is found peeled off or cracked open, use a little mica, tape, shellac, or armature varnish.

C. When ready to assemble the generator, put all bolts possible into place before tightening any. Close all oil cocks and fill up the bearings. Keep the armature leads away from the rotating armature.

D. When all is ready, slip on the belt, slide back the base to its former position and start the engine slowly, watching carefully the oil rings.

CHAPTER XV

DIAGNOSIS OF MOTOR AND GENERATOR TROUBLES

The electric motor and generator are sturdy pieces of apparatus when given the proper attention and operated within their normal ratings. The troubles which they develop can usually be traced to two main causes. 1. Faulty operating conditions. 2. Mechanical and electrical defects.

Faulty operating conditions may either bring to light existing mechanical and electrical defects or create new ones. Under normal conditions, therefore, correct operating conditions will reduce to a minimum, the troubles due to the second cause. The factors in faulty operating conditions may be classified as follows:

1. Lack of proper cleaning.
2. Operation in damp places.
3. Exposure to acid fumes and gases.
4. Lack of frequent inspection and replacement of worn parts.
5. Operating temperatures too high.

Lack of Proper Cleaning.—All machinery having moving parts requires lubrication and however well the provisions are made to confine the oil to the parts needing the lubrication, it will find its way in time to adjacent parts of the machine. In motors and generators the oil which is allowed to accumulate on the windings has a detrimental effect on the quality of the insulating materials used and is a frequent cause of short circuits and grounds. The presence of oil also invites the accumulation of dust and dirt which quickly fills up small spaces that have been provided for ventilation of windings and core. This results in an increase in temperature of the parts involved. The only remedy for troubles resulting from this cause on a repaired machine, or when a new one is substituted, is frequent cleaning at regular intervals. Motors

376

operated in especially dusty places, as in cement and flour mills, should be blown out daily with compressed air or a hand bellows. Care must be taken not to blow the dust into the windings. An air pressure of not more than 50 pounds per square inch with a ⅛-inch nozzle should be used to avoid injury to insulation.

Operation in Damp Places.—The materials employed in the insulation of windings of motors and generators consist of special papers, cotton tapes and cloth, and mica. With the exception of mica, all of these materials absorb moisture more or less or are said to be hydroscopic. In damp places where the operation of the machine is not continuous enough for the generated heat to keep moisture out, the insulation may absorb enough moisture to reduce the insulating strength to the rupture point resulting in all sorts of troubles. Motors and generators should not be installed in damp places except they be provided with windings having a special moisture-proof insulation which manufacturers can furnish when the conditions under which the machine is to operate are known. In case a machine has been exposed to dampness or been soaked with water in a fire without having the insulation damaged by the fire, it should be thoroughly dried out before being placed in operation. (For details of drying out a machine, see pages 181 to 185.)

Exposure to Acid Fumes and Gases.—As in the cases of oil and water, acid fumes destroy the insulating strength of most insulating materials. They also attack the metal of the machine and thus bring on commutator troubles. In chemical works and in industrial plants where acid fumes are present, small motors should be enclosed in a fume-tight case which can be ventilated. Where this is impossible specially insulated windings must be provided. The coils needed in the repair of such a machine should be secured from the manufacturer and in most cases it will be advisable for the manufacturer to do the repair work. Machines operated should be cleaned more frequently than under other conditions and the exposed windings painted regularly with an acid-resisting paint or a good linseed oil paint. The commutator should be wiped daily with a little vaseline. The metal parts of the machine should also receive a coat of acid-resisting paint at frequent intervals.

Lack of Frequent Inspection and Replacement of Worn Parts.—Short circuits and grounds are frequently traced to rubbing of the motor winding on field poles caused by a bent shaft or worn bearings. A worn or bent shaft may also cause the core of the armature to strike the pole faces and jam the punchings of the core enough to cut the coils and cause a ground in the winding. A loose fit of the commutator on the shaft, when it has been replaced after a repair job, may result in sufficient movement to break off the leads to armature coils at the necks of the commutator. The re-soldering of such a defect does not cure the trouble. An inspection should be made to locate the cause and eliminate it. In this case it will probably call for a new shaft. A mixture of dust and foreign material in the bearing oil cups or not enough oil is the start of many bearing troubles which can be eliminated by frequently draining the bearings and cleaning with kerosene. When oil is used that has stood for some time in a receptacle or been pumped from barrels to a tank, it is advisable to filter it before using it in motor or generator bearings. Wear of bearings should be inspected frequently when a large tight belt is used on the motor.

Roughness of the commutator should be guarded against. When it occurs and stoning does not remedy the trouble, the real cause should be searched out. The same applies to high mica. The air gap of the machine should also be frequently checked by thickness gauges for this is a good check on the condition of the bearings. A record made of all of these tests and inspections for reference when other troubles develop will save much time and trouble.

A frequent check for proper end play of the armature shaft in its bearings will prevent grooving of the commutator that otherwise might be suspected to be caused by unsuitable brushes.

Operating Temperatures Too High.—All insulating material such as paper and cotton materials have a maximum temperature limit above which they will not retain their insulating strength and will simply char and eventually crumble, causing electrical faults in the windings. The materials which have the highest maximum operating temperature are mica, and synthetic resins like bakelite. Where surrounding temperatures are known to be high as in the case of motors used to drive blowers in a boiler room or the scrapers on an economizer, special heat-resisting insulation must be provided instead of that ordinarily used.

For the ordinary design of industrial motor the Standardization Rules of the American Institute of Electrical Engineers recommend the following as maximum temperatures for the different kinds of insulating materials specified:

For cotton, silk, paper and other fibrous materials not so treated as to increase the thermal limit, 95°C. (203°F.). When measured by thermometer, 80°C. (176°F.).

For cotton, silk, paper and other fibrous material treated or impregnated and including enameled wire, 105°C. (221°F.). When measured by thermometer, 90°C. (194°F.). •

For mica, asbestos, or other material capable of resisting high tempera tures, in which the previous materials if used, are for structural purposes only and may be destroyed without impairing the insulating or mechanical qualities, 125°C. (257°F.). When measured by thermometer, 110°C. (230°F.).

All parts of electrical machinery other than those whose temperature affects the temperature of the insulating material, may be operated at such temperatures as may not be injurious in any respect. But no part of continuous-duty machinery subject to handling in operation, such as brush rigging, shall have a temperature in excess of 100°C. (212°F.) for more than a very brief time.

NOTE.—When a thermometer is used to measure the maximum (hottest spot) temperature, a correction of 15°C. is added to the thermometer reading in order to allow of the impossibility of locating the thermometer at the hottest spot, which will be beneath the insulation next to the metal of the conductor.

The hand is a very poor thermometer and should not be relied upon except as a general indicator of operating temperatures. Any temperature above 120°F. is very uncomfortable to the touch but is well within the range of safe operation. Until a surface temperature of about 176°F. is reached there is little danger to injury of insulation. The motor should however be closely watched at this temperature and not allowed to go much beyond it except for a very short time.

CAUSES AND REMEDIES FOR TROUBLES IN DIRECT-CURRENT MACHINES

Faults	Cause	How most readily detected	Remedy
1. Too high voltage.	1. Too high speed of engine.	1. Voltmeter reads greater than standard and lamps burn with undue brilliancy.	1. Slow the engine.
	2. Too strong magnetic field.	2. Same.	2. Introduce more resistance in shunt field.
2. Too low voltage.	1. Too low speed of engine.	1. Voltmeter shows lower than standard and lamps burn dimly.	1. Increase speed of engine.
	2. Too weak magnetic field.	2. Same.	2. Take out resistance in shunt field.
	3. Brushes not properly set.	3. Same.	3. Rock brushes back and forth till highest voltage consistent with sparkless commutation is shown.
3. Excessive current.	1. In a generator, too many lamps burning or motors running	1. By too high reading of ammeter for capacity of machine. By excessive sparking of dynamo brushes and too high reading of dynamo ammeter.	1. Cut out necessary number of lamps. Reduce load on motor circuits. In this case none of the motors may be doing too much work, but there may be too many in dynamo circuit.
	2. In a motor, too much mechanical work being done by it.	2. By excessive sparking of motor brushes nad too high reading of motor ammeter.	2. Reduce the load on the motor.
	3. Short circuit; leak or ground in external. circuit.	3. By excessive sparking of brushes, and heating of whole armature.	3. Locate and remove leaks or grounds.
	4. Short circuit in armature coil.	4. By heating of short-circuited coil more than the others.	4. Stop machine. Locate coil. If entirely burned out must be renewed.
	5. Grounds in armature. Two grounds to the core amount to a short circuit.	5. Same as 4.	5. Locate the grounds. Re-insulate the coils containing them.
	6. Due to excessive friction in bearings or by armature striking pole pieces. In general any cause tending to slow motor.	6. By sparking of brushes. By sound of armature striking while running. By heating of motor bearings.	6. File away pole pieces or re-center armature. Clean and oil journals, or re-fit bearings.

CAUSES AND REMEDIES FOR TROUBLES IN DIRECT-CURRENT MACHINES
(Continued)

Faults	Cause	How most readily detected	Remedy
4. Excessive sparking at brushes.	1. Excessive current; therefore due to any of the causes given under that head.	1. Same as given under "Excessive current."	1. Same as given under "Excessive current."
	2. Brushes improperly set.	2. By taking brushes out of holders and examining rubbing surface. By measuring the peripheral distance between brush sets.	2. Fit and set accurately, then shift the brushes backward or forward till sparking is reduced to a minimum.
	3. Brushes make poor contact with commutator.	3. By sighting underneath between brushes and commutator.	3. Sandpaper the brushes and adjust the spring tension until they rest evenly on commutator with light but even pressure.
	4. Rough, non-concentric commutator.	4. A rough commutator can be detected by lightly touching finger nail to it while running; an eccentric commutator by the regular rise and fall of the brushes.	4. Smooth commutator with fine sandpaper. If eccentricity is due to uneven wear of bearings, renew or re-line them.
	5. "High" or "flat" bars in commutator.	5. By the jumping or vibrations of the brushes.	5. Same as above, or turn down the commutator in lathe. Slot out the mica to a depth of $\frac{1}{10}$ or $\frac{1}{20}$ in.
	6. Broken circuit in armature or commutator.	6. Commutator flashes, and nearest the break is cut and burnt. Flashing continues when armature is slowly turned.	6. Locate coil by drop of potential method. If in commutator bridge over the break. If in armature coil, it must be renewed.
	7. Weak field magnetism, caused by broken circuit in field winding or short circuit in same; two or more grounds in windings; reversal of one or more field coils.	7. Dynamo fails to generate full emf. If very weak, motor runs very slow, taking a current many times full load current.	7. Short circuits or grounds are easily located and remedied if external to the windings. If internal, faulty coil must be rewound or repaired if only grounded. A reversed coil will lower the voltage instead of increasing it, and it is remedied by reversing the connections.

CAUSES AND REMEDIES FOR TROUBLES IN DIRECT-CURRENT MACHINES
(*Continued*)

Faults	Cause	How most readily detected	Remedy
	8. Unequal magnetism.	8. One brush sparks more than the other.	8. Only remedied by re-shaping pole pieces.
	9. Dirty commutator, causing brushes to vibrate, particularly if of carbon.	9. Flashing around commutator.	9. Clean commutator. (Methods given later.)
	10. Poor brushes, especially if of high-resistance carbon, hard blisters forming on them.	10. By ragged appearance of brushes around edges and formation of hard spots.	10. Renew brushes. Try different grades of hard and soft brush.
	11. Vibration, especially of brush holders, causing rapid vibration of brushes.	11. By a humming, singing sound of brushes.	11. Reduce cause of vibration or give the brushes a little greater pressure on commutator.
4(*a*) Excessive sparking in interpole machines.	12. Wrong interpole polarity.	12. With low field excitation, examine field polarity with a compass, the armature being first removed.	12. In motor, progressing in direction of armature rotation, polarity should be N-n-S-s, etc. In generator, progressing in direction of armature rotation, polarity should be N-s-S-n, etc.
	13. Interpoles not exactly over commutation belt.	13. By inspection.	13. Adjustable when poles are bolted to the frame.
	14. Brushes not set so that coils undergoing commutation are under interpole.	14. Trace out by following up coil ends.	14. Usual setting is in geometric neutral. Set for minimum sparking under average load.
	15. Interpole air gap too long or too short.	15. See if all interpole gaps are equal.	15. Adjustable when poles are bolted to the frame. Weaken interpole strength by shunting the interpole winding.
5. Heating of armature.	1. Excessive current through it and therefore due to any of the causes given under that head.	1. Same as given under "Excessive current."	1. Same as given under "Excessive current."
	2. Eddy currents and hysteresis in core.	2. Core becomes hotter than armature coils after running for a short time.	2. This can be corrected by improving ventilation by special fans or air guides.

CAUSES AND REMEDIES FOR TROUBLES IN DIRECT-CURRENT MACHINES
(Continued)

Faults	Cause	How most readily detected	Remedy
6. Heating of commutator.	3. Conduction from other parts as from commutator or bearings, the heat being conveyed to armature.	3. Other parts connected to armature, as commutator, shaft or bearings, hotter than the armature.	3. Locate source of heat by thermometer or feel by the hand and correct it by cleaning and lubrication.
	1. Too great pressure of brushes, friction causing heat.	1. By feeling the commutator with the hand.	1. Reduce pressure by adjusting spring.
	2. Excessive sparking.	2. Same.	2. Discover the cause of sparking and correct it according to the particular cause given under sparking.
	3. Excessive current.	3. Same.	3. Discover cause of excessive current and correct according to particular cause already given.
	4. Conduction from other parts.	4. Same.	4. If from bearings, lubricate orre-fit them.
7. Heating of field coils.	1. Excessive current in field circuit due to short circuits or grounds.	1. Too hot to bear the hand. If exceedingly hot, by smell of burning shellac or varnish or charring cotton.	1. Locate the particular coil in which fault lies and repair or re-wind. Methods given later.
	2. Eddy currents in pole pieces, heat being conducted to the coils.	2. The pole pieces are hotter than the coils after a short run.	2. Only remedied by better design, use laminated pole shoes.
8. Heating of bearings.	1. Lack of lubrication.	1. By feeling with hand. Oil cups empty or feeding pipes clogged.	1. Fill oil cups; clean feeding pipes.
	2. Dirty or gritty bearings.	2. By feeling with hand.	2. Remove cap and thoroughly clean.
	3. Bearings out of line.	3. Unequal wear of bearings, and shaft will not turn freely by hand.	3. Bearings must be lined up or shells rebabbitted. If very serious, new bearings will have to be made.
	4. Rough or cut shaft.	4. Shaft will show the roughness in the bearings.	4. Turn down shaft in lathe, or scrape the bearings.
	5. Shaft bent.	5. Unequal wear in bearings and armature will wobble. Very hard to move by hand.	5. Shafts can only be straightened by disconnecting from armature and re-heating and re-forging.

CAUSES AND REMEDIES FOR TROUBLES IN DIRECT-CURRENT MACHINES
(Continued)

Faults	Cause	How most readily detected	Remedy
	6. Oil rings stuck.	6. Inspection.	6. Adjust rings in grooves.
9. Too low speed (referring to motors).	1. Too much load.	1. By speed indicator; heavy sparking, heating of all parts and bearings.	1. Reduce the mechanical load.
	2. Any of the causes given under "Heating of bearings," causing excessive friction.	2. Same, and same as given under "Heating of bearings."	2. Discover particular cause and remedy same as given under "Heating of bearings."
	3. Short circuit or grounds in armature.	3. By motor taking excessive current without load as shown by ammeter or heavy sparking and heating.	3. Same as under 5, "Excessive current."
	4. Too low voltage at terminals.	4. By motor voltmeter or speed indicator. By heavy sparking and heating.	4. By increasing the line voltage.
10. Too high speed (referring to motors).	1. Too light load (in series motors).	1. By noticeable increase in speed.	1. Increase load.
	2. Weak field shunt motor.	2. Same.	2. Strengthen field.
	3. Too high voltage at terminals, due to high voltage of dynamo.	3. Same.	3. Correct line voltage by remedies 1 and 2 under "Too high voltage."
11. Dynamo fails to generate emf.	1. Too weak residual magnetism, caused by a jar or reversal of current not sufficient to reverse magnetism.	1. Very little attraction by the pole pieces when tested with a piece of iron.	1. Send a current through field from a few cells or from a running dynamo.
	2. Short circuit within machine, or grounds in field windings.	2. Magnetism very weak.	2. Locate the grounds or short circuits and correct them.
	3. Reversed field coils.	3. All poles should have alternate magnetism; if a coil is reversed it will show magnetism, but may not be of opposite polarity.	3. Make polarity opposite by reversing the connections of the coil. Each pole should be opposite to the one on each side of it.
	4. Series and shunt windings connected up opposite to each other.	4. Voltage falls as load is increased, the external circuit being closed showing that they are working against one another.	4. Reverse connections of either field, but not both

CAUSES AND REMEDIES FOR TROUBLES IN DIRECT-CURRENT MACHINES
(*Continued*)

Faults	Cause	How most readily detected	Remedy
	5. Brushes not properly placed.	5. Magnetism and emf. increased by shifting the brushes.	5. Find central position by experiment or from drawings of connections.
	6. Open circuit in field or armature. Brushes not making good contact with the commutator. Loose connections.	6. Test circuits with magneto.	6. Set up on all connections. Press brushes on commutator to start building up.
	7. Too much resistance in the shunt field circuit, *i.e.*, greater than the "critical" resistance. Shunt field bucks the residual magnetism.	7. Voltage does not exceed that due to residual magnetism. The voltage due to residual magnetism drops when the shunt field circuit is closed.	7. Cut all resistance out of the shunt field circuit. Reverse the shunt field.
12. Motor fails to start.	1. Too much load.	1. No motion and fuse in circuit melts or circuit-breaker acts. See if motor runs all right when light.	1. If motor does not start at once, turn off current and search for cause. Reduce load on motor.
	2. Excessive friction, due to any causes given under heading "Heating of bearings."	2. Same, and motor hard to turn when not loaded, and with no current.	2. Remedies same as given under "Heating of bearings."
	3. Short circuit of field or armature or among connections.	3. Motor refuses to revolve, though shows signs of strong magnetism. Will turn easily by hand if unloaded and with no current. If current is very great, it is indication of short circuit. If fault is in field, magnetism will be weak.	3. If connections are made wrong, consult maker's diagram and correct them. Test for continuity and short circuits as given later.
	4. Open circuits due to field switch open, fuse melted, loose or broken connections, or some fault at generator.	4. Weak magnetism shows a loose connection in field circuit; no magnetism, that field switch is open. May be heavy current in armature. If there is no armature current there will be no spark at brushes when raised.	4. Turn current from motor, and search for cause of discontinuity; examine all switch fuses and connections, tightening all. Test for continuity in machine circuits and repair broken or burnt-out coils.

25

CAUSES AND REMEDIES FOR TROUBLES IN DIRECT-CURRENT MACHINES
(Concluded)

Faults	Cause	How most readily detected	Remedy
13. Flickering of lamps.	1. Uneven running of engine, probably due to governor failing to properly function.	1. By flickering of lamps or vibration of voltmeter indicator.	1. Overhaul engine, specially governor.
	2. Loose connections, either on machine, switchboard or external circuit.	2. Same.	2. Examine all connections and see that they are firm and make good contact. Look for arcs.
14. Noise.	1. See third fault (6), fourth fault (4, 5, 9, 10, 11), eighth fault (3, 4, 5), and tenth fault.		
	2. Armature running against the brushes.	2. By unusual noise.	2. Correct direction of rotation.

Electrical Defects.—Troubles in motors and generators due to electrical defects show up in a variety of ways. Their location, however, is more often a simple than a difficult matter and depends upon a few testing devices and a great deal of patience and persistence. An experienced operator or repairman learns to diagnose electrical troubles by a process of elimination where there may be several causes. For such an analysis of common electrical troubles in motors and generators the table on pages 380 to 386 will be found useful. It was compiled by the authors of the *Naval Electricians Text Book* and has been taken from that most practical work.

CAUSES AND REMEDIES FOR TROUBLES IN ALTERNATING-CURRENT MACHINES

Induction Motor Troubles.—The most common troubles with induction motors show up by the machine failing to start or by stopping while connected to the line. When the machine refuses to start and the fuses are not blown, the cause may be in too large a load. The remedy in such cases is to either reduce the load or use a clutch for starting since the squirrel-cage motor has a limited starting torque but can often carry a much larger load while running. When investigating a trouble of this kind it is important to see that the voltage is normal and that the bearings are in good condition. If none of these conditions seem to cause the trouble a test should be made for open circuits in the windings. (See Chapter IX.)

An excessive current at starting may be due to a high voltage applied or too great a load. When the voltage is high an auto-transformer with suitable taps must be used for starting. When an auto-transformer is used and the starting current is excessive, a test should be made for proper connections. Too low taps on the starter should be avoided.

An overload on an induction motor will usually show up by the motor coming to rest or taking about 10 times more than normal current. When fuses and circuit breakers do not operate under such heavy current, the machine will burn out. It is therefore important that fuses and settings of circuit breakers be used to prevent such burn-outs. Since the torque of an induction motor varies with the square of the voltage, low supply voltage may be the cause of the machine stopping. Also worn bearings will allow the rotor to drop on the stator and thus block the former and stop the machine. For other details in testing and inspection of induction motors see Chapter XIV.

Locating Troubles in Winding of Induction Motors.— When the cause of trouble with an induction motor in starting or in operation has been traced to the stator windings, details of locating the fault are outlined in Chapter IX. When the stator has been repaired and again placed in service its connections should be carefully looked over. The points to be observed when inspecting such a stator are outlined on page 363. In case the connections of an auto-starter are reversed, the starting current will be excessive and insufficient torque with the switches in the running position will show up. If the motor refuses to start the cause may be due to a defect in the change-over switch or to a loose connection or open circuit in the auto-starter.

Mechanical Adjustments.—In those cases where induction motors are in continuous operation regular inspections should be made of the air gap to see that it is not appreciably reduced at the bottom of the rotor on account of wear of the bearings. When the air gap is reduced a test should be made before the trouble is attributed definitely to wear of the bearings. It is also important that an armature have a small play endwise in the bearings. This should be about $\frac{1}{16}$ inch. Excessive heating or excessive belt tension may be the cause of a great deal of bearing trouble on an induction motor which is belt-driven.

Troubles Due to Electrical Faults.—When errors have been made in winding an induction motor or in re-connecting the coils, trouble will usually show up in heating of the coils, a peculiar humming sound for large and unbalanced currents in the different phases. Before testing for faults of re-connection of coils, it must be determined that the connections of the winding to the supply circuit are correct and that none of the connections of the phase coils have been accidentally jammed together so as to short-circuit them. Troubles in rotors of induction motors are rare, however, in squirrel-cage types trouble may be located in soldered joints which have melted or corroded. High resistance at joints lowers the efficiency, increases the heating and also increases the starting torque of the motor. Heating or operation at reduced output or speed may be due to a three-phase motor running on one or two phases.

Troubles with Synchronous Motors.—When a synchronous motor fails to start the trouble is generally due to an overload. In testing out for such a condition the motor should be started light. If the operation is not satisfactory the load should be reduced. Poor starting may also be caused by reduced voltage or open or faulty connections in starting apparatus. An open circuit is usually indicated by no current flowing in a particular phase. An excessive current usually indicates a short circuit but may be due to grounds. An excessive current in a synchronous motor is a dangerous condition and the trouble should be located.

When a synchronous motor is used for power-factor correction overheating indicates an excessive current. The machine can usually be temporarily operated by reducing the load or reducing the amount of leading current. When a synchronous motor is operating satisfactorily the current in the armature phases should be about equal when the rotor is turning slowly.

Trouble in the field winding such as an open circuit causes a shutdown or excessive armature heating. When the field current seems excessive, a test should be made for polarity of the armature coils and reversal of connections. When a synchronous motor fails to show normal starting torque and will not carry the load, the trouble will frequently be found in the field circuit in the form of an open circuit, short circuit or reversal of one or more field windings.

Causes of A.-C. Motor Fuses Blowing.—In addition to overload on a motor, many other things cause fuses to blow. The following causes and symptoms have been formulated by Henry W. Zeuner, Milwaukee (Wis.) Electric Light Company (*Electrical World*, Sept. 20, 1919).

1. Operator throwing starting switch of compensators from starting to running position too quickly.

2. Operator throwing switch into running position without touching the starting position at all.

3. Motor winding becoming grounded.

4. Excessive current due to low voltage, short circuits in stator windings, single-phase operation, etc.

5. Starting switch being in running position when service comes back on line after interruption.

Wound-rotor motors and squirrel-cage motors which are not protected by a no-voltage release may be shut down at any time because of the last-mentioned cause. To overcome this trouble a group of such motors is often protected by an oil switch equipped with no-voltage release. The arrangement has the disadvantage, however, that whenever the oil switch opens it becomes necessary for some one to go around and open each individual motor switch before the oil switch is closed again.

A ground may only blow one fuse and leave the motor operating from one phase of the line. When a polyphase motor is running single-phase it not only gets hot but it makes a growling noise which is especially noticeable under heavy load. By the time these symptoms indicate the probable source of the trouble and it is decided to shut down the motor, a second fuse is sometimes blown by the excessive current per phase. If only the first defective fuse found is replaced, the motor may be started from the line side of the switch which is connected ahead of the fuses. When the switch is thrown over into the running position the motor is again operating on single phase. Because the motor continues to heat up the user often thinks there must be something wrong with the motor itself and calls for help, whereas if he had only tested all the fuses in the first place and replaced all of the burnt-out fuses instead of only one of them, he could have put the motor back in service without assistance and with a minimum loss of time. Another source of trouble which may be detected at the service fuses is low voltage. This causes excessive heating and often burns out stator coils. The voltage can be checked roughly with test lamps.

Inspection of Motor-starting Devices.—From the fuses it is customary to proceed to examine the motor-starting switch, compensator or controller. Contact fingers are often found bent or burned so that they do not make contact and the connecting leads are sometimes burned off. The two-minute starting resistance supplied by the manufacturers for starting slip-ring motors is often burned out by being used for speed-regulating duty which requires a much heavier resistance.

Testing Motor for Grounds.—When testing an alternating-current motor for grounds, a magneto or high-voltage testing transformer should be used as the line voltage will seldom show a ground unless it is making very good contact. National Electrical Code rules require that motor frames be grounded, but this requirement is not always carried out. When the motor frame is insulated from the ground the motor can be kept in operation with one phase grounded to the motor frame, but the defect should be remedied at the first opportunity. A second connection between the stationary windings and the motor frame will burn out the coils which it short circuits, and if not given prompt attention the two grounds may result in the burning out of the entire winding.

When both the supply system and the motor frames are grounded, as is usually the case, one ground on the stator winding will blow one of the motor fuses unless the fuse is too heavy, in which case the ground may burn out some of the stator coils. However, every ground which blows a fuse does not occur in the motor winding. If the motors test clear, the wiring leading to the motor may be found grounded to the conduit.

It is a good plan to run the defective motor while testing when it is practicable to do so. This makes it possible to conduct additional tests and very often to observe symptoms which do not appear when the motor is standing still. Under such operating conditions the speed should be tested. Low speed and inability to pull the load are usually an indication of bad connections between the rotor bars and the rotor end rings.

Hot Stator Coils.—Another condition to observe while the motor is operating is whether the stator coils are hotter in one place than in another. This is one of the signs of bearing trouble. When the bearings become worn the stator coils around the section of reduced air gaps get hotter than the coils adjacent to the section where the air gap has been increased. If the bearings are not renewed before the rotor begins to rub on the stator, the motor windings may be seriously injured, especially if the fuse is too large and does not blow. When it is impracticable to operate the motor the belt should be taken off and the bearings examined to find out if there is too much play in them.

Tension of Belts.—Much belt and bearing trouble is caused by the belt being too tight. This is especially true with vertical belt drives from squirrel-cage motors to high-speed machines. When bearing trouble is experienced with installations of this description it is usually because the pulley surface is too small to accelerate the driven machine as fast as a squirrel-cage motor comes up to speed, and consequently the belt comes off. In attempting to keep the belt on the pulley the belt is usually made so tight that the excessive tension soon wears down the bearings. This trouble can sometimes be overcome in installations of small motors by using larger pulleys, a larger motor, or by changing from a vertical belt drive to a horizontal belt drive with the slack side of the belt on top.   With large belted motors driving high-speed machines the slip-ring type of motor should be used in order to bring the driven machine up to speed more slowly.

Troubles in Rotor Windings.—A bad contact in the rotor winding is not so easily found when the end rings are cast on to the end of the rotor bars.   This cast construction was originally adopted to overcome the bad joints which developed with screwed and soldered connections in the rotor windings. The change has not entirely eliminated the trouble, however, because the molten metal does not always unite with the end of the copper bars when the end rings are being cast.   When this is the case trouble due to the poor contact often develops, especially if the motor is subject to much dirt and vibration. With a little experience a defective joint between the cast end rings and the rotor bars can be found by tapping the end rings with a hammer and noting the difference in sound at various places.   A bad joint in this type of construction can be repaired by welding the bar and end rings together.   Welded rotor windings have been very successful, and it is unusual to find bad joints in rotor windings which have been put together in this manner.

Examination of Stator Winding.—The stator winding should also be thoroughly examined while the end shields are off the motor.   If one or two coils are burned out, the other coils can in most instances be raised out of the slot and new coils slipped into place provided that the coil insulation is flexible and in good condition.   Should this be attempted, however, after the insulation on the coils has become brittle, there is a grave danger of damaging the insulation to such an extent that the entire stator winding may have to be renewed. When the condition of the insulation is doubtful and only one or two coils need replacing, it has been found a good plan to cut away the burnt-out coils and thread new wire through the slots turn by turn, without disturbing any of the other coils.

The damage from a local short circuit in the stator winding

can be limited to the one or two coils affected and the motor still kept temporarily in service by promptly cutting out the damaged coil with a jumper. However, if the trouble is neglected it will spread to other coils in the same phase, and then the windings of the other phase or phases will also burn out.

Sparking at Slip Rings.—This trouble in wound-rotor motors occurs when the tension spring has not been reset from time to time to keep the brushes in close contact with the slip rings. This is the most frequent cause of the trouble, and it can usually be eliminated by adjusting the tension of the spring and where necessary turning up the slip rings and renewing the brushes.

CHAPTER XVI

METHODS USED BY ELECTRICAL REPAIRMAN TO SOLVE SPECIAL TROUBLES

When called upon to locate troubles in electrical apparatus many electricians and repairmen find themselves in a state of wondering just what to do first. The mystery supposed for so long to be associated with the operation of electrical apparatus seems to discourage many able electrical men to attempt to search out an electrical trouble when it seems to be a complicated one. By the use of the same good sense that makes such men successful in the work with which they are familiar, most electrical problems in repair can be located and a satisfactory remedy applied. In a serious case where expert help is reasonable and within easy and prompt access, it may not always pay for an inexperienced man to spend the necessary time to handle a difficult trouble but in the ordinary run of plant operation such troubles are few. What is most needed is a little clear thinking aided by a few testing instruments.

One of the ways by which a repairman can develop confidence in his own ability to search out trouble and prepare himself to properly diagnose troubles, is to read and profit by the experiences related by those who have worked out puzzling troubles and have told in the columns of electrical trade journals how they proceeded. The author has made a selection of such experiences covering a wide range of operating troubles which are liable to come up at a time or under circumstances which make them difficult to handle. The details given will furnish suggestions as to methods of procedure in many other cases than those described.

Sparking at Commutator Caused by Poor Belt Joints.—In operating motors or generators with laced belts, it is important that the joints be flexible and the ends neatly laced close together to present as nearly as possible a continuous surface to the pulley. Where this is not done laced belts very frequently cause sparking due to any one of three causes: (1) The laced belt when passing over the pulley may cause a jerk or mechanical vibration of the armature which is severe enough to throw the brushes from the commutator and cause sparking due to the broken circuit. (2) When the bearings are loose in their housings or when the armature shaft is loose in its bearings, the jerk of the lacing may pull the armature to one side. This develops a higher voltage in a generator or a higher counter electromotive force in a motor in the part of the armature which is pulled closest to the pole faces. This will cause sparking due to a pulsating current or in severe cases due to a short circuit current between studs of the same polarity. (3) The belt may slip while the laced ends are passing over the pulley, which will permit a variation in the speed of the armature. This will cause a sudden change in the current and may produce sparking due to the inductance of the armature coils.

Plugging a Commutator.—When commutator bars show a tendency to blister and bead at the outer ends, "plugging" the commutator often gives relief. To do this, proceed as follows: Grind all of the "set" from the teeth of a piece of hacksaw blade. With this piece of blade saw the commutator side mica to the outline indicated at (*a*) in the accompanying diagram, Fig. 250. Next drive in mica wedges or "plugs" so called, to entirely fill and perfectly fit the grooves made by sawing. The best results are to be obtained by loosening the commutator before driving in the wedges, but this is not absolutely

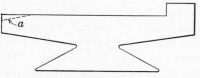

Fig. 250.—Method of repairing mica segment by sawing at (*a*) and plugging.

necessary. For other details of commutator repair see Chapter XII.

Knock in a Motor Armature Due to Band Wires Being Too High.—In the banding of many types of direct-current armatures, the bands are laid onto a layer of fish paper or of thin fiber which affords smooth bedding for the band wires and which also provides additional insulation between the band wires and the armature coils.   On many of the later designs of armatures the tension used in banding has been greatly increased, and as a further precaution against the bands cutting into the insulation of any coils that may be high in the slot, a layer of thin tin is interposed between the band wire and the insulating band.   That it may not be advisable to adopt this improved method on machines that have not been designed for it, is illustrated by the following experience (*Electrical Record*, June, 1918).

A 20-hp. direct-current motor which had just been repaired and shipped, was returned within a few days with the complaint that the armature "had a knock in it."   At the time of testing the motor, a slight vibration had been noticed, but leveling of the motor had eliminated the vibration.   Careful inspection of the motor this time, however, revealed that one of the tin clips of an end band had been striking one of the bottom pieces.   Investigation disclosed that a contributory cause of the knocking was that one of the bearing linings had been bored a little out of center, but even after this had been corrected a piece of $\frac{1}{64}$-inch fiber could not be inserted between the armature core and the bottom pole pieces in certain positions of the armature   The real cause of the trouble was, then, that the layers of insulation and tin under the band wires, projected the wires and their holding clips too far into the air gap.   As the air gap was thinner than ordinarily found on such motors, the remedy was to remove the tin and install band wires of smaller diameter and with less tension, and to use thin copper for the band wire clips.   These changes resulted in a $\frac{3}{32}$-inch air gap.   The testers were deceived as to the cause of the vibration because the tilting of the machine floated the armature to a position where the high clip cleared the pole piece it was striking.

Heating of an Armature Traced to Poor Soldering of Commutator Connections.—E. C. Parham has described (*Electrical Record*, March, 1919) an interesting case where it was necessary to replace the armature of an exciter that had been in operation so long that the commutator bars had worn so that the pressure of the end rings was beginning to buckle the bars up in the middle.   An extra armature was obtained because the exciter could not be spared from service. This armature was installed in place of the old one and the old one was repaired by re-filling its commutator. About a year later a switchboard short circuit which started by a stroke of lightning, so badly burned the new exciter commutator that it was necessary to take a cut off it. The repaired armature was taken from storage and installed but it could not be used, because it heated all over as soon as a field was put on the exciter. As the armature was the only equipment part that had been handled, the trouble evidently was in it. It was removed and the commutator disconnected for testing. The commutator was found to be perfectly clear but the armature leads where they were connected to the commutator were found to be a mass of short circuits due to the criminal carelessness of the man who had done the soldering. After picking out the solder, trimming the leads and re-connecting by a workman who knew that class of work, the operation was normal.

One lesson that stands out very prominently from this experience is this: When the armature of an indispensable machine must be replaced on account of the necessity of making repairs, after the repairs have been completed, re-install the repaired armature at once for test so that the armature that is *known* to be right, may be kept as the spare and with a fair degree of certainty that it will be all right when occasion arises for using it. Another lesson is that every shop or station that pretends to do connecting and soldering, should have access to a short-circuit test for locating just such trouble as described.

How a Commutator was Repaired under Difficulties.— In an instance related by R. L. Hervey (*Electrical World*, Feb. 26, 1916) the commutator of a generator had on a number of occasions given trouble because of the mica breaking down between the segments and at the end rings. After a member of the engine-room crew had failed to relieve the trouble, an electrician was called in. Two segments were located that had been hot enough to melt the solder out of the joint between the bars and the risers. This appeared to be the seat of the trouble.

Before the commutator was opened it was blown out with
an air blast at the front and back to remove the copper and
carbon dust and prevent it from falling into the commutator
and giving trouble when the latter was opened.   One of the
bars that showed signs of being hot had welded to the rear
end ring, forming a ground.   As this bar passed from one
brush to the other the ground changed from the positive to the
negative bar. causing the ground lamps to flicker.   Consider-

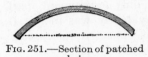

FIG. 251.—Section of patched
end ring.

able oil had crept along the shaft
and found its way into the commutator, starting the trouble by
causing the binder in the mica ring
to disintegrate.   Four segments were
removed so that a patch could be put in the mica ring, as shown
in Fig. 251.   The old ring was measured for thickness, and
two pieces of special ring mica were put in, with a thin piece
of clear mica covering each of the four joints.   A high-grade
shellac was used to hold the pieces in place until the commutator
was tightened and also to fill up the small openings in the
mica and keep oil out.

The risers used on this machine were poorly attached
to the commutator bars, being merely soldered in a shallow
slot in the center of the bar.   Before the heated segments
could be replaced it was found to be nesessary to scrape the
thin coating of solder from the riser and out of the slot in
order to make a good joint.   If a current is passed through a
soldered joint while the solder is hot enough to flow, the
structure of the solder is so changed that the resistance of the
joint is very much increased and will continue to give trouble
if worked near its original carrying capacity, although to all
appearance a good joint has been made.

When the commutator was built amber mica was used
between the bars.   About every two years it has been necessary to remove a few pieces, and these had been replaced by
micanite, which is supposed to be able to withstand the bad
effects of oil better than the former.   At this time 10 pieces
of mica that showed signs of pitting were taken out.   Two
pieces were of the original amber and the rest were micanite,
some of which had not been in service more than two years.

This case does not, however, afford a fair comparison between the two grades of mica.   If the leads had been poorly soldered into the riser or the riser into the bar, a high-resistance joint would have resulted, causing imperfect commutation with creepage of current across the mica between bars.   This creepage will in time break down the mica segment and thus short-circuit the bars.

In order to test for a short circuit, after the leads were soldered in and the commutator drawn tight the engine was started and the field switch closed.   If a short circuit had

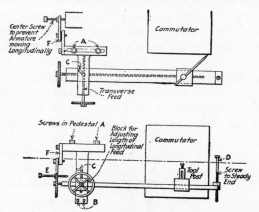

FIG. 252.—Method of attaching turning rig to machine showing its operation with tool upside down.

existed, it would have caused one or more coils to get hot in a few minutes, but such a condition was not observed in this case.

Since it had been necessary to turn this commutator so often, the owners had purchased a turning rig which was supposed to fit this machine.   A common difficulty of turning devices is that they seldom fit a machine unless made specially for it.   In this case if the rig had been put on the proper side of the pedestal it would have been necessary to leave the bearing cap off or to have the tool considerably above the center of the commutator.   In the latter instance, in case the tool caught, it would have dug into the commutator.   The only

other way by which the rig could be attached was to place it
so as to cut with the tool upside down. Although the rig
was not so steady as it would have been if worked in the correct position, no difficulty was encountered.

The turning rig used on this job was very easily attached.
It was unnecessary to remove a single brushholder in order
to put it in place. The screws at A in Fig. 252 held the main
part of the rig to the bearing cap. The two screws B were
screwed against the side of the pedestal to steady the end of
the rig. By loosening the screw C the transverse-feed length
was readily adjusted. The end of the transverse-feed arm
was supported by the long screw D resting on a brushholder
arm. To prevent any lateral motion of the armature, the
screw E was held in the center of the shaft by the adjustable
arm F.

Holder for Sandpapering Commutators.—In Fig. 253
there is shown a holder for use in sandpapering commutators
that makes it unnecessary to shape a block to fit the curved
surface of the commutator. This device as made by Peter
J. M. Clute (*Popular
Science Monthly*, June,
1919) consists essentially
of a handle which is
broadened at its lower
extremity, and has two
blocks, 2 by $2\frac{1}{2}$ in., with
an arc of a circle on each
face. These blocks are
pivoted, and will adjust
and accommodate them-
selves to any commu-
tator curvature. Two or
more of the blocks may be used, depending upon the size of
the commutator.

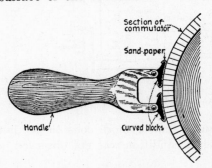

Fig. 253.—Convenient device for sandpapering a commutator.

**Use of a Portable Electric Drill to Undercut Mica of Com-
mutator.**—An interesting method of undercutting a commutator on which the mica had come to the surface after the
commutator had been turned, has been devised by R. H. N.
Lockyear, of Trail, B. C. (*Electrical Record*, June, 1918).

Mr. Lockyear describes as follows the circumstances under which the electric drill was successfully used for this purpose.

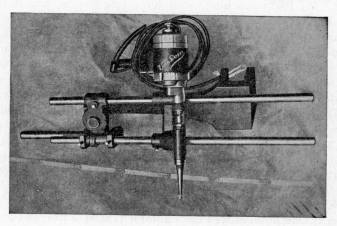

F𝗂g. 254.—Special arrangement to use a small portable electric drill to undercut mica on a commutator.

F𝗂g. 255.—Special rigging for the use of an electric drill shown mounted on a generator to undercut the commutator mica.

"The writer had occasion to undercut a commutator on a 500-kw. generator, the mica having come to the surface

26

after the commutator had been turned. Work had commenced by hand but it was found difficult to make headway. We had a machine for undercutting railway commutators having a width of about three inches. This machine was rebuilt with longer guide rods and a bracket made for mounting it on the brush shifting yoke of the generator. This machine was connected with a flexible shaft but soon discarded because of the vibration. It then occurred to the writer to direct connect a Van Dorn type DA-OO electric drill, which was available, to the spindle of a milling machine and undercut the mica with this equipment. The scheme proved most effective and since that time we have used it on 26 generators with a great saving of time, which is an important factor in a power plant when repairing large generators. In the tool we employ, the cutter has a speed of 1650 rpm., a diameter of $\frac{3}{4}$-in., and a thickness of 0.003 in."

Jerky Operation of New Commutator Traced to Burred Commutator Bars.—In some instances where it has been necessary to temporarily reduce the speed of a series motor and there have not been available suitable resistances for connecting in series with the armature, the desired result has been obtained by connecting a resistance across the brushes. The resistance so disposed not only diverts part of the line current from the armature, but also provides an external path through which the motor armature can act as a generator, thereby producing a braking effect. The extreme of this condition is active when a railway motor flashes over from brush to brush. The current generated through the short circuit formed by the arc is so great that the suddenly imposed load checks the speed of the armature, the sudden checking of the speed constituting what railway men call "bucking." An action which is similar in kind but which is milder in degree, occurs when an armature coil is short-circuited. The coil becomes a short-circuited loop moving in a strong field, and the local current of the coil is so heavy and the drag imposed by it so great that the remainder of the armature may be unable to support continuous motion. Under this condition the armature will turn in jerks, because the resisting drag of the short-circuited coil is greater in some positions than in others.

In a certain case (*Electrical Record*, June, 1918) a new commutator was installed on a direct-current armature which had operated normally up to the time of removing the old commutator. After installing the new commutator, on trying to start in the usual manner, the armature would turn very slowly and in jerks, and if the starter were advanced half of its travel the breaker would blow. An ammeter was connected in series with the armature, and the current was found to be of almost full-load value on the first notch of the starter. A bar to bar test was made around the commutator and nearly all of the armature coils appeared to have zero resistance. Just at this time, full-load current being in the armature, which was blocked so that it could not return, an explosion accompanied by a flash occurred on the commutator. Investigation disclosed a burn between two bars in the groove that is turned in the rear end of a commutator. Close inspection showed that the groove appeared as a continuous copper band extending entirely around the commutator. In cutting the groove the tool had been allowed to drag the copper over from bar to bar all round the commutator. On clearing the mica bodies of the copper bridges, operation became normal.

Why Brush Studs Heated on an Eight-pole Machine.—The accompanying diagram shows the paths of the current through a multiple connected armature that is used in a four-pole machine, the two brush studs of the same polarity being connected by means of copper busses with ends strung onto the studs that are to be connected. The incoming current arriving at brush *a* divides among three paths in order to reach

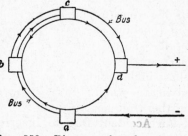

Fig. 256.—Diagram of paths of current through armature.

brush *d* to which the other end of the external circuit is connected. One path, *ad*, is directly through one-quarter of the armature to *d*; the second path is through one-quarter of the armature to brush *b* and thence by way of bus *bd* to brush *d* and out; the third path carries as much current as the two others combined; it runs through bus ac to c where it divides equally, half passing through the upper right hand quarter of the armature directly to d and out and the other half through the upper left hand quarter of the armature to brush b and thence by way of bd to d and out.   With the busses of negligible resistance and the sets of brushes equally spaced on the commutator all of the studs would carry approximately equal currents.

On an eight-pole machine there are more current ramifications because there are more studs and more busses and, therefore, there are more paths for the current.

It was on such a machine in a particular plant, that two of the brush studs would get so hot as to burn the insulating bushings by means of which the studs were insulated from the yoke.   Investigation disclosed that the machine was abusively overloaded and that all studs heated above normal but that only two got hot enough to burn bushings.   An inspector suggested that the heating was due to the generally poor condition of all contacts and especially to the poor contacts between the stud threads and the threads of the nuts by means of which the busses, the yoke, the washers and the studs were held together.

Acting on this theory, V-shaped pieces of copper strap were formed and so installed on the studs as to form a conducting bridge from the outside nut and washer over the yoke (without touching the yoke) to the inside nut and washer.   This bridge short-circuited all contacts with which the threaded parts of the studs were involved.   The scheme worked so well that similar bridges were installed on all of the studs.   After giving the whole stud construction a good cleaning there was no further trouble.

An Accident Due to Incorrectly Set Brushes.—In a case where an isolated plant was furnishing a meat packer with electric power at 110 volts for a 10-hp. motor, in order to provide emergency service, connections were made to the central station's 220-volt mains.   The higher voltage required the installation of an additional motor with its separate starter. When the new 220-volt motor was installed no electrical test was made until the work had been completed and the belt put on the pulleys. With all the machines connected to the line shaft, the motor was started with the following results. (R. L. Hervey, *Electrical World*, Jan. 13, 1917). An operator observed that the speed was excessive and ran to the switch box, missing by about six inches a piece of the rim of a 36-in. iron pulley; another piece went through the roof. Before the motor stopped the line shaft was bent and the boxes thrown out of line by the unbalancing of the pulleys. The dealer who sold the motor was held responsible for the damage, and therefore had an examination made. The connections were found correct, but the rocker arm was loose and the brushes were about 60 electrical degrees back of the neutral position.

Before the motor was started the brushes were set as closely to the neutral as could be by tracing out the armature leads. The line and armature wires were taken off the starter to test the magnetic switches, which were found to be working properly. The line wire was then re-connected and the shunt field tested and found complete by observing the flash when the switch opened and by holding an iron bolt against the field poles to test the pull of each pole. With the belt off, the brushes set approximately correct and a current in the shunt field, the armature connection was made and the switches closed, the motor started and ran as nicely as could be wished for. This little bit of carelessness in not testing the motor before putting on the belt caused a shutdown for seven hours, an expenditure of $24 in repairs and endangered the life of one man.

Wrong Setting of Brushes for Direction of Rotation Caused Motor to Flash.—If line voltage be applied to a shunt-wound motor without using any starting resistance in the armature circuit, the immediate result is likely to be the blowing of a fuse or the opening of a circuit breaker, because the armature resistance is so low compared to the resistance of the field winding that the latter is unable to get current for producing the field on which starting depends. In the case of a small motor, the fuse may hold and the motor may start without demonstration because the maximum current involved is small. A large motor is apt to flash and the brushes to burn owing to their being unable to handle an abnormal current. Shunt-wound motors operate better with their brushes set a little back of neutral than they do with the brushes set forward of neutral or on neutral, because with a slight backward shift field distortion helps commutation.

In one case mentioned by E. C. Parham (*Electrical Record*, October, 1918), a 20-hp. motor had been overhauled and was to be given a light running test. As there was no starting box available, it was necessary to start the motor from full voltage through a switch and also a circuit breaker. On closing the breaker and then closing the switch, there was a heavy flash at the brushes followed by blowing of the circuit breaker, but the motor failed to start. Thinking that the flashing might be due to full voltage being applied to armature and field connected in parallel and without a starting resistance, the motor was re-connected so that its field became energized on closing the breaker, the armature receiving current on closing the switch after closing the breaker. An attempt to start again caused flashing and blowing of the breaker, but this time the armature actually began to turn and it was observed to have started to turn in the wrong direction. On reversing the field connection, there was no further demonstration. All of the trouble was due to the brushes having a forward shift when the motor was connected to run in the wrong direction.

Proper Adjustment of a Reaction-type Brush-holder.— The angle at which a reaction-type brush-holder is set on a commutator plays an important part in the life of the brushes and commutator. When the brush is set against the direction of rotation of the commutator, as shown in Fig. 257, the correct setting of the brush is of greater importance than when set in the opposite direction. If the brush is set too straight, the friction will pull it away from the holder and cause a chattering and sparking. If it is set too flat, there will be a tendency for the brush to wedge between the holder and the commutator. Some machine manufacturers using this style of brush-holder furnish a templet by which the holder can be accurately set, and in such a case it should be carefully used.

R. L. Hervey (*Electrical World*, Jan. 22, 1916) relates a case where he was called upon to locate the cause of sparking on a generator using this type of holder. Upon making inquiries it was learned that the engineer had purchased a sheet of high-grade carbon, so called, and made his own brushes. To save carbon and work, both ends were made with the same angle and the holder was turned to suit the brush. The brush length had been made so great that the arm pushed the brush away from the holder instead of against it. The length L (Fig. 257) should never be so great that end of arm B will be above the line AO drawn perpendicular to the face and through the arm center O. The manufacturers of this holder recommend that the holder be set as shown; nevertheless, there are a great many installations working in the opposite direction.

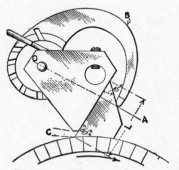

Fig. 257.—Diagram showing proper setting for reaction-type brush-holder.

Heating of Brush-holders Traced to Defective Contact Springs and Remedied by a Flexible Shunt.—R. L. Hervey (*Electrical World*, July 1, 1916) relates the following conditions in a case where his attention was called to the discoloring and heating of brush-holders on several generators. The holder was of the parallel-motion type, as shown in the sketch, Fig. 258. To prevent the burning of the hinge joints of the parallel motion, phosphor bronze springs 0.010 in. thick were used to carry the current around these points. As long as the contact between these thin springs and the moving arms was perfect no trouble occurred. But as soon as any part of the contact became defective an overload was thrown on the remaining contacts, causing overheating. The total contact area of the springs on the holders of the same polarity was 0.360 sq. in. for 250 amp. A properly designed contact to carry this amount of current should have $1\frac{3}{4}$ sq. in. of surface To relieve the trouble, the springs were taken out and replaced with a flexible shunt, as shown in the sketch. In such a case it should be mentioned that unless the soldering of the flexible wire into the lug is very carefully done the solder will get into the wire and stiffen it.   In order to prevent this, the shanks of the lugs were flattened with the wire in it, forming a very strong electrical joint.

The box type of construction of this holder afforded a substantial contact between the holder and the brush.   Due to the weight of the moving box and its supporting arms, however, this brush-holder was displaced by a stationary holder and sliding brush with a light spring.   With a high commutator speed, the heavy brush and holder does not follow the irregular-

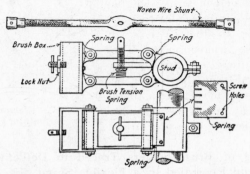

Fig. 258.—Substitution of woven wire shunt for springs of parallel motion brush-holder.

ities of the commutator as well as the lighter brush.   The brush that can move in its holder is better able to follow the grooves of the commutator as the armature weaves backward and forward in the bearings.   Although the brush-holder is usually considered a minor part of the motor or generator, it has held the attention of the designing engineer for a good many years and still needs the attention of the operator and repair man.

Simple Scheme for Banding Armatures.—The method shown in Fig. 259 has been found convenient in one repair shop (G. H. Vescelius, *Electrical World*, July 19, 1919, page 132) where a banding lathe and tension device was not available and only one man to do the work.   In using this scheme the free end of the banding wire is soldered to the armature anywhere and the latter rotated by means of a "dog" and pipe as indicated in the illustration until the wire has filled all of the banding grooves. In performing this operation no tension is exerted on the banding wire. Next, the remaining end of the wire is soldered to the armature and a weighted pulley hung on a loop of the banding wire nearest this end.

By selecting a weight twice as heavy in pounds as the desired tension in pounds per square inch the wire will be drawn up to the correct tension by rotating the armature backward. At any time when it is necessary to adjust the position of the banding wire this can be done easily by the person turning the armature because the tension will not be relieved as would happen when banding in the ordinary manner.

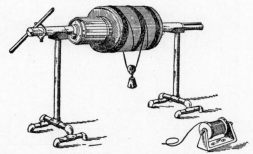

Fig. 259.—Weighted pulley in place for producing tension in banding wire.

Use of a Crane to Band an Armature in an Emergency.— In a large railway substation it was necessary to replace the banding wire on the armature of a 1000-kw. rotary converter. The bands required about 20 turns of steel wire. The scheme tried at first was to mount the steel wire reel so as to turn freely and pass the wire through a tension regulator consisting of two fiber-lined blocks bolted together. The wire was then wound on the armature as evenly as possible by turning it with bars, a method which was found slow and clumsy. The rotary was of the type that is brought up to speed with an induction motor with its rotor mounted on the shaft of the rotary armature. The idea was therefore conceived of removing the stator of the induction motor and using the rotor as a drum or pulley to rotate the rotary armature.

Three turns of a 1.25-inch rope were wound on this rotor and one end fastened to the hook of a traveling crane. The crane was then run the full length of the station with one man feeding the rope to the drum and keeping it taut. In this way a smooth, tight band was wound on the rotary armature with considerable saving in time over turning it by hand.

Method Used to Band a 2000-Hp. Rotor.—The banding of armatures and rotors, when done in a factory where such jobs are an every-day occurrence, has been more or less reduced to a science and the methods of procedure are many. When, however, the rotor to be banded reaches the 2000-hp. mark,

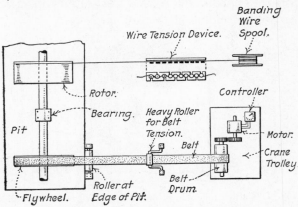

Fig. 260.—An arrangement devised to band a 2000-hp. motor armature.

it is out of the question to think of transporting it to the repair shop. Such a problem came up in a steel mill at one time when a 2000-hp. motor which operated the rolls became seriously grounded. The following method was decided upon (Maurice S. Clement, *Electrical Record*, April, 1919): The entire trolley of a traveling crane was lowered to the floor and placed in line with a huge fly-wheel which was on the same shaft as the rotor. The cable drum of the crane trolley was converted into a belt drum by covering it with canvas which was held in place by means of friction tape. This made a more or less flat surface and eliminated both the cable grooves and the grease from the face of the belt.

As the lower half of the fly-wheel was in a pit, it was necessary to place a roller at the edge of this pit as a belt runner. Another roller was placed on a frame somewhat resembling a large brace, both ends of which were secured to the floor, halfway between the crane trolley. The fly-wheel was arranged so as to ride the belt and serve as a belt tightener. The banding wire tension device used in this case was similar in principle to those used on wire nail machines, the sheaves being adjustable in the slots so as to tighten or slacken the wire at a moment's notice.

An Improvised Method Used to Turn a Commutator.—In a case where a rush order was received by a repair shop to turn the commutator of a generator at a large country house, R. L. Hervey (*Electrical World*, June 10, 1916) de-

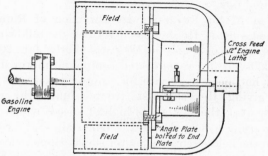

Fig. 261.—Method of using lathe cross-feed in turning a commutator.

scribes the following method of doing the work when the small turning rig which was taken along was found too small. In the garage, however, a large engine lathe was found. This started an examination to determine whether the armature could be taken out and swung in the lathe. This promised impossible. While looking around the shop an angle plate was uncovered. This plate and the cross-feed of the lathe were bolted together by a special screw of the rig. The plate was then bolted to the end plate of the generator frame, as shown in Fig. 261. There was but one bolt holding the angle plate on the generator frame, which made the equipment look very unsteady. A hole in the angle plate was selected so that, if the plate turned around the bolt, the tool would swing away from the commutator and not into it. The screw of the cross-feed was too short to take a cut across the commutator, therefore the tool had to be re-set for each cut. This was a little troublesome as the tool had to be tapped into position with a hammer. The commutator had grooves in it about ¼ inch deep, requiring considerable cutting. However, the job was satisfactorily done with this arrangement.

The generator was direct connected to a low-speed horizontal gasoline engine. While working on the commutator the valves were taken out to prevent compression, and the turning effort provided by a 1-hp. motor belted to the fly-wheel. The electrical equipment of the plant consisted of the generator and a storage battery of 58 lead cells. These supplied current for the lights, a motor-driven ice machine, laundry, water-pump and machine tools in the garage.

Cause of Motor Reversing its Direction of Rotation on High Speed.—R. L. Hervey has described the following peculiar performance of a motor (*Electrical World*, Jan. 20, 1917): A 2-hp. 220-volt direct-connected compound motor driving a band saw had been in service for approximately 18 months without giving the slightest trouble until the operator wanted to work the saw at its highest speed, which was obtained by using a field rheostat. When all of the resistance was cut in the field circuit the motor slowly came to a stop and started in the opposite direction. This was tried several times, and resulted in blowing the fuses most of the times. There could be but one condition that would cause this reversal of direction of rotation, namely, the compound winding being in opposition to the shunt field and overcoming it when the shunt field was weakened. By reversing the compound field leads the trouble was removed. This motor had been in operation for a year and a half without any indication of anything being wrong. The brushes and commutator were in excellent condition, which speaks well for the design of the machine.

Checking Connections of an Inter pole Motor.—The polarity of the interpole field coils should be the same as that of the preceding main poles in a direction against the rotation. The polarity of the interpole field with relation to the main fields for both directions of rotation of motors and generators is shown in Fig. 262. To determine the proper connections of interpoles proceed as follows:

As a rule one end of the interpole field and one armature lead are permanently connected together, and since the correct

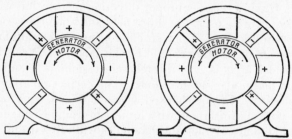

FIG. 262.—Polarity of interpole fields with relation to main fields for directions of rotation of motors and generators.

polarity is determined by the manufacturer, there is no occasion to change it. To reverse the direction of rotation the armature and the interpole field must be reversed as a unit. Reversed interpole connection is not noticeable at light load. As load is applied, a motor with reversed interpoles will spark

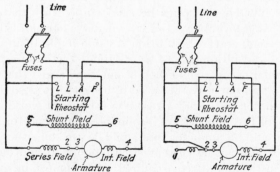

FIG. 263.—Connections for testing out correct connections of interpole windings for proper armature rotation.

badly and drop in speed, while on a generator difficulty will be experienced in maintaining rated voltage. Assuming that one end of the interpole field and one armature lead are permanently connected, wire the machine temporarily as a series motor with the shunt field disconnected. Care should be taken to apply the current only momentarily to prevent too high an armature speed.

The connections for this test are shown in Fig. 263.   If direction of rotation is wrong, interchange terminals 3 and 4 or 1 and 2.   Having secured proper direction of rotation with the series connection, insert the shunt field and open the series field as shown in Fig. 263.   Upon starting up again as a shunt motor, the direction of rotation should be the same as it was with the series field.   If it is not, interchange terminals 5 and 6 and make up permanent connections.   The correct polarity of the interpoles may then be checked with a compass or by bridging a main pole and interpole with a piece of iron, bearing in mind that unlike poles attract and like poles will repel it and checking with the diagrams in Fig. 263.

Heating of Field Coils Traced to Wrong Type of Starting Box.—On motors that are designed for field control of speed, E. C. Parham has pointed out (*Electrical Record*, February, 1919) that the shunt winding is likely to be lighter than that of a motor where the shunt winding is to be subjected continuously to full operating voltage.   Therefore if the shunt field of such a variable speed motor is connected to full voltage continuously, it will heat beyond the usual temperature guarantees. If the line voltage happens to run well above normal, as it often does, the temperature will reach a value liable to injure the insulation and ultimately to short-circuit the winding.

The owner of a machine shop at one time asked that a man be sent to find out why the speed of his motor was so low and why the motor got so hot after several hours of working.   As this was all the information obtainable, the inspector took a voltmeter and an ammeter that could be used on either direct-current or alternating-current circuits, only to find out later that no instruments were required.   The motor in question proved to be of the variable speed, field control, type.   There was no name plate on the motor, but the type was inferred from the type of resistance box which had been furnished with it but which was not being used.   The motor was being operated as a constant speed motor on voltage that was 15 per cent. above normal.   Of course the maximum speed obtainable was that due to full field hot.   The field coils heated too much but did not heat sufficiently for their increased resistance to give the speed required. In order to bring the speed to the necessary value and at the same time relieve the field coils, the resistance box, which had many taps, was connected in series with the field coils and different tap wires tried until one was found that gave approximately the proper speed. As the load of the motor was comparatively light there were no objectionable features attending the starting of the motor on a weakened field, so the connection was made permanent with the understanding that the operator would immediately get a starter that was adapted to the work.

Safe Operating Temperature of Portable Desk Fans.— A well-known manufacturer of fan motors points out that warm weather always brings a number of complaints in regard to heating of small motors. These complaints are usually from dealers or users who are possessed with the idea that if the motor-body does not feel nice and cool to the hand, the windings are in imminent danger of burning out. The latest standardization rules of the American Institute of Electrical Engineers provide that, in motors with the class of insulation used in reliable makes of motors, the temperature as recorded by a thermometer, should be within a limit of 80°C. This is equivalent to 176°F. No one would care to place his hand in contact with the frame of a motor at anywhere near that limit.

Let us say, for instance, that a small motor has a temperature rise of 40°F. when operated continuously. Such a motor operating on a day when the normal air temperature is 70°, would reach a temperature of only 110°, which would feel only comfortably warm to the hand. The same motor, operating on a mid-summer day when the thermometer runs from 90 to 95°, will attain a temperature between 130 and 140°F. Any temperature over 120° is quite uncomfortable to the touch and gives rise to alarm on the part of the inexperienced motor user.

However, a motor with a surface temperature of 140° is in no danger of injury from overheating, and motor users who make complaint of the heating effect under such conditions should be advised to continue operating their motors until it is apparent that the windings are being damaged. Unless there is some odor of burning insulation, the motor can not be considered in danger.

An Adjustable Shunt for Series Fields of Exciters.—In adjusting the compound characteristics of three exciters for parallel operation in conjunction with a Tirrill regulator, it was found impossible to get the necessary series-field shunt adjustment with the shunt taps provided by the manufac-

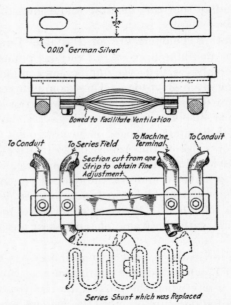

FIG. 264.—Construction of series-field shunt showing bowed formation to facilitate ventilation.

turers. Consequently each shunt was replaced by a very simple and easily adjustable shunt like that shown in Fig. 264, (Sydney Fisher, *Electrical World*, June 10, 1916). By means of these the characteristics of the machines were made practically identical. The shunt was made of strips of German silver slotted to permit the bowed formation shown. Rough adjustments were made by adding or removing strips, and finer adjustment obtained by varying the cross-section of one of the strips. The free passage offered to air through the shunt permits good ventilation with resulting low temperature from no load to full load. The construction of the shunt permited using the minimum number of connections, therefore they can be made much more readily than where more connections are required. This is an important consideration since the resistance of poor contacts becomes appreciable, the series-field resistance being small.

A Peculiar High-speed Motor Trouble.—On one occasion R. L. Hervey (*Electrical World*, Oct. 28, 1916) explains that a 500-volt 10-hp. direct-current motor, running at a speed of 3400 rpm., continued to open its circuit breakers every time an attempt was made to start it. The wiring contractor, after assuring himself that the connections were correct and that the trouble was inside the motor, refused to give more time to the job. The local representative of the machine company claimed that every machine turned out by his factory was given a 24-hour test, therefore the trouble could not be in the motor.

The motor was a shunt-wound, bipolar design, with two commutating poles. The three leads were marked A, F, and C, which were assumed to mean armature, field and line. After testing out the wiring between the starting box and the motor, the connections were made as stated above. Since the inertia of the machine parts to be started was large and the speed quite high, a large starting current was expected, so that the circuit breakers were set for their maximum current. An effort was made to start the motor to test the connections and also to observe its action when the voltage was applied, an ammeter having been connected in the circuit so that the starting current could be measured. When the starter handle reached the third button the current was 50 amp. The circuit breakers opened and the starter was smoking badly. These results indicated an open-field circuit. The internal connections of the motor were checked with considerable difficulty. The lead marked A was found to be the line and C the armature. After making this change the motor was started again with the same results. The machine representative objected to the motor being taken apart, but

27

yielded to persuasion. A small resistance tube connected in the shunt-field circuit was found in the bottom of the frame. While this tube could not be reached for examination, it was suspected of being the cause of the trouble, so a jumper was connected around it. Another effort to start the motor was successful. The motor speed was 3350 rpm. with a line voltage of 575. The resistance, after being patched, was connected in the field circuit when the speed measured 3730 rpm. As the motor was built for 3400 rpm. at 500 volts, it was thought that the factory test was made at that voltage and the resistance put in the field to bring up the speed. Since, however, the voltage was 575 at the place of installation, the speed of 3350 rpm. was high enough and as the resistance had had open-circuited once, it was decided to leave the resistance out to prevent future trouble.

Ways that End-play Variations Show Up.—The principal purpose of having end-play in the armature of a motor or of a generator is to keep the brushes from tracking in the same path and thereby wearing a groove in the commutator or in the collector rings as the case may be. To prevent such wearing of grooves, the armature end-thrust clearances are so disposed that when the armature is running in its normal zone, which is governed by the pull of the pole-pieces on the armature core, the thrust clearances at the two bearings are equal. Assuming the correct gear or pulley alignment to the connected load, the armature will never run sideways far enough to knock the bearing on either side; because when it has run over a certain distance, the field will pull it back toward and past the magnetic center. The same action will then be repeated but in the opposite direction. If, however, the end-thrust is unequally distributed for any reason, or if the machine as a whole is not level, knocking will occur which in the case of small, high-speed machines may take the form of serious vibrations that are likely to pound down the bearing linings.

E. C. Parham (*General Electric Review*, January, 1916) has mentioned a case where four motors of fractional horsepower, which were direct connected to tool grinding wheels, were installed and three of the outfits gave entire satisfaction, but the fourth one vibrated so badly that it shook the whole supporting structure. The rotating elements of two of the units were then interchanged and the vibrations remained with the same rotor. Spinning the rotating element of the troublesome machine in a high-speed lathe proved the shaft to be perfectly straight. Close inspection disclosed that the end-play was not distributed on the faulty outfit in the same manner as on the faultless ones. All vibration was eliminated by loosening the thrust collar so that the rotor when running could center itself, then starting the motor and letting it slow and stop, and then tightening the collar.

Connections for Two 220-volt Motors When Operated on 440 Volts.—It is practical to operate two 220-volt 7-hp.

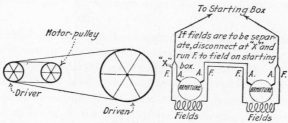

Fig. 265.—Belt arrangement for two motors operating in series and diagram for connecting two shunt motors in series.

motors in series on 440 volts and secure satisfactory results, providing that the motors are approximately the same as regards windings and speed. If the drive is by a belt and the motors run at the same speed a good plan is to set the motors with the pulleys in line and run a short belt from one to the other. That is, first belt the motors together by a short belt and then put the regular belt over the short belt as shown in Fig. 265. Another way is to couple the two armature shafts together with a suitable coupling and attach the driver pulley on one of the armature shafts.

The connections for two shunt-wound motors in series are shown in Fig. 265. The connections for two compound-wound motors in series and the connections for one shunt-wound motor and one compound-wound motor in series in Fig. 266.   (Frank Hoskinson, *Electrical Record*, September, 1917.)

In case one of the motors is higher in speed than the other one, it may be advisable to use different sizes of pulleys so as to secure the proper speed.

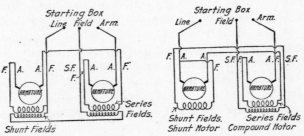

FIG. 266.—At the left, diagram for connecting two compound motors in series and, at the right, series connections for one shunt motor and one compound motor.

Cleaning Motors with Compressed Air.—When using compressed air to clean out dirt and dust from motor windings the pressure should not be higher than 100 lbs. gauge.   The air can be applied by the use of a rubber hose about ½ inch in diameter fitted with a short piece of ⅛-inch iron pipe to act as a nozzle and direct the air into the windings so as to blow out accumulated dirt.

Most motor windings are impregnated or painted with some sort of insulating varnish and this usually presents such a smooth surface that air, even at extremely high velocity, is not likely to lift the edges nor tear the insulating fabric.   If the dust that accumulates in the motor is of an abrasive character, it is by all odds more advisable to use a higher pressure than mentioned and get rid of the dust than to let the dust pile up until it stops ventilation of the windings and perhaps even cuts the insulation.

Testing out Phase-rotation.—Manufacturers of alternating-current generators generally have a standard direction of rotation—clockwise, for example—and likewise there is adopted a standard direction of phase-rotation.   This is necessary, because alternators that are to be operated in parallel must have their phase-rotations the same.   The adopted phase-rotation bears a definite relation to the numbering of the alternator terminal blocks. For example, the blocks of a three-phase alternator would be numbered 1, 2 and 3 and the standard phase-rotation would be in the same order. The phase-rotation of every alternator produced is tested by means of a phase-rotation tester. The tester is virtually an induction motor—in fact, a standard motor could be used as a phase-rotation indicator. The rotor of the tester, however, is simply a vane of iron free to turn under the influence of the stator magnetism. The stator winding of a three-phase indicator has three terminals, which are marked 1, 2 and 3. These terminals are connected to corresponding terminals of the alternator the phase-rotation of which is to be tested. Reduced voltage is applied to the stator of the alternator and the direction of rotation of the vane of the indicator shows the phase-rotation of the alternator.

When an induction motor is used as a phase-rotation indicator it should be connected first to the supply end of one machine and then to the other. If the motor rotates in the same direction it shows the phase-rotation of the two machines to be the same. If the rotation reverses, one phase of one of the alternators should be reversed.

An Induction Motor Trouble Due to Wrong Stator Connections.—The importance of checking up connections of induction motor windings is shown by the following trouble experienced by A. C. Hewitt (*Electrical World*, Jan. 16, 1916). In a cement plant where a 50-hp., three-phase, 440-volt, 60-cycle squirrel-cage induction motor operating at 450 rpm. was used to drive a 33-inch Fuller mill for pulverizing limestone the motor on several occasions was overloaded by feeding the material to the mill too fast and in large sizes. This overloading, combined with fluctuations of voltage as much as 30 per cent. below normal rating, caused the motor to heat and finally called for the replacing of several stator coils. The motor was repaired by the plant electrician and again placed in operation, but still it ran hot, with the mill showing a smaller output than a duplicate installation where the motor was running cooler.

When called to investigate the installation the repairman

noticed that the upper half of the motor was much hotter than the lower half. An inspection of the connections seemed to show that they were correctly made and that there were no grounds or open circuits. The fuses were in good condition and the auto-transformer motor starter operated satisfactorily. All of the connections for the starter windings checked with the diagram furnished with the motor.

The winding was a two-circuit delta arrangement and the motor had 16 poles. In checking over the number of poles in each of the two circuits it was finally found that the winding was divided in a horizontal plane through the stator, and that instead of each circuit having eight poles the upper circuit had only seven and the lower had nine poles. This explained why the upper half ran hotter than the lower. The electrician had made a miscount when connecting up the windings, with the result that the load was unevenly distributed. The connections were changed so that each circuit contained an equal number of poles, and the motor operated without the heating trouble previously experienced.

Stalling of Wound Rotor Induction Motor Explained.— A complete open circuit in the wound rotor of a polyphase induction motor, will prevent its starting because under such conditions there can be no secondary current. Such a complete open circuit may be caused by two of the rotor brushes being so stuck in their holders as to make no contact with the collector rings. An exception might obtain in the cases of fractional horsepower motors which are so small that the rotor may start by virtue of the eddy currents induced in the rotor laminations. However, the torque due to such reactions could support no load. The function of energy circuit of a repulsion induction single-phase motor is similar to that of the wound circuits of the rotor of a polyphase induction motor, in that both are the seat of the induced current by virtue of which the motor is able to do its duty Therefore a complete break in the energy circuit of a repulsion induction motor, will render the motor unable to start. That an incomplete open circuit in the energy circuit, may produce different results, is illustrated by the following experience.

A butcher complained that his motor-driven meat grinder

which had been working satisfactorily for months, was developing a tendency to slow down when coarse stock was fed into the hopper. With the finer stock, the motor apparently could do its work all right. On operating the motor with the end cover removed, vicious sparking was seen. At first this was thought to be caused by armature trouble but a close inspection disclosed that the sparking was due to the energy brushes being stuck in the brush-holders. The brushes had worn so short that the brush shunts were jammed into the boxes and a few more jobs of grinding probably would have burned and worn the brushes entirely out of contact with the commutator. Even with the arcing, the energy current had been sufficient to support the lighter loads, although after installing new brushes, it became evident that the motor had been operating at reduced speed at all loads.

Loose Bearing Caused Induction Motor to Fail to Start.—H. Wilson (*Power*, August 5, 1919, page 231) describes the following experience after repairing a large three-phase induction motor, when an attempt was made to put it back into service. On closing the compensator switch to the starting position, the motor failed to start, although it was evident from the sound of the machine that it was getting current through its winding. The first thing that suggested itself was an open circuit, so the starting compensator was tested to see if the current was coming through single-phase only. In order to do this quickly, we disconnected the motor lead at the machine, and while the switch was held on the starting position a test lamp was connected across the different leads,

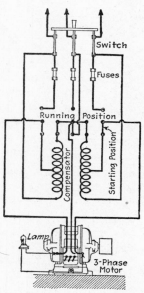

FIG. 267.—Method of testing for open-circuit.

as in Fig. 267. This showed current on each phase, at a reduced voltage, of course. We then put the switch on the

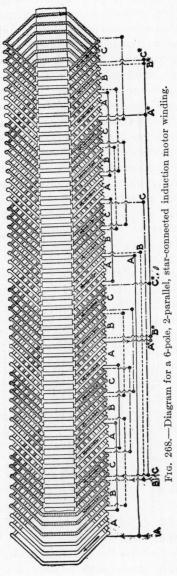

FIG. 268.—Diagram for a 6-pole, 2-parallel, star-connected induction motor winding.

running position and the test lamp burned brightly across each phase, showing that the motor was getting the current all right.

The rotor seemed to be rubbing a little on the stator, as it was somewhat hard to turn, so the clearance was adjusted by means of two draw-bolts on the bearing housings. This took some time, since when the bearings were moved one way a little, the rotor would bind; then we would shift it back slightly until finally getting it into a position where the rotor turned freely. Another attempt to start motor met with no better result than the first. The next step was to trace out the winding connections, which were found to be apparently correct. The winding being connected two parallel star made it somewhat complicated to trace out. However, by looking to see if the connections went under or over the winding, I would mark an arrow on the group of coils to show the polarity. We went around each phase in this way, starting with the outside lead in each case. The arrows on each group pointed alternately in opposite directions, showing the connections to be correct, as in Fig. 268.

The next suggestion was to test the polarity of the winding with a compass, when direct current was flowing through the coils. As a source of direct current an automobile starting and lighting battery was pressed into service. The three motor leads, A, B and C, Fig. 268, were joined together and connected to one terminal of the battery. A wire from the other battery terminal was taken to the common or neutral point on the winding, where the three phases connected together, such as $A*$, $B*$ and $C*$, Fig. 268. This connection was not attached permanently, as it would have run the battery down, owing to the low resistance of the circuit through the winding, but was attached each time only while the swing of the compass opposite each group was obtained. This test proved the connections to be correct, as the compass needle pointed in opposite directions on alternate groups as it was moved around the winding.

Since the polarity of the coils was undoubtedly correct, it left us all puzzled as to the cause of the trouble, as we had tested for grounds in the winding, open circuit, polarity, tested for the power at the motor terminal, and also mechanically, to see that rotor was free.

We had about decided to give the job up and send the machine to the manufacturers to have it fixed up, when one of the engineers came in on the job and after hearing our story remarked that the motor had given similar trouble, two or three years previous, after being repaired, due to the bearing letting the rotor rub on the stator. This gave us an idea that there might be a slight looseness in the bearing, sufficient to let the rotor lift up and rub on the stator. Acting on this, the bearing bolts were adjusted until the rotor would just clear the bottom of the stator. This proved to be the source of all the trouble; on closing the compensator the motor started up and ran satisfactorily, greatly to the relief of everybody concerned.

Three-phase Motors used on Single-phase Lines.—It often happens that utility customers have a supply of three-phase motors when only single-phase service is available, or that a customer is asked to purchase single-phase motors until the load becomes large enough to justify a three-phase line extension.   This difficulty can be overcome by a system patented by Professor Arno in which the inherent characteristics of three-phase motors are developed from a single-phase source of supply.

The system, which is used extensively in Australia, calls for the use of a three-phase master motor in addition to the three-phase power motors.   The master motor is a standard machine of either the squirrel-cage or wound-rotor type, and the larger the better.   The lower size limit of this motor is in practice about 10 to 15 per cent. of the total load connected to the system and is at least double the size of the next largest motor.

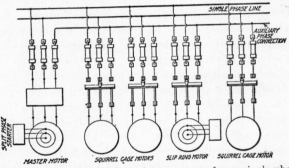

Fig. 269.—Method of operating 3-phase motors from single-phase line.
The four motors to the right are power motors, and the one to the left is a motor which has its third phase connected to the third phase of all the other motors.   The master motor is started up as a split-phase induction motor and runs light.   Its function is to supply auxiliary current to the third phase of the other motors, and by this means the 3-phase power motors are given practically the same characteristics as if they were operated from a 3-phase line.

All motors, including the master motor, are connected to the single-phase supply mains, and the third phases, which are not connected to the source of supply, are connected together.

The master motor is started up under no load with special starters equipped with an auxiliary winding similar to that used for the starting of split-phase induction motors.   The master motor should as a general rule run unloaded as a phase giver.   It is permissible, however, to load the master motor up to about 25 per cent. of its normal rating in special cases, but even when the master motor is running mechanically loaded, it may be electrically overloaded.   Any of the power motors becomes a master motor immediately its load is thrown off, and if the master motor cannot properly perform its function, a small unloaded power motor may become overloaded in helping out the master motor.

Through the voltage induced in the master motor's third phase, which is not connected to the supply mains, such motors at full speed are able to supply auxiliary current to the loaded motors during starting and overload periods. As long as the master motor is running the overload capacity of the loaded motors is raised, as compared with purely single-phase induction motors, and the three-phase motors are able to start up from the single-phase line with practically the same starting torque as they would have when connected to a polyphase line. Should all the motors including the master motor be loaded to the same extent in proportion to their rated capacity, no current would flow in the third-phase connections. After the master motor has been started up, the working motors can be started one after another as regular standard three-phase motors. The gain in efficiency by operating the individual motors as three-phase units is practically offset by the losses in the master motor, so that the overload efficiency of the whole installation is about the same as that of a straight single-phase system. The normal output of the power motors when operating in this manner is about 75 to 80 per cent. of their standard three-phase rating.

An Apparent Overload Trouble That was Traced to a Defective Fuse Block.—R. L. Hervey (*Electrical World*, June 24, 1916) relates the following trouble at a plating plant where a 5-hp. single-phase, induction motor, from apparent overload continued to blow fuses for several days and then refused to start. The motor had been in daily use for six years and the repairman, after examining the equipment, said that new bearings were needed as the rotor was rubbing the stator laminations. The shaft was also cut and grooved, which required it to be turned down so that the bearings could be properly fitted. After the motor had been replaced and in service for a few days the fuses started blowing again.

The repairman found one of the bearings hot, which was taken out and "eased up" a little. A few days later another shutdown occurred. This time the repairman reported that the motor was overloaded, and a larger motor was required. As the plant was being operated exactly as it had been for three years without a shutdown, the owner of the motor would not accept the report, and asked that a thorough examination be made to locate the trouble.

When putting in new reinforced fuses it was noticed that the fuse clips and block had been quite hot, for they were discolored and loose. The clips were closed up until they held the fuse tightly. A close examination of the motor and starter showed them to be in first-class condition. An ammeter was connected in the line and the motor started with no load. The current taken indicated that the winding was not defective. The load of two buffing wheels was then put on and the needle of the 50-amp. meter went off the scale. A further examination of the fuse block showed two loose connections. It was the heat generated by this high contact resistance that was causing the trouble with the fuses. It is very probable that while the rotor was rubbing the stator the motor was taking an excessive current and injured the fuse block. This instance shows the need of a careful inspection of all wiring when a repaired motor is again connected in circuit.

Cause of Noise in a Three-phase Motor Driving an Exhaust Fan.—The frequency of the current that is applied to the stator of an induction motor in commercial operation, ordinarily is constant within narrow limits if the speed of the prime mover to which the current is due, is as constant as it should be. The frequency of the current that is generated in the rotor of the motor, however, varies with the speed of the rotor, being greatest when the rotor is at rest and least when the rotor is operating at maximum speed. This is because the frequency of the rotor current depends on the difference of the speeds of the rotor and of the rotating field. In other words the frequency of the rotor current depends on the slip of the rotor. The principle of operation of frequency indicators of the vibrating type is, that the pendulum properties of each reed are such that it will respond synchronously to the impulses of but one value of frequency. On the same principle if a miscellaneous lot of pieces of iron and steel be subjected to the flux of an alternating current of varied frequency, some of the pieces will take up vibration at one value of frequency and other pieces will not be effected by that value of frequency but will take up vibration at some other value of the frequency.

In one case a large three-phase induction motor that was connected to an exhaust fan, was complained of on account of noise emitted and transmitted to all parts of the building when the motor was being started. The noise was described as a "clatter." An investigation disclosed that the noise occurred between narrow speed limits obtainable on the second notch of the controller and the sound was similar to that of rubbing a tin can with a piece of sandpaper. By throwing the controller back and forth between the first and second notches, there was obtained an average speed at which the noise was maintained almost continuously. By listening with the ear applied to different parts of the machine, and at the same time touching the machine here and there with a lead pencil, the source of the trouble was located in one of the slots in which slide the bolts that hold the motor frame to the sliding base. On each side of the machine extending from one bolt to the other, a steel strip was provided in order to keep the head of the bolt from turning when there was occasion to turn its nut with a wrench. The strip was so "bellied" that there was about $\frac{1}{16}$ inch clearance between the middle of the strip and the bottom of the machine which effectively constituted a reed supported at both ends, and the time element of the construction was such that the strip vibrated in response to rotor current frequency that obtained on the second notch of the controller. On removing the strip and re-bending so as to bring the bulged part up against the bottom of the rail, no further trouble was experienced with noise.

Cause of a Burned Out Starting Winding in a Single-phase Motor.—Unless of the commutator type, a single-phase motor, in order that it may be started without manual assistance, must include some phase-splitting device that is effective in producing the rotating field so necessary to self-starting of such motors. The phase-splitting device usually takes the form of an auxiliary starting winding and of an arrangement of resistance and inductance or of resistance and reactance, so disposed that the currents in the main stator winding and in the starting winding shall be out of phase with each other. As the starting winding is intended to be active for only a second or more, it is not proportioned to stand continuous application of the voltage. Accordingly, a centrifugal switch that turns with the rotor, is provided for automatically cutting out the starting winding as soon as the rotor approaches full speed. If for any reason the starting winding is left in circuit for appreciable time, the winding is likely to be injured.

In a certain instance (*Electrical Record*, August, 1918) one of these motors stopped a few minutes after having been started for the first time and, as the owner expressed it, "the motor had no more life in it." The motor was of the resistance-inductance self-starting type, in which the phase splitting was accomplished without the use of any external resistance or reactance. Examination of the motor disclosed that its failure had been due to the main stator winding being in series with the automatic switch which should have included only the starting winding. The motor would start all right, but the opening of the centrifugal switch would cut out the main winding, leaving the starting winding connected across the line. It developed that the motor had been bought at a low price because it was in bad condition and had been re-wound by a local repair man, who did o good job of winding, but a poor job of connecting.

Cause of One Motor Failing to Start While Another was Running on the Same Circuit.—At an industrial plant where 440-volt, three-phase, 60-cycle service was used to operate motors of many different sizes, a peculiar trouble was experienced by A. C. Hewitt (*Electrical World*, Jan. 8, 1916) when one of three fuses was blown on a feeder circuit. One feeder circuit supplied some four or five motors, one of which was rated at 75 hp. and the others at 10 hp. each. Each motor was equipped with a knife switch, fuses and starting compensator, and the feeder circuit was fused at the distributing switchboard. The 75-hp. motor was delta-connected, while the 10-hp. motors were connected "Y" (Fig. 270).

The 75-hp. motor was carrying a load of about 50 hp. Only one of the 10-hp. motors was in use, and it was driving a 7-hp.

load at the time the trouble developed. Both motors had been running for about four hours when it became necessary to stop the small motor for a few minutes. Upon trying to operate it again it refused to start. The electrician tested the motor fuses with two 250-volt lamps in series, without removing the fuses from the circuit, and found them good. The lamp test seemed to show, however, that the voltage between the middle and either outside wire was not as high as it should be. He then tested the fuses on the 75-hp. motor while the motor was running and found the same conditions

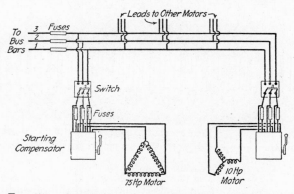

FIG. 270.—Connections when 10-hp. motor failed to start.

as with the 10-hp. motor. Evidently something was wrong, and with reduced voltage between the middle and outside wires it was natural to suppose that there was a high-resistance connection somewhere in that feeder. The large motor was stopped, and the fuses were tested as before, but this time no voltage at all was found between the middle and the outside wires. Then the electrician tried to check up the first results by starting the large motor, but since it was a squirrel-cage three-phase induction motor it would not start on a single-phase circuit.

He next tested the main-feeder fuses and found one of them had blown. A new feeder fuse was put in, and everything started off all right. The reduced voltage between the middle and the outside wires was just one-half of the line voltage, or 220 volts, since the middle wire amounted to a 50 per cent.

tap on the winding of the large motor when it was running single-phase. This case seemed quite a puzzler at the time, and it was thought at first that the reduced voltage on the middle wire was being generated in the large motor. However, a little study of the conditions soon made plain the real reason as explained.

Cause of Synchronous Motor Failing to Start.—E. C. Parham (*Power*, June 24, 1919) explains the following trouble with a synchronous motor in a large mill when it was necessary to repair the winding which had been damaged in a fire.

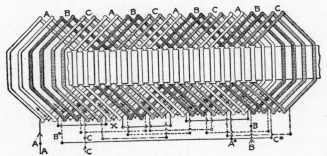

Fig. 271.—Pole-phase group shown reversed at ✕.

A complete set of coils was available and the rewinding was done by local repairmen. After completing the job, however, connecting the motor to its source of power failed to turn the rotor, although it had started very promptly before being damaged. Higher compensator taps were tried, but to no avail. An expert alternator winder was called from the factory and found that one pole-phase group of coils had been reversed as at *X*, Fig. 271. The interchanging of the leads of this group, as in Fig. 272, restored normal starting torque. It will be noticed that by tracing each phase through to the star connection in Fig. 272, the arrows point in opposite directions on adjacent pole-phase groups, which is the correct condition. In Fig. 271 the wrong connection is indicated by three adjacent arrows pointing in the same direction.

The existence of such a condition may be proved by connecting ammeters into each phase conductor and observing the intake currents while the rotor is turned by hand; a re-

versed pole-phase group of coils will greatly unbalance the
currents of the three wires. It is essential that the rotor be
rotated so as to equalize impedances due to different phases
including different amounts of iron in their magnetic circuits.

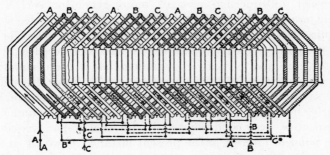

Fig. 272.—Correct connection for a 4-pole series-star winding.

**Effect of Decreased Frequency on Operation of an Induc-
tion Motor-generator Set.**—The immediate effect of operating
a generator below its rated speed is to increase the amount of
field current required in order to maintain normal voltage.
This is due mainly to the fact that the maintenance of normal
voltage under given load conditions requires that certain
number of field lines of force be cut each second by the armature conductors, and if the necessary rate of cutting can not
be obtained from the existing conductor rate of motion through
the existing field, the field strength must be increased until
the increase makes up for the lack of conductor speed. If
the field strength can not be increased in proportion to the
speed deficiency, voltage can not be maintained at its normal
value.

One effect of decreasing the frequency of the voltage that is
applied to an induction motor is to decrease proportionally
the speed of the motor and of its connected load. It follows,
then, that if an induction motor is the driving member of a
motor-generator set of which the driven member is a con-
tinuous-current generator, the effect of low frequency will be
to reduce the speed of the set. If the speed decrease is too
great, the generator field will not have sufficient margin to
permit of maintaining normal voltage at full load—the load

28

itself producing further speed reduction incident to the increase of the amount of motor slip.

E. C. Parham (*Electrical World*, Jan. 1, 1916) has referred to such a situation where an operator on a 50-cycle system specified, in ordering a small motor-generator set, a 60-cycle motor because he knew that ultimately his service would require 60-cycle operation. In ordering the 60-cycle set for temporary 50-cycle operation he had considered only the motor, and had felt safe in assuming that it could stand the larger current incident to operating on the lower frequency. The safety of such an assumption would largely depend on how nearly the motor would operate at its normal rating under the prospective load conditions and with the proper frequency. The point of interest in the present instance, however, is that when the 60-cycle set was put into service it was found impossible to maintain the generator voltage at normal value even with the generator field rheostat resistance all cut out. In order to get out of the difficulty it was necessary to install upon the generator a set of shunt-field coils that had a greater number of ampere-turns.

Alternating-current motors are designed and are rated to stand a reasonable departure from their voltage, current and frequency specifications, but before abusing them with eyes wide open it would be advisable for operators to ascertain the permissible limits of abnormal use.

Simple Rules for Re-connecting Alternating-current Motors. —The repairman should devise simple rules that he can remember easily so as to be able to handle simple changes in motors without having to study up the connections or ask his neighbor to explain them. A few such suggestions are given here as used by Maurice S. Clement (*Electrical Record*, October, 1918) for re-connecting a motor to suit changes in voltage, speed, etc. For example, if a three-phase, four-pole motor is to be changed to two-phase, four-pole, at the same time retaining the same speed, the grouping must be changed. A three-phase, four-pole connection has 12 groups; that is, one group to each pole, of which there are four, and four poles to each phase, giving 12 groups. Therefore, the number of poles multiplied by the number of phases gives the number of groups. By this rule a two-phase, four-pole machine has eight groups. The next element to be taken into consideration is the number of coils in each group.

In a three-phase, four-pole machine with 48 coils there would be four coils per group; with 36 slots, three coils per group. In a 48-coil, four-pole, three-phase machine there are 12 groups of four coils each. To change this to a two-phase, four-pole winding without change of speed, the following is the rule:

(Number of coils) ÷ (Number of poles × Phases)
$$= 48 \div (4 \times 2) = 6.$$

Therefore the new grouping will be arranged with six coils per group.

In changing the grouping of a 36-coil machine from four-pole, three-phase to four-pole, two-phase, the result becomes a trifle puzzling, as it apparently gives four and one-half coils per group. Since we know that cutting a coil in half to suit a particular grouping can not be done, the grouping of coils will be in the following order: 4, 4, 5, 5, 4, 4, 5, 5. This method accounts for the half coils and will be found to be evenly balanced. If the machine is to be changed from two-phase to three-phase, simply reverse the operation that is described above.

For general details for connecting alternating current motors, see Chapter XI.

Changing 440-volt Motor for 220-volt Operation.—The accompanying illustrations show how a 440-volt, 4-pole, 2-phase motor was reconnected for 220-volt operation by reconnecting the coils in parallel. The diagram of Fig. 273 (a) shows the original connections of the motor, and Fig. 273 (b) indicates the connection after the necessary alterations had been made. The changes indicated in the diagram, Fig. 273 (b), were made as follows:

Terminal X_1 was joined to the beginning of coil group A_1 and end of group A_4. Then the beginnings of groups A_3 and A_4 and ends of A_1 and A_2 were connected. Terminal X_2

was joined to the beginning and end of groups A_2 and A_3 respectively.   The *B*-phase coils were connected in a similar manner.

The foregoing alterations give very well-distributed end windings, which are considered essential to obtain a uniform flux distribution; but the impedance of the parallel circuits will be changed if the rotor runs off center, as may happen with a worm bearing, thus causing overheating.   On account of the small air gap usually found in alternating-current motors, there is small probability of this happening because worn bearings would cause the rotor to rub the stator before

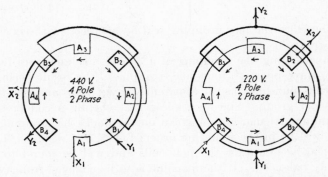

Fig. 273.—Motor winding before and after changing from 440 volts to 220 volts.

it would bring about overheating.   Unequal distribution of current between parallel windings due to a change of impedance may be avoided by connecting the coil groups which are diametrically opposite   Of course, this cannot be done with two parallel windings if one-half the number of poles is an odd number.

Multiple Connection Diagram for A.-C. Motor Windings. — Maurice S. Clement of Youngstown, Ohio, makes use of the diagram shown in Fig. 274 and claims that it saves a great deal of time in re-connecting alternating-current motors (*Electrical Record*, February, 1919).   This multiple connection winding diagram takes the place of four diagrams, since it can be used to show connections for single star, single delta, parallel star and parallel delta windings for alternating-current motors. In this instance a four-pole, three-phase diagram is shown, but the same plan can be used with different polarity and phasing.

The following are the formulas for the different connections:

SINGLE STAR

7, 9, 11 = Line
8 & 10 & 12 = Star
1 & 4   2 & 5   3 & 6 in Series

SINGLE DELTA

7 & 8 = Line
9 & 10 = Line
11 & 12 = Line
1 & 4   2 & 5   3 & 6 in Series

PARALLEL STAR

4 & 7 = Line
6 & 9 = Line
2 & 11 = Line
1 & 3 & 5   8 & 10 & 12 = Stars.

PARALLEL DELTA

7 & 4 & 8 & 5 = Line
2 & 11 & 3 & 12 = Line
1 & 10 & 9 & 6 = Line

When connecting a stator it is always well to look forward to the fact that some day the connections may be changed to suit other conditions, and that if the long connection is used it will be much easier to change. By long connection is meant this. If the reader will trace out the first phase of a single star on the sketch, he will find it to be 1 to 7 to 10 to 4; whereas, it is sometimes connected as follows: 1 to 4 to 7 to 10. By studying the sketch closely it will be seen that if the long connection method is used, the connection can be changed to any of the other three much easier than by the latter method, as half the connections do not have to be opened. Although the short connection is per-

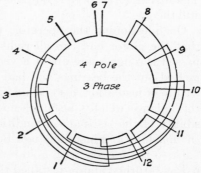

FIG. 274.—Diagram that can be used for connecting terminals of pole-phase-groups for single and parallel star and delta connections.

haps a wire saver by a couple of inches, the long connection is easier to understand and makes a much neater job.

Brush and Slip-ring Sparking Traced to Absence of Rotor Balancing Weights.—Manufacturing companies take particular care that the rotors of alternating-current machines and the armatures of direct-current machines are perfectly balanced before they are shipped either in machines or as extras. Some go so far as to balance rotors before and after installing the coils and the higher speed rotors of the slip-ring type may be balanced before and after installing the slip rings. Most of the balancing weight is applied by forcing lead into pockets provided in the core end plates for that purpose. That the absence of these weights may set up vibrations that cause roughening of the slip rings and ultimate sparking, is proven by the following experience:

In one shop (*Electrical Record*, August, 1918) a slip-ring motor had given much brush and slip-ring trouble. Turning of the rings and changing of the rings, brushes and holders, had given no permanent relief. A factory inspector at once diagnosed the cause of the trouble as vibration—which no one had suspected because it was in one of those shops where everything that moves vibrates. He tested the rotor in a lathe and found that the shaft was bent. The shaft was then straightened and it was thought that all trouble was at an end; but not so. The machine ran better, but there was considerable vibration still there.

On questioning the operator, the statement was obtained that the motor had run all right up to the time that it had passed through a fire about a year previously. The fire had melted out the bearings and had destroyed everything in the nature of insulation; also it had distorted the shaft and melted the balance weights although no one had considered the possibility of the last-named conditions at the time of re-winding the machine and installing new bearings. The rotor was sent back to the factory with a statement of its history and when it was returned and re-installed the motor, in the words of the owner, "ran like a new machine." Probably it was a new machine.

Overheating of an Induction Motor Traced to a Variation of Frequency.—Provided that an induction motor is not already overloaded, it is not considered abusive to operate the motor at less than 10 per cent. over voltage or at 10 per cent. under frequency. Manufacturers are careful to specify, however, that the motor should not be expected to stand without material increase in heating, the continuous application of 10 per cent. over voltage and 10 per cent. under frequency, because both of these variations are in the direction that tends to increase the heating. If the ammeter of an induction motor circuit be observed while the motor is being started, it will be seen that when the motor reaches nearly normal speed, the current drops suddenly to a value far below what existed immediately preceding the sudden drop. It is conceivable that certain voltage-frequency-load conditions might exist whereby the motor would be operating just on the high side of the critical point indicated. Under this condition the current would be abnormally large.

In one case a mill operator complained of the heating of one of his larger induction motors. He admitted that the motor was overloaded, but the overload was constant and this did not explain why the heating was so much greater during some periods than during others. When taking the motor speed during a period of maximum load, the inspector was much surprised to find that the speed was five per cent. above synchronism. The mill operator stated that over speeds had never been noticed, but he felt certain that there were times when the speed was considerably under normal. Investigation of the engine room equipment, disclosed that at times the steam pressure became so low that it was necessary for the engineer to operate the overload valve of the turbine in order to maintain its speed, hence frequency. The turbine generator was excited from an engine-driven exciter, the speed of which was not materially affected by the variations of steam pressure. As the frequency of the service applied to the motors depended on the speed of the turbine, which speed depended on steam conditions, while the voltage of the service applied to the motors depended on the turbine voltage which in turn depended not only on the turbine speed but on the turbine excitation which was independent of steam pressure variations, the extreme conditions of high voltage and low frequency, which may have obtained at times, can better be imagined than estimated. As the engine room conditions could not immediately be relieved, the duty of the abused motor was lightened by removing a few of the connected machines that constituted its load.

Relief for a Hot Bearing.—In case of a hot bearing, feed plenty of heavy oil, loosen the nuts on the bearing cap and slacken the belt if one is used. If no relief is shown, take off the load and run the machine slowly until the shaft is cool so that the bearing will not "freeze." If the bearing is of babbitt examine it to see that the oil grooves are still intact. If they are and the surface of the bearing has not been injured, renew the oil supply and start the machine again. Watch the oil rings to see that they are revolving properly and carrying plenty of oil to the shaft. A new machine or one in which the bearings have been renewed should be run at slow speed for an hour or more before the load is applied in order to see that the bearings are properly adjusted and worked in.

Static Sparks from Belts (*Instruction Book*, Westinghouse Electic & Mfg. Co.).—It sometimes occurs on belted machines, especially in dry weather, that charges of static electricity of considerable potential on the belt cause discharges to the ground. If the frame of the machine is not grounded, these charges may jump to the armature or field winding and then to the ground, puncturing the insulation. The belt and frame may be discharged by placing close to the belt, at a point near the machine pulley, a number of sharp metal points like a comb, which are carefully grounded. If the field frame is grounded, there should be no danger to the insulation.

Ratings of A.-C. Generators.—In the case of a single-phase generator, the rating in kva. is equal to the product of amperes and volts.

For a two-phase generator, the rating in kva. is equal to twice the output of one phase when the load is balanced.

For a three-phase generator the total rating in kva. is equal to the output of one phase multiplied by 1.732. That is, the readings or amperes and volts for one phase times 1.732 is equal to the kva. rating of the machine, when it carries a balanced load.

Alternating-current Motor Phase-rotation (*Instruction Book*, Westinghouse Electric & Mfg. Co.).—In order that the alternating-current wiring connections between the motor and its supply circuit may be correctly made to obtain a given direction of rotation, it is necessary to know the phase-rotation of the motor and the supply circuit. By "phase-rotation of the motor" is meant the order in which each phase reaches its maximum voltage of one polarity. When the machines are arranged for clockwise rotation, looking at the commutator end, the phase-rotation is given by the order of terminal notation. Using letters to designate the terminals of Westinghouse machines, the order for three-phase machines is B-C-A and for two-phase B_1-A_1 B_2-A_2.

The sequence of phase-rotation of the supply system can be found by tracing the wiring back to the generating station or else by the use of a phase-rotation indicator. When there are flexible cable leads on the alternating-current side, the simplest method of determining the proper order in which to connect the motor leads is to connect the leads in any convenient order and start the motor. If the direction of rotation is opposite to that desired, reverse any two leads in the case of a three-phase motor or interchange the two leads of either phase, in the case of a two-phase motor.

End Bells or Heads.—An end bell which is cracked can easily be welded, which process makes it just as good as new. If a bearing has been worn out or burned out, it must be relined. This work must be done by a machinist who appreciates the importance of a good bearing.

Brushes and Brush Holders.—When a brush holder is damaged to any great extent, it is advisable to order a new set from the factory as it would not pay to make a set in a repair shop. Carbon brushes are easily made, however, and dimensions should be exact so as to insure their working easily in the holder.

The Rotor.—Under certain conditions, a rotor will become so heated as to cause the solder to melt from its bars. When this happens the affected parts will rattle when the machine is run; resoldering the bars will remedy this. If the bars become damaged or bent, they should be removed, straightened, the slots reinsulated and rotor reassembled.

The Stator.—The troubles occurring in an alternating-current stator may be said to be very similar to those of an armature and most of the tests described can be used. For details of checking up errors in connections see Chapter XI, page 288.

Sizes of Fuses for A.-C. Motors.—The National Electrical Code does not specify the size of wire which should be used to connect up any given motor, nor does it give the sizes of starting and running fuses to be used. A committee of the

SQUIRREL-CAGE THREE-PHASE INDUCTION MOTORS EQUIPPED WITH AUTO-STARTERS

Average horsepower	Full-load amp.		Starting fuse amp.		Running fuse amp.	
	220 volts	550 volts	220 volts	550 volts	220 volts	550 volts
0.5......	1.8	0.7	5	5	5	5
1.0......	3.5	1.3	10	5	5	5
2.0......	6.5	2.6	20	10	10	5
3.0......	9.5	3.8	30	10	15	5
5.0......	15.4	6.2	40	15	20	10
7.5......	22.4	9.0	60	25	25	15
10.0......	29.0	11.8	70	30	35	15
15.0......	42.5	17.4	85	40	45	20
20.0......	55.0	22.5	110	55	60	25
25.0......	68.0	27.0	140	65	75	30
30.0......	80.0	32.0	160	70	90	35
35.0......	94.0	37.0	190	75	110	40
40.0......	105.0	42.0	210	85	115	45
50.0......	130.0	52.0	260	110	145	60
60.0......	155.0	62.0	310	125	170	70
75.0......	192.0	77.0	390	160	210	85
100.0......	252.0	101.0	500	200	280	110
150.0......	368.0	148.0	730	300	410	160
200.0......	484.0	195.0	920	390	530	215
250.0......	595.0	240.0	1200	480	650	265
300.0......	710.0	285.0	1420	570	780	315

Western Association of Electrical Inspectors has compiled the accompanying table based on the code rules which give this information for single-phase, two-phase and three-phase motors. Excerpts from the report and the recommendations for three-phase motors follow:

No consideration was given to limiting the voltage drop at the motor. Motors without a starting device and those operating at less than 600 r.p.m. require, in the majority of cases, one size larger wire or cable than the table calls for.

The wires in the table are calculated for two and one-half times the full load current of motors up to 30-amp. rating and for twice the full-load current of larger motors.

Wire or cable sizes for other types of continuous-duty induction motors should be based on the following multiples of the full-load current: Squirrel-cage motors up to 7.5 hp. without starters, three times full-load current; squirrel-cage motors with star-delta starting switch, one and a half times full-load current; wound-rotor motors with resistance in rotor, one and a tenth times full-load current, and single-phase repulsion motors up to 15 hp., twice, and single-phase motors with split-phase starting, three times full-load current.

CHAPTER XVII

MACHINE EQUIPMENT AND TOOLS NEEDED IN A
REPAIR SHOP

The work that comes to the average electrical repair shop varies from the re-winding a fan motor to the overhauling and re-winding of large station generators. In the latter case the work must, in the majority of cases, be done at the location of the machine and calls for more portable tools than machine equipment. To meet the requirements of work between these limits in size of machine there is needed a fairly well equipped machine shop. Most motor repair and armature winding work can be properly handled if the following equipment is available:

> Lathe.
> Coil-winding lathe heads.
> Shaper, or undercutting attachment for lathe.
> Drill press.
> Band saw.
> Emery wheel.
> Portable hand crane.
> Chain block.
> Welding outfit.
> Vices.
> Coil-pulling machine.
> Coil-taping machine.
> Banding machine or tension device for lathe.

In case only one lathe is available this should be large enough to accommodate a good sized armature and have a spread between head and tail post of about 60 inches. The shaper and band saw are rather special machines for a repair shop but very useful. The former serves as a rapid and accurate method for undercutting the mica of a commutator. The latter saves a great deal of time when many coil forms are to be cut for several coil winders.

In the electrical repair shop of a large industrial plant where a number of armatures are re-wound and repaired the following equipment is provided:

1   12-inch speed lathe.
1   24-inch armature-banding lathe.
1   24-inch commutator grooving lathe.
1   Commutator turning device.
1   Double head emery wheel grinder.
1   3-inch bench vice.
1   5-inch bench vice.
2   6-inch bench vices.
2   Field-winding machines.
2   Armature coil-taping machines.
1   One-ton electric hoist and carriage.

Fig. 275.—Armature winders' hand tools. (Numbers refer to their names and uses, page 446.)

Armature Winder's Tools.—The experienced armature winder usually has a variety of tools either designed according to his own ideas or convenience for a particular job or for use in connection with armatures of different sizes. In Figs. 275 and 276 a varied assortment of hand tools and drifts are shown. The names of these tools and their uses are given in the following tabulations.

Fig. 276.—Drifts used by armature winders. (Numbers refer to types and uses, page 447.)

ARMATURE WINDER'S HAND TOOLS (FIG. 275)

Number in illustration	Name of tool	Uses in winding armatures
1	Coil hook..................	To lift coils out of slots.
2	Medium file...............	For cleaning commutator necks before soldering.
3	Knife edge file..............	For trimming edges of mica segments.
4	16-oz. machinist's hammer.....	For use on metal surfaces.
5 and 6	No. 1 and No. 2 rawhide mallets.	For drifting coils into slots.
7	12-oz. machinist hammer.......	For use on metal surfaces.
8	Tinsmith's hammer...........	For peening slots of commutator necks.
9	Cold chisel.................	For cutting coil leads to commutator.
10	Coil lifter and shaper.........	For lifting coils out of slots and shaping when rewinding.
11 and 12	Metal drifts................	For driving down coil terminals in commutator necks.
13 and 15	Two sizes of wedge drivers.....	For driving wedges into slots.
14	Undercutting tool............	For undercutting mica on commutators.
16	Coil scraper................	For scraping cotton insulation off wires.
17	Diagonal cutters.............	Special pliers for rewinding work.
18	Half-round duck bill pliers.....	Special pliers for rewinding work.
19	Round-nose pliers............	Special pliers for rewinding work.
20	Small screw driver...........	For general use.
21	Shoemaker's knife,...........	For triming and cutting slot insulation.
22	Scissors....................	For cutting tape, and cotton duck.
23	Tinsmith's shears.............	For cutting tin clips for banding wires.
24	6-in. parallel pliers...........	For gripping wires in winding coils, etc.
25	8-in. side cutting pliers........	For cutting heavy wire coil terminals.
26	Flat duck bill pliers..........	For shaping coils.
27	Long metal coil drift..........	For lifting tight coils out of slots.
28	Monkey wrench..............	For tightening commutator, etc.
29	Large screw driver...........	For general use.

DRIFTS USED BY ARMATURE WINDERS (FIG. 276)

Number in illustration	Name of drift	Particular uses
1	Coil sliders or guides...........	For sliding top sides of coils into slots.
2	Different sizes of fiber slot drifts.	For driving coils into slots. They vary in width and length according to size of slot.
3, 4 and 5	Fiber coil shapers.............	The curved surfaces are used to shape ends of coils.
6	Fiber coil drift tapered.........	For lifting tight coils in small machines.
7	Small metal coil lifter..........	For lifting tight coils out of slots.
8	Center punch..................	For marking location and pitch of coil when stripping armature.
9, 10, 11 and 12	Lead lifters....................	For driving soldered ends out of commutator necks when stripping armature.
13, 14, 15, 18, 19, 20, 21 and 22	Metal drifts..................	For seating coil terminals in commutator necks.
16	Ordinary dividers.............	For laying out fiber collars.
17 and 23	Tee slot drifts................	For partly closed slots to drive coils down in slots.

Device for Shaping Insulating Cells of Armature Slots.—

For shaping the fish paper in making cells for armature and stator slots the cell shaper shown in Fig. 277 is very useful. It consists of two pieces of wood hinged together so that they will make a neat 90-deg. fold. The permanency of the correct-

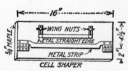

FIG. 277.—Device for shaping insulating cells of armature slots.

fold maker is insured by means of a metal strip attached to the wood slot. The cell shaper is used by inserting a piece of fish paper in the opening between the two blocks of wood, which is the length of the slot plus twice the height and whose width is the width of the slots. The metal straight-edge, which is adjustable by means of wing nuts, allows the paper to be folded so as to be made the height of the slot.

Tool for Cutting Cell Lining at Top of Slot.—

For cutting the projecting insulation of an armature slot after the coils have been assembled, the tool shown in Fig. 279 is recommended by Maurice S. Clement (*Electrical World*, Oct. 12, 1918). This

FIG. 218.—Convenient adjustable bench frame for winding small direct-current armatures and the tools most frequently needed.

tool as well as those of Figs. 280 and 282 and the insulating cell shaping device shown in Fig. 278 are home-made designs he has devised. It consists of a piece of forged steel 14 inches long by ¾ inch wide by 3⁄16 inch thick with a set of beveled knife-edges at one end and a file handle at the other.

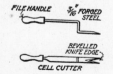

Special Winding Tools.—In Fig. 280 three convenient tools are shown that can be easily made by any armature winder. From left to right in the illustration they are a coil-taping needle, coil raiser, and wire scraper. The coil-taping needle can

FIG. 279.—Tool for cutting insulation that projects from slots.

be made from one foot of No. 14 banding wire shaped so that it can be used for taping coils in closed-slot stators. After the user is accustomed to this device high speed may be attained.

The coil raiser consists of a piece of steel, 16 inches by 1 by 3⁄16 inch with a four-inch one-sided taper on one end for strip-

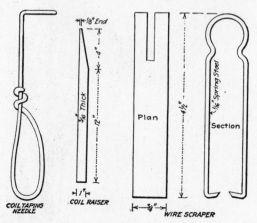

FIG. 280.—Convenient designs of coil taping needle, coil raiser and wire scraper.

ping open-slot armatures and stators. This also can be used to good advantage in removing grounded coils from a newly wound armature or in raising coils sufficiently to allow for insulating weak spots in the coils, the main object in this case

33

FIG. 281.—Tools most frequently used when winding stators of induction motors.

being to lift out a tight-fitting coil without damaging the insulation.

The wire scraper is very simply made and very economical, because it eliminates the use of a knife, whose life is short on account of the rough treatment accorded it. This device is made of spring metal, 12 inches by $\frac{3}{4}$ inch by $\frac{1}{16}$ inch. The knife-edges can be sharpened by means of a file and the tool used indefinitely. A section the shape of a rectangle is cut from the metal at the handle end, greatly increasing the spring effect of the device.

For driving fiber wedges between the top of a coil and the lamination overhanging closed-slots, a wedge drift, made of a piece of tool steel, eight inches by five inches by $\frac{3}{32}$ inch, over which is fitted a loose-fitting steel sleeve, $\frac{1}{16}$ inch thick, is very convenient. This is used by inserting the fiber wedge about $\frac{1}{4}$ inch into the slot; then, with the drift pulled back into the sleeve, the sleeve is fitted over the wedge, which is driven into the proper place, the sleeve holding the wedge in position.

Repair Tools that Can be Made from Old Hack-saw Blades.
Seven tools that have been made from old hack-saw blades

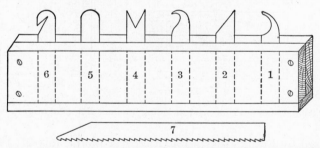

Fig. 282.—Seven armature repair tools made from old hack-saw blades that are useful around a motor repair bench.

and found useful in the re-winding of motors are shown in Fig. 282. A small wooden case to stow away these tools can be made as follows: Cut out two pieces of any suitable hard wood eight inches long, one and one-half inches wide and $\frac{1}{2}$ inch thick. Then on the flat side of one of these pieces cut several grooves, large enough to allow a hack-saw blade to fit in it snugly. The two pieces should then be nailed together so that the grooves will be between both pieces. When a third piece of wood, eight inches long, one inch wide and $\frac{1}{4}$ inch thick is nailed on as a bottom piece, the case is ready for the tools.

While each of the tools can be used for several different operations, a few of the most important uses are as follows: Tools one, two and five (from the right) are used mostly in taping coils. Tools one and two are used to best advantage in digging stray drops of solder out of the winding of a stator after the connections have been soldered. Tools four and six, which have both edges of the V sharpened to a knife-edge, are very well adapted to cutting insulation and scraping wires or leads. Number seven is used to drive wedges into tight slots. By setting the saw-teeth on the wedge and pounding on the beveled end with a hammer, the teeth are made to grip the wedge and drive it to its proper place.

Special Coil-winding Device.—For winding coils of practically any shape the special device shown in Fig. 283 has been

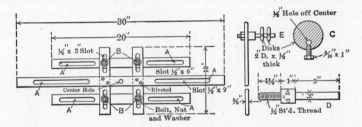

Fig. 283.—Framework for use in winding different shapes of armature coils.

devised by Frank Huskinson (*Electrical World*, July 27, 1918). It consists of an iron framework held together with four bolts shown at *B*. By loosening the nuts of these bolts the two outside members can be adjusted for any width of coil needed. To give the coil the proper shape, disks such as marked *C* are clamped on the piece *D* and the latter inserted in the slots marked *A* in the frame. The view at *E* shows how these disks appear when the bolt *D* is in its proper place in the frame. When forming the coils the wire is wound around six of the bolts or pegs and between the disks mounted on them.

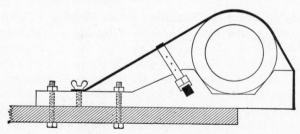

Fig. 284.—Convenient bench device for holding the stator of a small motor when repairing windings.

Fig. 285.—At the left a vertical stand is shown for use in mounting the commutator on small armatures. At the right, a large armature being wound with pushed-through coils.

Steadying Brace for Repairing Small Motors.—The device shown in Fig. 284 has been devised by Maurice S. Clement (*Electrical Record*, December, 1918) for use in repairing fan motors or other small motors when it is necessary to remove the winding of the stator from the frame. To remove these windings from the frame the laminations must be removed with the winding. When once removed it is very difficult to work on it as it has a tendency to roll away all the time.

This brace is constructed as follows: A block is cut as shown and bolted to the bench. One end of a length of ribbon copper wire about $\frac{1}{16}$ inch thick and $\frac{1}{2}$ inch wide is then screwed to the end of the block and passed over the winding which sets in the cut out portion of the block. The other end of the copper ribbon is held down by means of a wing nut placed between the bolts. A leather strap is arranged from one side of the block, over the copper ribbon and fastened to a buckle on the other side. This is a tension strap and takes the slack out of the copper ribbon.

Tension Block For Use When Banding Armatures.—A tool is shown in Fig. 286 which has been devised by Maurice S.

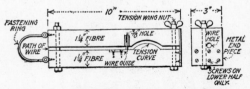

Fig. 286.—Tension block for use when winding armatures.

Clement (*Electrical World*, Oct. 12, 1918) for banding an armature in a small repair shop where a banding lathe is not available. By use of the device the armature can be banded on an ordinary winding stand which is securely fastened to the floor or work bench. When this device is used about one foot of stout line with a hook attached to one end is made fast to the ring on the tension block and hooked to an eye-bolt which is set in the floor for that purpose. The spool of banding wire is placed on a small stand beside the eye-bolt and the wire is passed between the two blocks at the rear end through the hole in the first wire guide over the tension curve and through the second wire guide hole and then to the armature. The tension can be regulated by the wing nut placed at the forward upper end of the block. By screwing down the wing nut both sides of the block are brought nearer together, thus

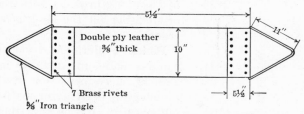

Fig. 287.—Armature sling made up of double-ply leather belting.

narrowing the tension curve over which the wire must pass. This increases the tightness of the band when a pipe wrench can be used to revolve the armature.

Fig. 288.—Method of using a rope sling in handling armatures with a crane.

Armature Sling.—For handling heavy armatures in repair shops a sling is sometimes used instead of lifting by means of a rope attached to the ends of the shaft as a bale handle for the crane hook. The sling prevents the possibility of springing the shaft. A sling which can be used for handling small armatures is shown in Fig. 287. It is constructed of a piece of double ply belting about ⅜ inch thick, 10 inches wide and

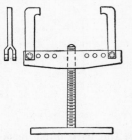

5½ feet long, provided with triangles of steel bar for the hook of a shop crane.

Pinion Puller.—A device which can be made up as shown in Fig. 289 is convenient for removing pinion gears from motor shafts without injury. By making the head sufficiently long and providing holes at suitable distances, pinions of

FIG. 289.—Convenient device for removing pinions from a motor shaft.

different sizes can be removed by adjusting the end pieces.

Coil-winding Machines.—In Fig. 290 a device is shown which does not require the use of forms when winding armature coils. It consists of an adjustable metal frame with jaws which may be clamped in various positions so as to make a form over which the wire can be wound into the

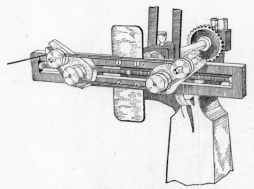

FIG. 290.—Segur armature coil winder for winding hair-pin loop, obtuse loop and rectangular loop coils. (*Electrical Manufacturers Equipment Company.*)

With this device loops from 3 inches to 36 inches can be wound. By means of the spreader shown in Fig. 291 the coil shapes shown in Fig. 292 can be formed from these loops.

shape of the coil desired. Jaws are provided for forming hairpin loop coils, that is, coils with parallel sides and curved ends.

Another set of jaws provided with the machine has four points and gives four curves to the coil, the jaws being set so as to form a rectangular coil with two angles obtuse and two angles acute. These same jaws may be set in another way so as to give a triangular or square loop. With these attachments, coils of various shapes can be wound, some of the shapes being suitable for use directly in various types of motors and generators and other coils requiring further operations on a machine called a spreader. The purpose of this machine (Fig. 291) is to form the coil to the throw required when it is

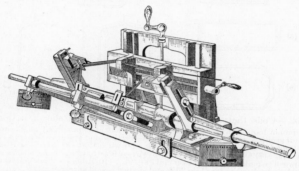

FIG. 291.—Coil spreader for shaping the coils shown in Fig 292 as wound on the machine shown Fig. 290. (*Electrical Manufacturers Equipment Company.*)

inserted in the armature or stator. The spreader takes the coil as it is wound upon the winding machine and opens it and twists it at both ends, so that it conforms to the shape desired. Some of the forms of coils as wound on these machines and as finally shaped on the spreader are shown in the accompanying illustrations, Fig. 292.

Coil-taping Machines.—Field and armature coils for medium and large-sized motor and generators are wound from bare copper wire and are insulated after the winding operation has been completed. The material usually employed for winding coils is treated or untreated tape which is wound on the complete coil by hand using rolls of treated or untreated tape or by the use of a taping machine. The taping machine consists essentially of a rotating circular element which has an opening, by means of which the coil is placed inside of the ring

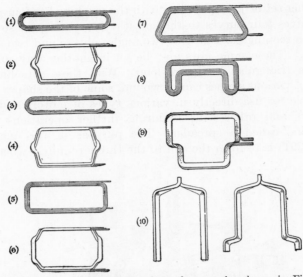

FIG. 292.—Coils that can be shaped on the spreader shown in Fig. 291.

(1) Common loop, 3 wires wide with 5 turns that can be spread as shown in (2)·
(3) a 5-coil group 3 wires wide, wound 5 wires vertical and spiral shown formed in (4)·
(5) a rectangular loop 3 wires wide, 2 turns of 6 wires that can be shaped to make a
3-coil bundle.   (7) Obtuse loop, 5 turns, 3 wires wide that can be formed as shown in
(8) and spread to make an Eickemeyer coil like (9).   (10) Ribbon copper coil formed into
a hair-pin loop by bar bender (Fig. 293) and shaped in coil spreader.

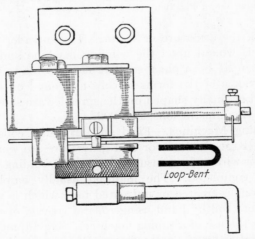

FIG. 293.—Top view of a Segur bar bender for shaping armature coils made
of copper strip from 0.05 to 0.125 inch thick by any width up to 1⅛ inch.
(*Electrical Manufacturers Equipment Company.*)

(Fig. 294). Tape is then attached by hand and the rotating element which carries the spool of tape winds it symmetrically about the bundle of wires forming the coil.

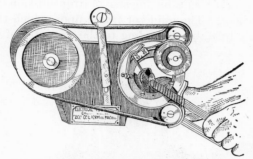

FIG. 294.—Segur armature coil-taping machine.
(*Electrical Manufacturers Equipment Company.*)

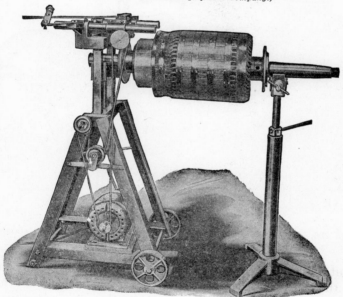

FIG. 295.—Portable commutator slotting machine that will handle armatures up to 18 inch in diameter. (*Electric Service Supplies Company.*)

Commutator-slotting and Grinding Machines.—In Fig. 295 is shown a commutator-slotting outfit. This machine consists of a frame in which the commutator is held either before or after the commutator has been placed on the armature, and a rotating disk saw mounted on slides which are parallel to the direction of rotation of the disk. The rotating saw is driven by belts or other suitable means of transmission from the source of power. The guide or frame upon which the saw is mounted is adjustable according to the diameter of the com-

FIG. 296.—Commutator slotting maching that can be attached to a standard engine lathe. (*Electric Service Supplies Company.*)

mutator to be worked on and after the correct height and depth of the cut have been ascertained, the frame is clamped firmly in position. The operator then starts the saw and moves it forward on its guide by means of a lever, so that it comes into contact with the commutator, thus cutting a slot. The armature is moved through a space corresponding to the width of a single bar, and the saw is again brought forward cutting another slot, and so the operation continues until the commutator has been slotted all around.

The face of the commutator must be smooth and perfectly circular so as to secure sparkless operation and the minimum wear of brushes. This result is obtained by grinding the commutator after it has been assembled or slotted. The com-

Fig. 297.—Combination armature banding and tension machine. (*Electric Service Supplies Company.*)

mutator grinder operates by bringing a stationary grinding tool or abrasive material into contact with the rotating commutator which is mounted in its final position on the armature, in this case the entire armature being mounted in a lathe and rotated. Another method is to apply a rotating grinding wheel to the armature. The commutator grinding or truing machine is essentially a lathe and operates in the same manner as any other machine for grinding a circular surface.

Armature-banding Machine.—This machine usually consists of a suitable stand with bearings upon which the armature shaft rests, and some means for rotating the armature by means of a belt, chain or gear drive from a line shaft or from an individual motor.   A band wire tension device similar to the tension device employed for winding coils is incorporated in the machine or is built as a separate machine, which may be attached to the armature stand.   With an armature in position, the band wire is attached at several points throughout the length

FIG. 298.—A machine equipped so that coil-winding, banding and grinding operations may be performed on it.

of the armature, one at each end and one or more at equal distances between the ends, and the machine is started.   The rotation of the armature causes the wire to be wrapped about the armature, the tension device and guide laying the wires evenly, to a width which is determined by the setting of the guide.

Combination Machines.—A combination coil-winding, banding and grinding machine is shown in Fig. 298.   This machine combines into one, the following tools: (*a*) a banding machine with a self-contained tension carriage for the band wire, designed to handle large or small railway, locomotive or stationary armatures; (*b*) a commutator slotting machine with independent motor drive; (*c*) a commutator grinding machine with independent motor drive; (*d*) a commutator cutting or turning attachment; (e) a field and armature coil plate mounted on the main spindle suitable for all classes of heavy form coil winding. This machine closely resembles a large power lathe but is provided with the special attachments for performing the work above outlined. After an armature has had the coils placed in the slot and the leads soldered to the commutator, it may be placed in this machine and the work completed without removing the armature from the machine. The banding attachment is capable of heavy duty, the rotation being under control of the operator. When the machine is stopped it automatically locks and prevents slack in the band wire due to backing motion of the armature. Uniform tension is secured by a tension device mounted on the feed carriage and traveling with it. The feed carriage is moved along by means of a rack and pinion and pilot wheel and is adjustable vertically in or out.

The slotting attachment is supported by a bracket clamped to the tail-stock spindle and is removed by loosening two cap screws. The commutator truing or grinding attachment consists of a traveling grinding wheel supported from the tail stock and motor driven. The casting which supports the two rods carrying the grinding wheel and the independent motor are adjustable along two other steel rods projecting backward from the tail stock and bringing the grinding wheel parallel to the face of the commutator. These rods are adjustable in or out to suit the length or location of the commutator, and the grinding wheel is moved along by means of the screw and hand wheel. Cutting is done in both directions of travel of the wheel. Power is applied either through belt and pulley from a countershaft or by an individual motor drive which may readily be installed. The control is by means of a clutch which is operated by a treadle running the full length of the machine. The machine is provided with two changes of speed, a low speed for banding and coil winding and a high speed for commutator cutting, grinding and truing. The head stock is provided with a coil-winding plate to which may be attached forms for winding coils of various sizes and shapes, upon the same principle as the independent coil-winding machines, designed to do this work only.

APPENDIX

DATA AND REFERENCE TABLES

How to Remember the Wire Table.—The wire table for B. & S. gauge copper wire has simple relations, such that if a few constants are remembered the whole table can be constructed mentally with approximate accuracy.

A wire which is three sizes larger than another wire has half the resistance, twice the weight and twice the area. A wire which is ten sizes larger than another wire has one-tenth the resistance, ten times the weight and ten times the area.

No. 10 Wire is 0.10 inch in diameter (more precisely 0.102); it has an area of 10,000 circular mils (more precisely 10,380); it has a resistance of 1 ohm per thousand feet at 20°C. (68°F.), and weighs 32 pounds (more precisely 31.4 pounds) per thousand feet.

The weight of one thousand feet of No. 5 wire is 100 pounds.

The relative values of resistance (for decreasing sizes) and of weight and area (for increasing sizes) for *consecutive* sizes are: 0.50, 0.60, 0.80, 1.00, 1.25, 1.60, 2.00.

The relative values of the diameters of *alternate* sizes of wire are: 0.50, 0.63, 0.80 1.00, 1.25, 1.60, 2.00.

The "mil," whose value is one-thousandth (0.001) of an inch, is the practical basis for determining the diameters and thereby the areas of all wires used as electric conductors. The diameter being given, the area is obtained by the well-known rule, "the area of a circle, in circular units, is equal to the square of its diameter," hence, the square of the diameter of a wire expressed in mils equals the area of its cross-section. $D^2 = A$, which area is expressed in circular mils or CM; hence, $D^2 = CM$.

Circular Mils.—Conductors of large size are usually specified in circular mils as 500,000 circular mils, 750,000 circular mils.

To find resistance, drop one cypher from the number of circular mils; the result is the number of feet per ohm.

To find weight, drop four cyphers from the number of circular mils and multiply by the weight of No. 10 Wire.

Copper for Various Systems of Distribution.—When the power transmitted, distance, line loss and voltage of lamps is constant and all wires of each system are of the same size, the following is the relationship of the copper required.

	System.	Copper Required
2 Wire, single-phase or direct current		1.000
3 Wire, single-phase or direct current		0.375
4 Wire, single-phase or direct current		0.222
4 Wire, two-phase		1.000
4 Wire, three-phase with neutral		0.333
3 Wire, three-phase Delta		0.75

Classification of Wire Gauges.—Wire gauges are known under a variety of names so that it is important to know the difference when conditions require that the values of one gauge shall be converted into those of another. The following is a classification of gauges by names and uses:

Brown & Sharpe (B. & S.) = American Wire Gauge (A. W. G.).

New British Standard (N. B. S.) = British, Imperial, English Legal Standard and Standard Wire Gauge, and is variously abbreviated by S. W. G. and I. W. G.

Birmingham Gauge (B. W. G.) = Stubs, Old English Standard and Iron Wire Gauge.

Roebling = Washburn Moen, American Steel and Wire Co's. Iron Wire Gauge.

London = Old English (not Old English Standard).

As a further complication:

Birmingham or Stubs' Iron Wire Gauge is not the same as Stubs' Steel Wire Gauge.

Uses of Various Gauges.—B. & S. Gauge.—All forms of round wire used for electrical conductors. Sheet copper, brass and German silver.

U. S. S. Gauge—Sheet iron and steel. Legalized by act of Congress, March 3, 1893.

B. W. Gauge.—Galvanized iron wire. Norway iron wire.

American Screw Co.'s Wire Gauge—Numbered sizes of machine and wood screws, particularly up to No. 14 (0.2421 inch).

Stubs' Steel Wire Gauge—Drill rod.

Roebling & Trenton—Iron and steel wire. Telephone and telegraph wire.

N. B. S.—Hard drawn copper. Telephone and telegraph wire.

London Gauge—Brass wire.

DIFFERENCE BETWEEN WIRE GAUGES

Gauge No.	Brown & Sharpe's	Old English or London	Stubs' or Birmingham	New British Standard
0000	0.460	0.454	0.454	0.400
000	0.40964	0.425	0.425	0.372
00	0.36480	0.380	0.380	0.348
0	0.32495	0.340	0.340	0.324
1	0.28930	0.300	0.300	0.300
2	0.25763	0.284	0.284	0.276
3	0.22942	0.259	0.259	0.252
4	0.20431	0.238	0.238	0.232
5	0.18194	0.220	0.220	0.212
6	0.16202	0.203	0.203	0.192
7	0.14428	0.180	0.180	0.176
8	0.12849	0.165	0.165	0.160
9	0.11443	0.148	0.148	0.144
10	0.10189	0.134	0.134	0.128
11	0.09074	0.120	0.120	0.116
12	0.08081	0.109	0.109	0.104
13	0.07196	0.095	0.095	0.092
14	0.06408	0.083	0.083	0.080
15	0.05706	0.072	0.072	0.072
16	0.05082	0.065	0.065	0.064
17	0.04525	0.058	0.058	0.056
18	0.04030	0.049	0.049	0.048
19	0.03589	0.040	0.042	0.040
20	0.03196	0.035	0.035	0.036
21	0.02846	0.0315	0.032	0.032
22	0.025347	0.0295	0.028	0.028
23	0.022571	0.027	0.025	0.024
24	0.0201	0.025	0.022	0.022
25	0.0179	0.023	0.020	0.020
26	0.01594	0.0205	0.018	0.018
27	0.014195	0.01875	0.016	0.0164
28	0.012641	0.0165	0.014	0.0148
29	0.011257	0.0155	0.013	0.0136
30	0.010025	0.01375	0.012	0.0124
31	0.008928	0.01225	0.010	0.0116
32	0.00795	0.01125	0.009	0.0108
33	0.00708	0.01025	0.008	0.010
34	0.0063	0.0095	0.007	0.0092
35	0.00561	0.009	0.005	0.0084
36	0.005	0.0075	0.004	0.0076
37	0.00445	0.0065		
38	0.003965	0.00575		
39	0.003531	0.005		
40	0.003144	0.0045		

Equivalents of Wire Sizes (B. & S. Gauge)

0000 = 2	No. 0 = 4	No. 3 = 8	No. 6 = 16	No. 9 = 32	No. 12 = 64	No. 15
000 = 2	No. 1 = 4	No. 4 = 8	No. 7 = 16	No. 10 = 32	No. 13 = 64	No. 16
00 = 2	No. 2 = 4	No. 5 = 8	No. 8 = 16	No. 11 = 32	No. 14 = 64	No. 17
0 = 2	No. 3 = 4	No. 6 = 8	No. 9 = 16	No. 12 = 32	No. 15 = 64	No. 18
1 = 2	No. 4 = 4	No. 7 = 8	No. 10 = 16	No. 13 = 32	No. 16 = 64	No. 19
2 = 2	No. 5 = 4	No. 8 = 8	No. 11 = 16	No. 14 = 32	No. 17 = 64	No. 20
3 = 2	No. 6 = 4	No. 9 = 8	No. 12 = 16	No. 15 = 32	No. 18 = 64	No. 21
4 = 2	No. 7 = 4	No. 10 = 8	No. 13 = 16	No. 16 = 32	No. 19 = 64	No. 22
5 = 2	No. 8 = 4	No. 11 = 8	No. 14 = 16	No. 17 = 32	No. 20 = 64	No. 23
6 = 2	No. 9 = 4	No. 12 = 8	No. 15 = 16	No. 18 = 32	No. 21 = 64	No. 24
7 = 2	No. 10 = 4	No. 13 = 8	No. 16 = 16	No. 19 = 32	No. 22 = 64	No. 25
8 = 2	No. 11 = 4	No. 14 = 8	No. 17 = 16	No. 20 = 32	No. 23 = 64	No. 26
9 = 2	No. 12 = 4	No. 15 = 8	No. 18 = 16	No. 21 = 32	No. 24 = 64	No. 27
10 = 2	No. 13 = 4	No. 16 = 8	No. 19 = 16	No. 22 = 32	No. 25 = 64	No. 28
11 = 2	No. 14 = 4	No. 17 = 8	No. 20 = 16	No. 23 = 32	No. 26 = 64	No. 29
12 = 2	No. 15 = 4	No. 18 = 8	No. 21 = 16	No. 24 = 32	No. 27 = 64	No. 30
13 = 2	No. 16 = 4	No. 19 = 8	No. 22 = 16	No. 25 = 32	No. 28	
14 = 2	No. 17 = 4	No. 20 = 8	No. 23 = 16	No. 26 = 33	No. 29	
15 = 2	No. 18 = 4	No. 21 = 8	No. 24 = 16	No. 27 = 32	No. 30	
16 = 2	No. 19 = 4	No. 22 = 8	No. 25 = 16	No. 28		
17 = 2	No. 20 = 4	No. 23 = 8	No. 26 = 16	No. 29		
18 = 2	No. 21 = 4	No. 24 = 8	No. 27 = 16	No. 30		
19 = 2	No. 22 = 4	No. 25 = 8	No. 28			
20 = 2	No. 23 = 4	No. 26 = 8	No. 29			
21 = 2	No. 24 = 4	No. 27 = 8	No. 30			

General Wiring Formula For Alternating- and Direct-current Circuits.
The following general formula may be used to determine the size of copper conductors, volts loss in lines, current per conductor, and of copper per circuit or any system of electrical distribution.

$$\text{Area of conductor, circular mils} = \frac{D \times W \times C}{P \times E^2}$$

$$\text{Volts loss in lines} = \frac{P \times E \times B}{100}$$

$$\text{Current in main conductors} = \frac{W \times T}{E}$$

$$\text{Pounds copper} = \frac{D^2 \times W \times C \times A}{P \times E \times 1,000,000}$$

W = Total watts delivered.
D = Distance of transmission (one way) in feet.
P = Loss in line in per cent. of power delivered, that is of W.
E = Voltage between main conductors at receiving or consumer's end of circuit.
For continuous current $C = 2160$, $T = 1$, $B = 1$, and $A = 6.04$

System	Value of A	Value of C					Value of T				
		Per cent., power factor					Per cent., power factor				
		100	95	90	85	80	100	95	90	85	80
Single-phase..........	6.04	2160	2400	2660	3000	3380	1.00	1.05	1.11	0.17	1.25
Two-phase (4 wire)....	12.08	1080	1200	1330	1500	1690	0.50	0.53	0.55	0.59	0.62
Three-phase (3 wire)..	9.06	1030	1200	1330	1500	1690	0.58	0.61	0.64	0.68	0.72

APPLICATION OF THE FORMULA

The value of C for any particular power factor is obtained by dividing 2160, the value for continuous current, by the square of that power factor for single-phase, and by twice the square of that power factor for three-wire, three-phase, or four-wire, two-phase.

The value of B depends on the size of wire, frequency and power factor. It is equal to 1 for continuous current, and for alternating current with 100 per cent. power factor. For sizes of wire given in the tables of wiring constants (pages 470 and 471), and other power factors and cycles the values of B are given.

The figures given are for wires 18 inches apart and are sufficiently accurate for all practical purposes provided the displacement in phase between current and emf. at the receiving end is not very much greater than that at the generator; in other words, provided that the reactance of the line is not excessive, or the line loss unusually high. For example, the constants should not be applied at 125 cycles if the largest conductors are used and the loss 20 per cent. or more of the power delivered. At lower frequencies, however, the constants are reasonably correct even under such extreme conditions. They represent about the true values at 10 per cent. line loss, are close enough at all losses less than 10 per cent., and often, at least for frequencies up to 40 cycles, close enough for even much larger losses. When the canductors of a circuit are nearer each other than 18 inches, the volts loss will be less than given by the formula, and if close together, as with multiple conductor cable, the loss will be only that due to resistance.

The value of T depends on the system and power factor. It is equal to 1 for continuous current and for single-phase current of 100 per cent. power factor.

The value of A and the weights of the wires in the table are based on 0.00000302 pound as the weight of a foot of copper wire of 1 circular mil area.

In using the above formula and constants, it should be particularly observed that P stands for the per cent. loss in the line of the delivered power, not for the per cent. loss in the line of the power at the generator; and that E is the potential at the end of the line and not at the generator.

When the power factor cannot be more accurately determined, it may be assumed to be as follows for any alternating system operating under average conditions: Incandescent lighting and synchronous motors, 95 per cent.; lighting and induction motors together, 85 per cent.; induction motors alone, 80 per cent.

In continuous current, three-wire systems, the neutral wire for feeders should be made of ⅓ the section obtained by the formula for either of the outside wires. In both continuous and alternating-current systems, the neutral conductor for secondary mains and house wiring should be taken as large as the other conductors.

The three wires of a three-phase circuit and the four wires of a two-phase circuit should be made all the same size, and each conductor should be of the cross-section given by the first formula.

GENERAL WIRING DATA FOR FORMULA FOR DIRECT- AND ALTERNATING-CURRENT CIRCUITS—25 AND 60 CYCLES

Size of wire B. & S.	Area wire cir. mils	Wt. lbs. bare wire per 1000 ft.	Resistance ohms per 1000 ft. at 20°C.	Value of B for formula (page 468)								Size of wire B. & S.
				25 cycles				40 cycles				
				Per cent. power factor				Per cent. power factor				
				95	90	85	80	95	90	85	80	
0000	211,600	640.73	0.04879	1.23	1.29	1.33	1.34	1.52	1.53	1.61	1.67	0000
000	167,805	508.12	0.06154	1.18	1.22	1.24	1.24	1.40	1.41	1.48	1.51	000
00	133,079	402.97	0.07758	1.14	1.16	1.16	1.16	1.25	1.32	1.35	1.37	00
0	105,560	319.00	0.09775	1.10	1.11	1.10	1.09	1.19	1.24	1.26	1.26	0
1	83,694	253.43	0.1234	1.07	1.07	1.05	1.03	1.14	1.17	1.18	1.17	1
2	66,373	200.98	0.1556	1.05	1.01	1.02	1	1.11	1.12	1.12	1.10	2
3	52,633	159.38	0.1962	1.03	1.02	1	1	1.07	1.08	1.07	1.05	3
4	41,742	126.40	0.2473	1.02	1	1	1	1.05	1.06	1.03	1	4
5	33,102	100.23	0.3120	1	1	1	1	1.03	1.01	1	1	5
6	26,250	79.49	0.3934	1	1	1	1	1.02	1	1	1	6
7	20,816	63.03	0.4959	1	1	1	1	1.01	1	1	1	7
8	16,509	49.99	0.6250	1	1	1	1	1	1	1	1	8
9	13,090	39.60	0.7886	1	1	1	1	1	1	1	1	9
10	10,382	31.40	0.9940	1	1	1	1	1	1	1	1	10

GENERAL WIRING DATA FOR FORMULA FOR DIRECT- AND ALTERNATING-CURRENT CIRCUITS—60 AND 125 CYCLES

Size of wire B. & S.	Area wire cir. mils.	Wt. lb. bare wire per 100 ft.	Resistance ohms per 1000 ft. at 20°C.	Value of B for formula (page 468)								Size of wire B. & S.
				60 cycles				125 cycles				
				Per cent., power factor				Per cent., power factor				
				95	90	85	80	95	90	85	80	
0000	211,600	640.73	0.04879	1.62	1.84	1.99	2.09	2.35	2.86	3.24	3.49	0000
000	167,805	508.12	0.06154	1.49	1.66	1.77	1.95	2.08	2.48	2.77	2.94	000
00	133,079	402.97	0.07758	1.34	1.52	1.60	1.66	1.86	2.18	2.40	2.57	00
0	105,560	319.00	0.09775	1.31	1.40	1.46	1.49	1.71	1.96	2.13	2.25	0
1	83,694	253.43	0.1234	1.24	1.30	1.34	1.36	1.56	1.75	1.88	1.97	1
2	66,373	200.98	0.1556	1.18	1.23	1.25	1.26	1.45	1.60	1.70	1.77	2
3	52,633	159.38	0.1962	1.14	1.17	1.18	1.17	1.35	1.46	1.53	1.57	3
4	41,742	126.40	0.2473	1.11	1.12	1.11	1.10	1.27	1.35	1.40	1.43	4
5	33,102	100.23	0.3120	1.08	1.08	1.06	1.04	1.21	1.27	1.30	1.31	5
6	26,250	79.49	0.3934	1.05	1.04	1.02	1	1.16	1.20	1.21	1.21	6
7	20,816	63.03	0.4958	1.03	1.02	1	1	1.12	1.14	1.14	1.13	7
8	16,509	49.99	0.6250	1.02	1	1	1	1.09	1.10	1.09	1.07	8
9	13,090	39.60	0.7886	1	1	1	1	1.06	1.06	1.04	1.02	9
10	10,382	31.40	0.9940	1	1	1	1	1.04	1.03	1	1	10

Amperes in Alternating-current Circuits.—The following tables give the amperes per lead wire per kilowatt for single-phase and three-phase balanced loads. The single-phase table can be used for two-phase balanced loads by using a current value corresponding to twice the stated potential of the circuit or by dividing the current value at the potential of the circuit by two. That is, each wire of a two-phase circuit carries one-half of the current indicated at the load specified. These tables show the value of the current at power factors varying from unity to 70 per cent. The power of any circuit in kilowatts can, therefore, be computed by dividing the reading of the ammeter by the tabulated value corresponding to the measured power factor and voltage of the circuit. These values are correct only for a balanced load (and there is generally a slight unbalancing of the loads on the phases), but the table is useful in computing the sizes of wire required for transmission purposes.

This table was derived from the following formulas:

For single-phase circuits: Amperes per wire = watts ÷ (volts × power factor).

For three-phase circuits: Amperes per wire = total watts ÷ (volts between wires × power factor × $\sqrt{3}$).

For two-phase circuits: Amperes per wire = total watts ÷ (volts between wires of one phase × power factor × 2).

In making the computations the number of watts was assumed as 1000, and the amperes were computed for various values of emf. to a sufficient number of decimal places to insure accuracy. The tables were then extended by multiplication and division. If desired, these tables can be further extended to cover voltages outside of their limits by using the tabular values corresponding to potentials of one-tenth (or 10 times) the desired potential, care being used to shift the decimal point in the proper direction.

The values for intermediate power factors can be approximated from the tables. For lower power factors, the value of the current for unity power factor can be divided by actual power factor of the circuit or multiplied by the reciprocal of this power factor.

SINGLE-PHASE CIRCUITS—AMPERES FOR ONE KILOWATT AT DIFFERENT POWER FACTORS

Power factor in per cent.

Volts	100	95	90	85	80	75	70
110	9.0909	9.5693	10.1010	10.6952	11.3636	12.1211	12.9870
220	4.5455	4.7847	5.0505	5.3476	5.6819	6.0606	6.4936
440	2.2727	2.3923	2.5252	2.6738	2.8409	3.0303	3.2467
550	1.8182	1.9139	2.0202	2.1390	2.2728	2.4242	2.5974
1100	0.9091	0.9569	1.0101	0.0695	1.1364	1.2121	1.2987
2200	0.4545	0.4785	0.5050	0.5348	0.5682	0.6061	0.6494
3300	0.3030	0.3190	0.3367	0.3565	0.3788	0.4040	0.4329
6600	0.1515	0.1595	0.1684	0.1783	0.1894	0.2020	0.2165
11000	0.0909	0.0957	0.1010	0.1070	0.1136	0.1212	0.1299

THREE-PHASE CIRCUITS—AMPERES PER WIRE FOR ONE KILOWATT AT DIFFERENT POWER FACTORS

Power factor per cent.

Volts	100	95	90	85	80	75	70
110	5.2486	5.5249	5.8319	6.1749	6.5608	6.9982	7.4980
220	2.6243	2.7624	2.9159	3.0874	3.2804	3.4992	3.7490
225	2.5660	2.7010	2.8511	3.0188	3.2075	3.4213	3.6657
440	1.3122	1.3812	1.4579	1.5437	1.6402	1.7495	1.8745
550	1.0497	1.1050	1.1664	1.2350	1.3121	1.3996	1.4996
1100	0.5249	0.5525	0.5832	0.6175	0.6561	0.6998	0.7498
2200	0.2624	0.2762	0.2916	0.3087	0.3280	0.3499	0.3749
3300	0.1749	0.1842	0.1944	0.2058	0.2187	0.2333	0.2499
6600	0.0875	0.0921	0.0972	0.1029	0.1093	0.1167	0.1249
11000	0.0525	0.0552	0.0583	0.0617	0.0656	0.0700	0.0750

MINIMUM SIZE WIRE FOR MOTOR SERVICES—WHEN CONCEALED OR
PARTLY CONCEALED WIRES ARE USED

Hp.	Size wire B. & S. gauge		
	110 volts	220 volts	550 volts
½	14	14	14
1	14	14	14
2	12	14	14
3	10	14	14
4	8	12	14
5	6	10	14
7½	4	8	14
10	3	6	12
15	0	5	10
20	00	3	8
25	000	1	6
30	0000	0	5
40	....	00	3
50	....	000	2
60	....	0000	1
70	....	....	0
80	....	....	00
90	....	....	000
100	....	....	0000

VALUES OF FIELD CURRENT IN DIRECT-CURRENT GENERATORS

It has been found that a fair average for the field amperes of different
sizes of generators is as follows:

Kw..................	1	5	10	20	30	50	75	100
Per cent..............	8	6	5	4	3.5	3	3	2.75

The field current (expressed as a percentage of full-load current on
lines) is determined with all of the resistance cut out, that is, with the
rheostat on the first notch.

SIZES OF LEADS REQUIRED FOR MOTORS AND GENERATORS

	MOTOR LEADS								GENERATOR LEADS																
	115 volts				230 volts					115 volts							230 volts							Field	
		Wire or cable No.	Con-duit				Con-duit				Wire or cable per leg		Conduit per leg					Wire or cable per leg		Conduit per leg					
													R. C.		L. C.					L. C.		R. C.			
Hp.	Amps.		No. of	Size, in.	Amps.	Wire No.	No. of	Size, in.	Kw.	Amps.	No. of	Size B. & S.	No. of	Size, in.	No. of	Size, in.	Amps.	No. of	Size B. & S. No.	No. of	Size in.	No. of	Size, in.	Wire No.	Cond't, in.
1	9	14	1	¾	5	14	1	¾	5	44	1	6					22	1	10					14	¾
2	17	12	1	¾	9	14	1	¾	7½	65	1	4					33	1	8					14	¾
3	25	8	1	1	13	12	1	¾	10	87	1	2					44	1	6					14	¾
4	34	6	1	1	17	12	1	¾	12½	109	1	0	All legs in one				55	1	4					14	¾
5	42	6	1	1	21	10	1	¾	15	132	1	00	conduit				66	1	2					14	¾
6	50	4	1	1¼	25	8	1	1	20	176	1	0000	1	1	1	1¼	88	1	2	All legs in one				14	¾
8	67	2	1	1¼	34	6	1	1	25	220	1	250,000	1	1½	1	1½	110	1	0	conduit				14	¾
10	84	2	1	1¼	42	6	1	1	50	440	1	600,000	1	2	1	2½	220	1	250,000	1	1½	1	1½	14	¾
12	100	1	1	1½	50	4	1	1¼	60	522	1	800,000	1	2	1	2½	261	1	300,000	1	1½	1	1½	14	¾
15	125	0	1	1½	63	4	1	1¼	75	660	1	1,000,000	1	2½	1	2½	330	1	400,000	1	1½	1	2	14	¾
17	142	00	1	1½	71	2	1	1¼	100	870	2	600,000	2	2	2	2½	435	1	600,000	1	2	1	2½	14	¾
20	167	000	1	2	84	2	1	1¼	125	1090	2	800,000	2	2	2	2½	545	1	800,000	1	2	1	2½	14	¾
25	209	0000	1	2	105	1	1	1½	150	1326	2	1,000,000	2	2½	2	2½	660	1	1,000,000	1	2½	1	2½	12	¾
30	250	300,000	2	1½	125	0	1	1½	200	1740	3	900,000	3	2	3	2½	870	2	600,000	2	2	2	2½	10	¾
35	292	400,000	2	1½	146	00	1	1½	250	2175	4	800,000	3	2½	3	3	1088	2	800,000	2	2	2	2½	10	¾
40	334	500,000	2	1½	167	000	1	2	300	2610	4	1,000,000	4	2½	4	2½	1305	2	1,000,000	2	2½	2	2½	8	¾
45	375	500,000	2	1½	188	0000	1	2	400	3580	5	1,200,000	5	2½	5	3	1790	3	800,000	3	2	3	2½	6	¾
50	317	600,000	2	2	209	0000	1	2	500	4350	6	1,200,000	6	2½	6	3	2175	3	1,200,000	3	2½	3	3	6	¾

DATA FOR WIRING DIRECT-CURRENT MOTORS ACCORDING TO NATIONAL ELECTRICAL CODE RULES

Table showing maximum hp. allowed on wires according to National Electrical Code Rules, and carrying capacities. Assumed efficiency of motors, 0.90.

Carrying capacities		B. & S. gauge	110 volts				220 volts				440 volts				550 volts			
Other insulation	Rubber insulation		Mains		Branches		Mains		Branches		Mains		Branches		Mains		Branches	
			O. I.	Rub.	O. I.	Rub.	O. I.	Rub.	O. I.	Rub.	O. I.	Rub.	O. I.	Rub.	O. I.	R. I.	O. I.	Rub.
16	12	14	2.1	1.6	1.7	1.2	4.2	3.2	3.4	2.4	8.4	6.4	6.8	4.8	10	8	8	6
23	17	12	3.0	2.2	2.4	1.8	6.0	4.4	4.8	3.6	12.0	8.8	9.6	7.2	15	11	12	9
32	24	10	4.2	3.2	3.4	2.5	8.4	6.4	6.8	5.0	16.8	12.8	13.6	10.0	21	16	17	12
46	33	8	6.1	4.4	4.8	3.5	12.2	8.8	9.6	7.0	24.4	17.6	19.2	14.0	30	22	24	17
65	46	6	8.6	6.1	6.9	4.8	17.2	12.2	13.8	9.6	34.4	24.4	27.6	19.2	43	30	34	24
77	54	5	10.2	7.2	8.2	5.7	20.4	14.4	16.4	11.4	40.8	28.8	32.8	22.8	51	36	41	28
92	65	4	12.2	8.6	9.7	6.9	24.4	17.2	19.4	13.8	48.8	34.4	38.8	27.6	61	43	48	34
110	76	3	14.6	10.1	11.7	8.0	29.2	20.2	23.4	16.0	58.4	40.4	46.8	32.0	73	50	58	40
131	90	2	17.4	12.0	13.9	9.5	34.8	24.0	27.8	19.0	69.6	48.0	55.6	38.0	87	60	69	47
156	107	1	20.8	14.2	16.6	11.3	41.6	28.4	33.2	22.6	83.2	56.8	66.4	45.2	104	71	83	56
185	127	0	24.6	16.9	19.7	13.5	49.2	33.8	39.4	27.0	98.4	67.6	78.8	54.0	123	84	98	67
220	150	00	29.3	20.0	23.4	15.9	58.6	40.0	46.8	31.8	117.2	80.0	93.6	63.6	146	100	117	79
262	177	000	34.9	23.6	27.8	18.8	69.8	47.2	55.6	37.6	139.6	94.4	111.2	75.2	174	118	139	94
312	210	0000	41.6	28.0	33.2	22.3	83.2	56.0	66.4	44.6	166.0	112.0	132.8	89.2	208	140	166	111

Under the proper voltage and conditions of wiring, find a number equal to or greater than the given hp. In the same horizontal line, under the heading B. & S. gauge, will be found the number of the smallest wire permissible. For other efficiencies than 0.90, divide hp. given by 1.06 for 0.95; 0.95 for 0.85; 0.89 for 0.80; 0.84 for 0.75, and 0.78 for 0.70 per cent. efficiency.

DATA FOR WIRING ALTERNATING-CURRENT MOTORS ACCORDING TO NATIONAL ELECTRICAL CODE RULES

Table showing maximum hp. allowed on wires according to National Electrical Code rules and carrying capacities. P. F., 0.85; Efficiency, 0.90.

Volts	Carrying capacities Other insulation	Carrying capacities Rubber insulation	B. & S. gauge	Single phase Mains O.I.	Single phase Mains R.I.	Single phase Branches O.I.	Single phase Branches R.I.	2 phase, 4 wire Mains O.I.	2 phase, 4 wire Mains R.I.	2 phase, 4 wire Branches O.I.	2 phase, 4 wire Branches R.I.	3 phase, 3 wire Mains O.I.	3 phase, 3 wire Mains R.I.	3 phase, 3 wire Branches O.I.	3 phase, 3 wire Branches R.I.
110	16	12	14	1.8	1.3	1.4	1.0	3.6	2.6	2.8	2.1	3.1	2.2	2.4	1.8
	23	17	12	2.6	1.9	2.1	1.5	5.2	3.8	4.2	3.0	4.4	3.2	3.6	2.6
	32	24	10	3.6	2.7	2.9	2.2	7.2	5.4	5.4	4.3	6.2	4.6	5.0	3.8
	46	33	8	5.2	3.7	4.2	3.0	10.4	7.4	8.4	6.0	8.9	6.4	7.1	5.2
	65	46	6	7.4	5.2	5.9	4.2	14.8	10.4	11.8	8.4	12.7	8.9	10.1	7.2
	77	54	5	8.7	6.1	7.0	4.9	17.4	12.2	14.0	9.8	15.0	10.5	12.0	8.4
	92	65	4	10.4	7.4	8.3	5.9	20.8	14.8	16.6	11.8	17.9	12.8	14.3	10.1
	110	76	3	12.5	8.6	10.0	6.9	25.0	17.2	20.0	13.8	21.5	14.8	17.2	11.9
	131	90	2	14.9	10.2	12.0	8.2	29.8	20.4	24.0	16.4	25.7	17.6	20.7	14.1
	156	107	1	17.7	12.1	14.2	9.7	35.4	24.2	28.4	19.4	30.5	20.8	24.5	16.7
	185	127	0	21.0	14.4	16.8	11.5	42.0	28.8	33.6	23.0	36.0	24.8	28.9	19.8
	220	150	00	25.0	17.0	20.0	13.6	50.0	34.0	40.0	27.2	43.0	29.3	34.5	23.4
	262	177	000	29.7	20.1	23.8	16.1	59.4	40.2	47.6	32.4	51.2	34.6	41.0	27.7
	312	210	0000	35.4	23.8	28.3	19.1	70.8	47.6	56.6	38.2	61.0	41.0	48.8	32.9

220

												hp	hp	B. & S.	hp	hp
3.6	4.8	4.4	6.2	4.2	5.6	5.2	7.2	2.1	2.8	2.6	3.6	16	12	14	12	16
5.2	7.2	6.4	8.8	6.0	8.4	7.6	10.4	3.0	4.2	3.8	5.2	23	17	12	17	23
7.6	10.0	9.2	12.4	8.6	10.8	10.8	14.4	4.4	5.8	5.4	7.2	32	24	10	24	32
10.4	14.2	12.8	17.8	12.0	16.8	14.8	20.8	6.0	8.4	7.4	10.4	46	33	8	33	46
14.4	20.2	17.8	25.4	16.8	23.6	20.8	29.6	8.4	11.8	10.4	14.8	65	46	6	46	65
16.8	24.0	21.0	30.0	19.6	28.0	24.4	34.8	9.8	14.0	12.2	17.4	77	54	5	54	77
20.2	28.6	25.6	35.8	23.6	33.2	29.6	41.6	11.8	16.6	14.8	20.8	92	65	4	65	92
23.8	34.4	29.6	43.0	27.6	40.0	34.4	50.0	13.8	20.0	17.2	25.0	110	76	3	76	110
28.2	41.4	35.2	51.4	32.8	48.0	40.8	59.6	16.4	24.0	20.4	29.8	131	90	2	90	131
33.4	49.0	41.6	61.0	38.8	56.8	48.4	70.8	19.4	28.4	24.2	35.4	156	107	1	107	156
39.6	57.8	49.6	72.0	46.0	67.2	57.6	84.0	23.0	33.6	28.8	42.0	185	127	0	127	185
46.8	69.0	58.6	86.0	54.4	80.0	68.0	100.0	27.2	40.0	34.0	50.0	220	150	00	150	220
55.4	82.0	69.2	102.4	64.8	95.2	80.4	118.8	32.4	47.6	40.2	59.4	262	177	000	177	262
65.8	97.6	82.0	122.0	76.4	113.2	95.2	141.6	38.2	56.6	47.6	70.8	312	210	0000	210	312

440

												hp	hp	B. & S.	hp	hp
7.2	9.6	8.8	12.4	8.4	11.2	10.4	14.4	4.2	5.6	5.2	7.2	16	12	14	12	16
10.4	14.4	12.8	17.6	12.0	16.8	15.2	20.8	6.0	8.4	7.6	10.4	23	17	12	17	23
15.2	20.0	18.4	24.8	17.2	21.6	21.6	28.8	8.8	11.6	10.8	14.4	32	24	10	24	32
20.8	28.4	25.6	35.6	24.0	33.6	29.6	41.6	12.0	16.8	14.8	20.8	46	33	8	33	46
28.8	40.4	35.6	50.8	33.6	47.2	41.6	59.2	16.8	23.6	20.8	29.6	65	46	6	46	65
33.6	48.0	42.0	60.0	39.2	56.0	48.8	69.6	19.6	28.0	24.4	34.8	77	54	5	54	77
40.4	57.2	51.2	71.6	47.2	66.4	59.2	83.2	23.6	33.2	29.6	41.6	92	65	4	65	92
47.6	68.8	59.2	86.0	55.2	80.0	68.8	100.0	27.6	40.0	34.4	50.0	110	76	3	76	110
56.4	82.8	70.4	102.8	65.6	96.0	81.6	119.2	32.8	48.0	40.8	59.6	131	90	2	90	131
66.8	98.0	83.2	122.0	77.6	113.6	96.8	141.6	38.8	56.8	48.4	70.8	156	107	1	107	156
79.2	115.6	99.2	144.0	92.0	134.4	115.2	168.0	46.0	67.2	57.6	84.0	185	127	0	127	185
93.6	138.0	117.2	172.0	108.8	160.0	136.0	200.0	54.4	80.0	68.0	100.0	220	150	00	150	220
110.8	164.0	138.4	204.8	129.6	190.4	160.8	237.6	64.8	95.2	80.4	118.8	262	177	000	177	262
131.6	195.2	164.0	244.0	152.8	226.4	190.4	283.2	76.4	113.2	95.2	141.6	312	210	0000	210	312

To find the smallest wire permissible for a given number of hp., find the number nearest equal to the desired hp. in the column pertaining to the system, condition of wiring and voltage. In the same horizontal line, under the heading B. & S. gauge, will be found the number of the proper wire. These tables are figured for a power factor of 0.85 and an efficiency of 0.90. For other power factors and efficiencies, consult table of efficiencies, and multiply the given hp. by the number found where the lines pertaining to the proper power factors and efficiencies cross, and use the wire indicated by this product. *Prepared by Engineering Department, Toledo Railways & Light Co.*

General Motor Data.—The following table gives the horsepower, voltage and speed of standard motors at various frequencies for two- and three-phase operation:

VOLTAGE, HORSEPOWER AND SPEEDS OF STANDARD MOTORS

Windings	Cycles	Volts	Hp.	Rpm.
2- and 3-phase	60	110, 220, 440, 550	1, 2, 3, 5, 7.5, 10, 15	1800
2- and 3-phase	60	110, 220, 440, 550	0.75, 1.5, 2, 3, 5, 7.5	1200
3-phase	40	220, 550	1,1.5, 2, 3, 5,	1200
3-phase	40	220, 550	1, 2, 3	800
3-phase	25	110, 220, 440	1, 2, 3, 5	1500
3-phase	25	110, 220, 440	1, 2, 3, 5	750

STANDARD POTENTIALS FOR WHICH SKELETON FRAME MOTORS ARE WOUND

Style of winding	Cycles	Volts	
		Under 50 hp.	50 hp. and above
3- and 2-phase	60	220	440–2200
3-phase	40	220	550
3-phase	25	220	440

Standard motors will develop considerably more torque than that given at the rated speed and voltage, so that there is ample margin to carry full load or temporary overloads under ordinary variations of voltage.

The maximum output of an induction motor varies with the square of the voltage at the motor's terminal, but motors will give their rated output even with a drop of 10 per cent. in the voltage, as their maximum output is greatly in excess of the rated value. At the lower potential the efficiency and power factor will be increased at light loads; the full load values, however, are usually somewhat lower.

Transformer Rating for Alternating-current Motors.—For the larger motors the capacity of the transformers in kilowatts should equal the output of the motor in hp. Small motors should be supplied with a somewhat larger transformer capacity, especially if, as is desirable, they are expected to run most of the time near full load, or even at slight overload. Transformers of less capacity than those given in the following table should not be used even when a motor is to be run at only partial load.

For the operation of industrial motors, from three-phase systems, three single-phase units or one three-phase unit are recommended, although, if desired, two single-phase transformers may be used. The use of the three-phase transformer greatly reduces the space required and makes

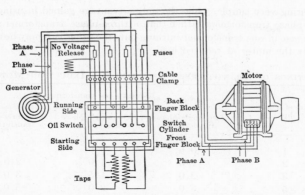

FIG. 299.—Connections for a 2-phase auto-starter for a 4-wire circuit.

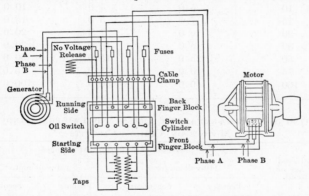

FIG. 300.—Connections for a 2-phase auto-starter for a 3-wire circuit.

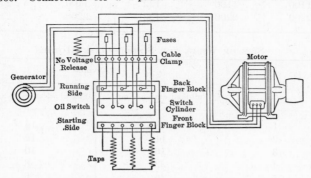

FIG. 301.—Connections for a 3-phase auto-starter.

the wiring very simple, while the only advantage gained in using three single-phase transformers rather than a three-phase transformer is that in the case of one transformer burning out, the other two may be used to operate the motor at reduced load.

RATINGS OF TRANSFORMERS REQUIRED FOR INDUCTION MOTORS

Size of motor hp.	Kilowatts per transformer		
	Two single-phase transformers	Three single-phase transformers	One three-phase transformer
1	0.6	0.6	. . . . . .
2	1.5	1.0	2.0
3	2.0	1.5	3.0
5	3.0	2.0	5.0
7½	4.0	3.0	7.5
10	5.0	4.0	10.0
15	7.5	5.0	15.0
20	10.0	7.5	20.0
30	15.0	10.0	30.0
50	25.0	15.0	50.0
75	40.0	25.0	75.0
100	50.0	30.0	100.0

RATING OF TRANSFORMERS FOR THREE- AND TWO-PHASE INDUCTION MOTORS ON VARIOUS CIRCUITS

Delivered voltage of circuit	Single-phase transformer voltages			
	110-volt motor		220-volt motor	
	Primary	Secondary	Primary	Secondary
1100	1100	122	1100	244
2200	2200	122	2200	244

SIZE OF WIRES FOR SINGLE-PHASE MOTORS

Hp.	220 volts	
	Full-load current-amp.	Size of wire—B. & S. gauge
1	6	14
2	11	12
3	16	10
4	22	8
5	26	6

SIZE OF WIRES OF DIRECT-CURRENT MOTORS

Horsepower	220 Volts		
	Full load current, amp.	Size of wire, mains, B. & S. gauge	Size of wire, branches, B. & S. gauge
1.0	4	14	14
2.0	8	14	14
3.0	12	14	14
4.0	15	14	12
5.0	19	12	10
7.5	28	8	8
10.0	38	6	6
12.5	47	6	4
15.0	56	5	4
17.5	65	4	3
20.0	75	3	1
25.0	94	1	0
30.0	113	0	2/0
35.0	131	2/0	3/0
40.0	150	2/0	4/0
45.0	169	3/0	4/0
50.0	188	4/0	250,000 C.M.
55.0	206	4/0	300,000 C.M.
60.0	225	4/0	300,000 C.M.
65.0	244	250,000 C.M.	350,000 C.M.
70.0	263	300,000 C.M.	400,000 C.M.
75.0	281	300,000 C.M.	500,000 C.M.
80.0	300	350,000 C.M.	500,000 C.M.
85.0	319	400,000 C.M.	500,000 C.M.
90.0	338	500,000 C.M.	600,000 C.M.
95.0	356	500,000 C.M.	600,000 C.M.
100.0	375	500,000 C.M.	700,000 C.M.
125.0	463	700,000 C.M.	900,000 C.M.
150.0	563	800,000 C.M.	1,100,000 C.M.
200.0	750	1,300,000 C.M.	1,700,000 C.M.
250.0	938	1,700,000 C.M.	2–900,000 C.M.
300.0	1,125	2–800,000 C.M.	2–1,100,000 C.M.

Column headed "Size of wire, branches" gives size of wire for branches and for mains supplying one motor and is based on 50 per cent. overload.

Column headed "Size of wire, mains" gives size of wire to be used for mains, but in no case must the size of these mains be less than that required for the 50 per cent. overload on the largest motor such mains supply.

The question of drop is not taken into consideration in these tables.

31

Size of Wires for Three-phase Motors

Horsepower	220 Volts			440 Volts		
	Full load current, amp.	Size of wire mains, B. & S. gauge	Size of wire, branches, B. & S. gauge	Full load current, amp.	Size of wire, mains, B. & S. gauge	Size of wire, branches, B. & S. gauge
1.0	3	14	14	2	14	14
2.0	5	14	14	3	14	14
3.0	8	14	14	4	14	14
4.0	10	14	14	5	14	14
5.0	13	14	12	6	14	14
7.5	19	12	8	10	14	14
10.0	26	8	6	13	14	12
12.5	32	8	6	16	12	10
15.0	38	6	4	19	12	8
17.5	45	6	4	22	10	8
20.0	51	6	3	26	8	8
25.0	64	4	1	32	8	6
30.0	77	3	0	38	6	6
35.0	90	2	2/0	45	6	4
40.0	102	1	2/0	51	5	4
45.0	115	0	3/0	58	4	3
50.0	128	0	4/0	64	4	2
55.0	141	2/0	4/0	70	4	1
60.0	154	3/0	250,000 C.M.	77	3	0
65.0	166	3/0	300,000 C.M.	83	2	0

70.0	179	3/0	300,000 C.M.	90	2	2/0
75.0	192	4/0	350,000 C.M.	96	1	2/0
80.0	205	4/0	400,000 C.M.	102	1	2/0
85.0	218	4/0	400,000 C.M.	109	0	3/0
90.0	230	4/0	500,000 C.M.	115	0	3/0
95.0	243	300,000 C.M.	500,000 C.M.	122	0	4/0
100.0	256	300,000 C.M.	500,000 C.M.	128	0	4/0
125.0	320	400,000 C.M.	700,000 C.M.	160	3/0	250,000 C.M.
150.0	384	500,000 C.M.	900,000 C.M.	192	4/0	350,000 C.M.
200.0	512	700,000 C.M.	1,300,000 C.M.	256	300,000 C.M.	500,000 C.M.
250.0	640	1,000,000 C.M.	1,800,000 C.M.	320	400,000 C.M.	700,000 C.M.
300.0	768	1,300,000 C.M.	2-900,000 C.M.	384	500,000 C.M.	900,000 C.M.

Column headed "Size of wire, branches" gives size of wire for branches and for mains supplying one motor and is based on 50 per cent. overload.

Column headed "Size of wire, mains" gives size of wire to be used for mains, but in no case must the size of these mains be less than that required for the 50 per cent. overload on the largest motor such main supplies.

The question of drop is not taken into consideration in these tables.

WIRING DATA FOR DIRECT-CURRENT MOTORS, 115 VOLTS

Horsepower	Approx. full load current, amp.	Size of fuses, amp.	Size of fused switches, amp.	Size of wire, B. & S. gauge	Size of conduit, inches
¼	2.5	3	30	14	½
½	4.4	5	30	14	½
1	8.4	10	30	14	½
2	17.0	20	30	12	½
3	23.6	30	30	8	¾
5	38.7	50	60	6	1
7½	57.6	75	100	4	1
10	75.1	85	100	2	1¼
15	113	150	200	00	2
20	151	175	200	000	2
25	191	225	400	0000	2
30	226	275	400	300000	2½
35	264	325	400	400000	2½
40	300	375	400	500000	3
50	375	*450	500	600000	3
55	405	*500	500	700000	3½
65	480	*600	600	900000	4
70	520	*650	700	1000000	4½
75	555	*700	700	1100000	4½

*When fuse sizes exceed 600 amperes, circuit breakers of approved type should be substituted.

WIRING DATA FOR DIRECT-CURRENT MOTORS, 230 VOLTS

Horsepower	Approx. full load current, amp.	Size of fuse, amp.	Size of fused switches, amp.	Size of wire, B. & S. gauge	Size of conduit, inches
¼	1.3	3	30	14	½
½	2.3	3	30	14	½
1	4.2	5	30	14	½
2	8.6	10	30	14	½
3	11.8	15	30	12	½
5	19.0	25	30	10	¾
7½	28.6	35	60	8	¾
10	37.6	45	60	6	1
15	55.0	70	100	4	1
20	73.8	90	100	2	1¼
25	95	125	200	0	1½
30	113	150	200	00	2
35	130	175	200	000	2
40	150	175	200	000	2
50	185	225	400	0000	2
55	200	250	400	250000	2
60	219	275	400	300000	2½
65	238	300	400	350000	2½
70	260	325	400	400000	2½
75	274	350	400	450000	3
80	288	375	400	500000	3
85	308	400	400	500000	3
90	328	*425	*500	500000	3
100	368	*450	*500	600000	3

*When fuse sizes exceed 600 amperes, circuit breakers of approved type should be substituted.

WIRING DATA FOR DIRECT-CURRENT MOTORS, 550 VOLTS

Horse-power	Approx. full-load current-amp.	Size of fuses, amp.	Size of fused switches, amp.	Size of wire, B. & S. gauge	Size of conduit, inches
¼	0.52	1	30	14	½
½	0.94	2	30	14	½
1	1.80	3	30	14	½
2	3.50	5	30	14	½
3	4.93	6	30	14	½
5	8.00	10	30	14	½
7½	12.00	15	30	12	½
10	15.60	20	30	12	½
15	22.80	35	60	8	¾
20	30.70	40	60	6	1
25	40.00	50	60	6	1
30	47.00	60	60	6	1
35	55.00	70	100	4	1
40	62.00	75	100	2	1¼
50	78.00	95	100	2	1¼
55	84.00	100	100	1	1½
60	92.00	125	200	0	1½
65	98.00	125	200	00	1½
70	108.00	150	200	00	2
75	114.00	150	200	00	2
80	120.00	150	200	00	2
85	129.00	150	200	00	2
90	138.00	175	200	000	2
100	152.00	200	200	0000	2

WIRING DATA FOR INDUCTION MOTORS—SINGLE-PHASE—110 VOLTS, ALL FREQUENCIES, STANDARD SPEEDS

Horse-power	Approx. full current-amperes	Size wire B. & S. gauge	Size of switches in amperes	Size of starting fuses, amperes	Size of running fuses, amperes	Size of conduit, inches
1	16.4	10	30	25	20	¾
2	24.0	8	60	45	30	1
3	33.6	6	100	70	45	1¼
4	43.6	4	100	85	60	1¼
5	54.0	4	100	100	70	1¼
7½	80.0	1	200	200	100	1½
10	106.0	0	200	200	125	2

WIRING DATA FOR INDUCTION MOTORS—SINGLE-PHASE—220 VOLTS, ALL FREQUENCIES, STANDARD SPEEDS

Horse-power	Approx. full current-amperes	Size of wire, B. & S. gauge	Size of switches in amperes	Size of starting fuses, amperes	Size of running fuses, amperes	Size of conduit, inches
1	8.2	14	30	15	10	½
2	12.0	10	30	25	15	¾
3	16.8	8	60	35	20	1
4	21.8	6	60	45	25	1¼
5	27.0	6	60	55	35	1¼
7½	40.0	4	100	75	50	1¼
10	53.0	2	100	100	65	1½

WIRING DATA FOR INDUCTION MOTORS—THREE-PHASE—110 VOLTS, ALL FREQUENCIES, STANDARD SPEEDS

Horse-power	Approx. full current-amperes	Size of wire, B. & S. gauge	Size of switches in amperes	Size of starting fuses, amperes	Size of running fuses, amperes	Size of conduit, inches
1	6	14	30	15	9	½
2	12	12	30	25	18	½
3	18	10	60	35	27	¾
5	27	6	100	65	40	1
7½	39	4	100	80	58	1¼
10	51	2	200	125	75	1½
15	75	1	200	150	112	1½
20	101	00	400	225	150	2
25	125	000	400	250	187	2
30	150	0,000	400	325	225	1½
35	175	300,000	400	400	262	2½
40	210	400,000	500	*500	315	3
50	246	450,000	500	*500	369	3

* When fuse sizes exceed 600 amperes, circuit breakers of approved type should be substituted.

WIRING DATA FOR INDUCTION MOTORS—THREE-PHASE—220 VOLTS, ALL FREQUENCIES, STANDARD SPEEDS

Horsepower	Approx. full current-amperes	Size of wire, B. &. S. gauge	Size of switches in amperes	Size of starting fuses, amperes	Size of running fuses, amperes	Size of conduit, inches
¼	1.0	14	30	.....	5	½
½	2.0	14	30	.....	5	½
1	3.0	14	30	10	5	½
2	6.0	14	30	15	10	½
3	9.0	12	30	25	15	½
5	13.3	10	60	35	20	¾
7½	19.5	8	60	45	30	1
10	25.5	6	100	65	40	1
15	37.5	4	100	100	60	1¼
20	50.5	2	200	130	75	1½
25	62.5	1	200	150	95	1½
30	75.0	0	200	200	100	1½
35	87.5	0	200	200	125	1½
40	105.0	00	400	225	150	2
50	123.0	000	400	250	175	2
75	186.0	300,000	400	400	275	2½
100	243.0	450,000	500	*550	350	3
150	362.0	800,000	800	*850	*550	3½
200	480.0	1,200,000	1,000	*1,150	*725	4

* When fuse sizes exceed 600 amperes, circuit breakers of approved type should be substituted.

WIRING DATA FOR INDUCTION MOTORS—THREE-PHASE—440 VOLTS, ALL FREQUENCIES, STANDARD SPEEDS

Horse-power	Approx. full current-amperes	Size of wire, B. & S. gauge	Size of switches in amperes	Size of starting fuses, amperes	Size of running fuses, amperes	Size of conduit, inches
1	1.5	14	30	5	3	½
2	3.0	14	30	10	5	½
3	4.5	14	30	15	6	½
5	6.7	14	30	20	10	½
7½	9.8	12	30	25	15	½
10	12.8	10	60	35	20	¾
15	18.8	8	60	50	30	1
20	25.2	6	100	75	35	1
25	31.3	6	100	75	50	1
30	37.5	4	100	90	55	1¼
35	43.8	4	100	100	65	1¼
40	52.5	2	200	135	75	1½
50	61.5	0	200	175	90	1½
75	93.0	00	400	225	140	2
100	121.5	000	400	275	175	2
150	181.0	300,000	400	400	275	2½
200	240.0	450,000	400	*550	350	3

* When fuse sizes exceed 600 amperes, circuit breakers of approved type should be substituted.

Circuit-breakers for Overload Protection of Motors.—There are two overload conditions that may injure an electric motor. (1) A continuous load beyond the overload rating of the motor and (2) by an excessive momentary overload   Overloads of the second class can obviously be much larger than those of the first class without exceeding safe limits. For example, a continuous overload of 50 per cent. may injure a motor, while the safe momentary overload may be three or four times the full load. If a motor is subjected to overloads of both these classes, adequate overload protection may be difficult with either a circuit-breaker or fuses. Both devices must be set for maximum allowable current, usually considerably in excess of the continuous safe carrying capacity of the motor, and a continuous overload current inside this limit may work injury. Such conditions are unusual, however, and either fuses or a properly designed circuit-breaker will ordinarily afford all necessary protection.

For Induction Motors.—In case the squirrel-cage induction motors is protected by a circuit-breaker, the motor should be so connected as to be without overload protection when the starter handle is in the starting position; in addition, the circuit-breaker should be provided with a time element device to prevent opening when the starter handle is thrown to the running position. Without this time element the circuit-breaker when connected as just described, must be calibrated for two or three times the rated full-load current of the motor. If the circuit-breaker must be effective in the starting position it must be provided with a time element and be calibrated for from three to five times the rated full-load current; with this calibration no protection will be afforded from continuous overloads which might work injury.

For Motors Carrying a Uniform Load.—That is, motors driving line shafts, fans, machine tools, or any machines which give them a fairly uniform load, carrying maximum continuous rated output at least part of the time and possibly full-rated overload for short periods. In general, the overload protection for such motors should have a normal calibration equal to 125 per cent. of normal full-load motor current. If no standard circuit-breaker is listed for this rating, the next larger listed size should be used. A circuit-breaker selected in this manner will have a maximum calibration at least twice full-load current. Where overloads greater than 200 per cent. of normal current are regularly experienced for periods not exceeding two seconds, a time element device should be added to the circuit-breaker. For heavy overloads frequently recurring and continuing for periods of five seconds or longer, the circuit-breaker should have a maximum calibration of at least 10 per cent. in excess of the maximum current.

For Motors Started and Stopped Frequently.—Motors on cranes, elevators, pumps, air compressors, or other apparatus requiring frequent starting and stopping, should have circuit-breakers with a calibration of at least 25 per cent. in excess of the maximum current actually required by the motor during any continuous period of more than five seconds. A time element device should be supplied to care for greater overloads lasting less than five seconds.

Belting.—Rubber belts should always be kept free from grease or animal oils. If they slip, moisten the inside of the belt with boiled linseed oil. Some fine chalk, sprinkled on over the oil, will help the belt.

Length of Belts.—Add the diameter of the two pulleys together, multiply by three and one-seventh, divide the product by two, add to the quotient the distance between the center of the shafts, and the product will be the required length.

Ordinarily Accepted Equivalents of Belting

2-ply Rubber—Light single leather.
3-piy Rubber—Medium single leather.
4-ply Rubber—Heavy single leather.
5-ply Rubber—Light double leather.
6-ply Rubber—Medium double leather.
7-ply Rubber—Heavy double leather.
8-ply Rubber—Triple leather.

The thickness of rubber belting is usually figured at $\frac{1}{16}$ inch per ply.

Horsepower Transmitted by Belting.—One-inch single belt moving at a velocity of 1000 ft. per minute equals one horsepower. One-inch double belt moving 700 ft. per minute equals one horsepower. The horsepower of any belt equals its velocity in feet per minute, multiplied by its width and divided by 1000 for single, and by 700 for double belts.

The following table is based on single belts running on pulleys of equal diameter, revolving at 100 rpm. The power transmitted at other speeds is in direct proportion. For double belts, multiply by ten-sevenths.

HORSEPOWER TRANSMITTED BY BELTING

Diameter of pulley in inches	Width of belt in inches												
	2	3	4	5	6	8	10	12	14	16	18	20	22
6	.44	.65	.87	1.09	1.31								
7	.51	.76	1.01	1.27	1.53								
8	.58	.87	1.16	1.45	1.75								
9	.65	.98	1.31	1.64	1.97								
10	.73	1.09	1.45	1.81	2.18								
11	.80	1.20	1.60	2.00	2.40								
12	.87	1.31	1.75	2.18	2.62								
13	.95	1.42	1.89	2.36	2.83								
14	1.02	1.52	2.02	2.53	3.05								
15	1.09	1.64	2.19	2.73	3.29								
16	1.16	1.74	2.32	2.91	3.48								
17	1.24	1.85	2.47	3.09	3.70								
18	1.31	1.96	2.62	3.27	3.92								
19	1.39	2.07	2.76	3.45	4.14								
20	1.45	2.18	2.91	3.64	4.36								
22	1.60	2.40	3.20	4.00	4.80								
24	....	....	3.50	4.40	5.20	7.0	8.7	10.5	12.2	14.0	16.0	17.0	19.0
26	....	....	3.80	4.70	5.70	7.6	9.5	11.3	13.2	15.1			
28	....	....	4.10	5.10	6.10	8.1	10.2	12.2	14.3	16.3			
30	....	....	4.40	5.40	6.60	8.7	10.9	13.1	15.3	17.4	19.0	22.0	24.0
32	....	....	4.70	5.80	7.00	9.3	11.6	14.0	16.3	18.6			
34	....	....	4.90	6.20	7.40	9.9	12.4	14.8	17.3	19.8			
36	....	....	5.20	6.50	7.80	10.5	13.1	15.7	18.3	20.9	24.0	26.0	29.0
38	....	....	5.50	6.90	8.30	11.0	13.8	16.6	19.3	22.1	25.0	28.0	30.0
40	....	....	5.80	7.30	8.70	11.6	14.6	17.5	20.4	23.3	26.0	29.0	32.0
42	....	....	6.10	7.60	9.20	12.2	15.3	18.2	21.4	24.3	28.0	31.0	34.0
44	....	....	6.40	8.00	9.60	12.8	16.0	19.2	22.4	25.6	29.0	32.0	35.0
46	....	....	6.70	8.40	10.00	13.4	16.8	20.1	23.4	26.8			
48	....	....	7.00	8.80	10.40	14.4	17.4	21.0	24.4	28.0	31.0	35.0	38.0
50	....	....	7.20	9.00	10.90	14.6	18.2	21.8	25.4	29.0	33.0	36.0	40.0
54	....	....	7.80	9.80	11.80	15.6	19.6	23.6	26.4	31.2	35.0	39.0	43.0
60	....	....	8.80	10.80	13.10	17.4	21.8	26.2	30.6	34.8	39.0	44.0	48.0
66	....	....	9.60	12.00	14.40	19.2	24.0	28.8	33.6	38.4	43.0	48.0	53.0
72	....	....	10.40	13.00	15.60	21.0	26.2	31.4	36.6	41.8	47.0	52.0	58.0
78	....	....	11.40	14.20	17.00	22.6	28.4	34.0	39.8	45.4	51.0	57.0	62.0
84	....	....	12.20	15.20	19.40	24.4	30.6	36.4	42.8	48.6	55.0	61.0	67.0

Belting Rules.—The power transmitted by a belt depends upon its width and its thickness and the speed at which it travels. Hence it is customary (as mentioned under "Horsepower Transmitted by Belting") to express the transmitting capacity as the speed in feet per minute required by a belt one inch wide to transmit one horsepower. For single or light double belt, this expression is usually given a value of about 700, and for heavy double belt approximately 450. Thus a double belt four inches wide, running at 2250 ft. per minute will transmit 20 hp.

Roughly, belt speeds should not exceed one mile per minute; this speed is given when the diameter of either pulley in inches multiplied by its rpm. equals 20,000 (D × rpm. = 20,000).

Minimum diameter of pulleys for long life of heavy belts:

For double belts............................... 12 in.
For double belts, extra flexible.................. 10 in.
For double 3-ply belts......................... 18 in.

Ordinarily,
$$wd = \frac{hp.}{rpm.} \times \frac{126,500}{P}$$

where w = width of belt, d = diameter of pulley (both in inches), and P = belt stress per inch width. Safe values for P are as follows:

Single belts, above 4000 ft. per min., 33 lb.; below 4000, 46 lb.; max. stress never over 50 lb. Double belts, 40 to 70 lb.; 3-ply belts, 70 to 95 lb.

With standard construction and normal belt stress, the stress on the shaft and bearings is within safe limits as long as d exceeds w. To find length L (length) of belt when the pulley diameters D, d and the distance A between centers are known, use the formula

$$L = 1.62\ (D + d) + 2A$$

To determine distance between pulley centers use the formula

$$A = K\ (D - d)$$

where the value of the constant K ranges from 3 to 4, 3.5 being a good average value when the diameter D is from 4 to 6 times that of d.

The following precautions should be observed:

a. The formula does not apply when pulleys are of nearly the same diameter; in this case the distance should be great enough to allow some belt sag.

b. As a general rule the distance A should not exceed 25 ft. in any case.

Rules for Pulley Sizes.—The following formula can be used to calculate sizes of pulleys for motor drives:

$$d = \frac{D \times N}{n} \qquad n = \frac{D \times N}{d}$$

D = Diameter of driver.
d = Diameter of driven pulley.
N = Revolutions per minute of driver.
n = Revolutions per minute of driven pulley.

Speed of Pulleys.—When the diameter of the driven pulley is given, to find its number of revolutions proceed as follows: Multiply the diameter of the driver by the number of its revolutions, and divide the product by the diameter of the driven. The quotient will be the number of revolutions of the driven pulley.

When the diameter and revolutions of driver pulley are given, to find the diameter of the driven pulley that will make any given number of revolutions in the same time, proceed as follows: Multiply the diameter of the driver pulley by its number of revolutions, and divide the product by the number of revolutions of the driven pulley. The quotient will be the diameter of the driven pulley.

To ascertain the size of the driver pulley proceed as follows: Multiply the diameter of the driven pulley by the number of revolutions you wish to make, and divide the product by the revolutions of the driver pulley. The quotient will be the diameter of the driven pulley.

Chain Drives.—Chains are now made to transmit power for any purpose in sizes varying from $\frac{1}{4}$ hp. at 3000 rpm. to 3000 hp. at 50 rpm. By the use of a chain instead of a belt or gears, power may be transmitted with a positive speed ratio on short centers quietly and with a very high efficiency. Chains should be lubricated with a heavy paste grease containing no solid matter such as automobile transmission grease.

Approximate Weight of Solid Pinions and Armed Sprockets.—When T is the number of teeth; F the face in inches; C a constant in pounds per inch in face per tooth. Then $T \times F \times C$ = weight of armed sprocket. Add 25 per cent. if the sprocket is split and add 50 per cent. if spring sprocket and split. For solid pinions, weight $= C \times T^2 \times (F + 1)$.

Points to Consider when Calculating Size of Chain—*Morse Chain Co.*—When the number of teeth equals T and the exact outside diameter is D, then T should be less than 20 when D equals the pitch diameter. When T is more than 20 teeth, D is equal to the pitch diameter plus twice the addendum.

The following points should be considered in this connection:

(1) Use sprockets having an odd number of teeth whenever possible.

(2) When specially authorized, a larger number of teeth than shown may be cut in large sprocket.

(3) Thickness of sprocket rim, including teeth, should be at least 1.2 times the chain pitch.

(4) The number of grooves in the sprocket, their width and distance apart, varies according to pitch and width of chain.

(5) The width of the sprocket should be $\frac{1}{8}$ to $\frac{1}{4}$ inch greater on small drives, and $\frac{1}{4}$ to $\frac{1}{2}$ inch greater on large drives than nominal width of the chain.

(6) An even number of links in the chain and an odd number of teeth in the wheels are desirable.

(7) Horizontal drives preferred with slack on top strand, but for short drives without center adjustment slack thould be on the bottom strand.

(8) Adjustable wheel centers desirable for horizontal drives and necessary for vertical drives.

CHAIN AND SPROCKET DATA (MORSE CHAIN CO.)

Pitch	½	⅝	¾	9⁄16	1 3⁄10	1½	2	3
Min. No. of teeth } Small sprocket driver...	13	13	13	15	15	17	17	17
Small sprocket driven...	17	17	21	25	29	29	31	35
Desirable number of teeth in driver sprockets...	15–17	17–21	17–21	17–23	17–23	17–27	17–31	19–31
Maximum number of teeth in sprockets. (See note 3.)...	99	109	115	125	129	129	129	131
Desirable number of teeth in driven sprockets...	55–75	55–75	55–85	55–95	55–105	55–115	55–115	55–115
To find pitch diameter of wheel multiply number of teeth by (inches).	.159	.199	.239	.2865	.382	.477	.636	.955
Addendum—For outside diameter of sprockets 20 to 130T. (See note 1): (ins.)...	.05	.06	.075	.09	.12	.15	.20	.30
Maximum rpm...	2400	1800	1200	1100	800	600	400	250
Tension per inch width chain, lbs. } Small sprocket driver.	80	100	120	150	200	270	450	750
Small sprocket driven.	65	80	95	120	160	210	350	600
Radial clearance beyond tooth required for chain in inches...	.50	.62	.75	.90	1.2	1.5	2.0	3.0
Constants for solid pinions...	.0045	.0063	.009	.013	.023	.035	.058	.145
Constants for armed sprockets...	.16	.25	.35	.45	.7	1.0	2.0	4.0

(9) Avoid vertical drives.

(10) Allow a side clearance for chain (parallel to axis of sprockets and measured from nominal width of chain) equal to the pitch.

(11) Maximum linear velocity for commercial service, 1200 to 1600 feet per minute.

HORSEPOWER TRANSMITTED BY STEEL SHAFTING

Diameter of shaft in inches	Revolutions per minute									
	100	125	150	175	200	225	250	300	350	400
$\frac{15}{16}$	1.2	1.4	1.1	2.1	2.4	2.6	3.1	3.6	4.3	5.0
$1\frac{3}{16}$	2.4	3.1	3.7	4.3	4.5	5.5	6.1	7.3	8.5	9.7
$1\frac{7}{16}$	4.3	5.3	6.4	7.4	8.5	9.5	10.5	12.7	14.8	16.9
$1\frac{11}{16}$	6.7	8.4	10.1	11.7	13.4	15.1	16.7	20.1	23.4	26.8
$1\frac{15}{16}$	10.0	12.5	15.0	17.5	20.0	22.5	25.0	30.0	35.0	40.0
$2\frac{3}{16}$	14.3	17.8	21.4	24.9	28.5	32.1	35.6	42.7	49.8	57.0
$2\frac{7}{16}$	19.5	24.4	29.3	34.1	39.0	44.1	48.7	58.5	68.2	78.0
$2\frac{11}{16}$	26.0	32.5	39.0	43.5	52.0	58.5	65.0	78.0	87.0	104.0
$2\frac{15}{16}$	33.8	42.2	50.6	59.1	67.5	75.9	84.4	101.3	118.2	135.0
$3\frac{3}{16}$	43.0	53.6	64.4	75.1	85.8	96.6	107.3	128.7	150.3	171.6
$3\frac{7}{16}$	53.6	67.0	79.4	93.8	107.2	120.1	134.0	158.8	187.6	214.4
$3\frac{11}{16}$	65.9	82.4	97.9	115.4	121.8	148.3	164.8	195.7	230.7	243.6
$3\frac{15}{16}$	80.0	100.0	120.0	140.0	160.0	180.0	200.0	240.0	280.0	320.0
$4\frac{7}{16}$	113.9	142.4	170.8	199.3	227.8	256.2	284.7	341.7	398.6	455.6
$4\frac{15}{16}$	156.3	195.3	234.4	273.4	312.5	351.5	390.6	468.7	546.8	625.0

HORSEPOWER TRANSMITTED BY SINGLE ROPES
(Working strain $= 200d^2$ where d is diameter of rope)

Speed of rope in feet per minute	Diameter of rope in inches						
	$\frac{5}{8}$	$\frac{3}{4}$	1.0	1.25	1.50	1.75	2.0
1000	1.24	2.25	3.57	5.59	8.02	10.85	14.20
2000	2.70	3.84	6.84	10.68	15.39	20.93	27.36
2500	3.30	4.71	8.38	13.10	18.86	25.66	33.54
3000	3.83	5.46	9.80	15.39	21.87	29.74	38.88
3500	4.30	6.23	10.09	17.33	24.94	34.03	44.35
4000	4.74	6.83	12.15	18.98	27.33	37.17	48.59
4500	5.01	7.24	12.89	20.15	29.00	39.45	51.57
5000	5.20	7.47	13.29	20.76	29.89	40.65	53.15
5500	5.29	7.60	13.53	21.14	30.43	41.39	54.11
6000	5.08	7.32	13.10	20.36	29.32	39.77	52.12
6500	4.74	6.83	12.13	19.00	27.34	37.21	48.63
7000	4.12	5.93	10.54	16.47	23.72	32.26	42.18
Smallest sheave, diameter, inches.................	26.00	30.00	42.00	54.00	60.00	72.00	84.00
Allowable weight, tension carriage, lb............	80.00	110.00	200.00	300.00	450.00	600.00	750.00

NOTE.—The horsepower decreases when the velocity is above 5500 feet on account of centrifugal force.

GEAR TABLE—DIAMETRAL PITCH (Nuttall)

Diametral Pitch is the Number of Teeth to Each Inch of the Pitch Diameter

To Get	Having	Rule
The Diametral Pitch	The Circular Pitch	Divide 3.1416 by the Circular Pitch
The Diametral Pitch	The Pitch Diameter and the Number of Teeth	Divide Number of Teeth by Pitch Diameter
The Diametral Pitch	The Outside Diameter and the Number of Teeth	Divide Number of Teeth plus 2 by Outside Diameter
Pitch Diameter	The Number of Teeth and the Diametral Pitch	Divide Number of Teeth by the Diametral Pitch
Pitch Diameter	The Number of Teeth and Outside Diameter	Divide the Product of Outside Diam. and No. of Teeth by No. of Teeth plus 2
Pitch Diameter	The Outside Diameter and the Diametral Pitch	Subtract from Outside Diam. the Quotient of 2 divided by the Diametral Pitch
Pitch Diameter	Addendum and the Number of Teeth	Multiply Addendum by the Number of Teeth
Outside Diameter	The Number of Teeth and the Diametral Pitch	Divide Number of Teeth plus 2 by the Diametral Pitch
Outside Diameter	The Pitch Diameter and the Diametral Pitch	Add to the Pitch Diameter the Quotient of 2 divided by the Diametral Pitch
Outside Diameter	The Pitch Diameter and the Number of Teeth	Divide Product of Number of Teeth plus 2 and Pitch Diameter by the Number of Teeth.

Outside Diameter	The Number of Teeth and Addendum	Multiply the Number of Teeth plus 2 by Addendum
Number of Teeth	The Pitch Diameter and the Diametral Pitch	Multiply Pitch Diameter by the Diametral Pitch
Number of Teeth	The Outside Diameter and the Diametral Pitch	Multiply Outside Diameter by the Diametral Pitch and subtract 2
Thickness of Tooth	The Diametral Pitch	Divide 1.5708 by the Diametral Pitch
Addendum	The Diametral Pitch	Divide 1 by the Diametral Pitch, or $s = \dfrac{D'}{N}$
Root	The Diametral Pitch	Divide 1.157 by the Diametral Pitch
Working Depth	The Diametral Pitch	Divide 2 by the Diametral Pitch
Whole Depth	The Diametral Pitch	Divide 2.157 by the Diametral Pitch
Clearance	The Diametral Pitch	Divide .157 by the Diametral Pitch
Clearance	Thickness of Tooth	Divide Thickness of Tooth at Pitch Line by 10

Some Handy Rules

Diameter of a circle $\times$ 3.1416 = Circumference.

Radius of a circle $\times$ 6.283185 = Circumference.

Square of the radius of a circle $\times$ 3.1416 = Area.

Square of the diameter of a circle $\times$ 0.7854 = Area.

Square of the circumference of a circle $\times$ 0.07958 = Area.

Half the circumference of a circle $\times$ by half its diameter = Area.

Circumference of a circle $\times$ 0.159155 = Radius.

Sqare root of the area of a circle $\times$ 0.56419 = Radius.

Circumference of a circle $\times$ 0.31831 = Diameter.

Square root a the area of a circle $\times$ 1.12838 = Diameter.

Diameter of a circle $\times$ 0.86 = Side of inscribed equilateral triangle.

Diameter of a circle $\times$ 0.7071 = Side of an inscribed square.

Circumference of a circle $\times$ 0.225 = Side of an inscribed square.

Circumference of a circle $\times$ 0.282 = Side of an equal square.

Diameter of a circle $\times$ 0.8862 = Side of an equal square.

Base of a triangle $\times$ by $\frac{1}{2}$ the altitude = Area.

Multiplying both diameters and .7854 together = Area of an ellipse.

Surface of a sphere $\times$ by $\frac{1}{6}$ of its diameter = Solidity.

Circumference of a sphere $\times$ by its diameter = Surface.

Square of the diameter of a sphere $\times$ 3.1416 = Surface.

Square of the circumference of a sphere $\times$ 0.3183 = Surface.

Cube of the diameter of a sphere $\times$ 0.5236 = Solidity.

Cube of the radius of a sphere $\times$ 4.1888 = Solidity.

Cube of the circumference of a sphere $\times$ 0.016887 = Solidity.

Square root of the surface of a sphere $\times$ 0.56419 = Diameter.

Square root of the surface of a sphere $\times$ 1.772454 = Circumference.

Cube root of the solidity of a sphere $\times$ 1.2407 = Diameter.

Cube root of the solidity of a sphere $\times$ 3.8978 = Circumference.

Radius of a sphere $\times$ 1.1547 = Side of inscribed cube.

Square root of ($\frac{1}{3}$ of the square of) the diameter of a sphere = Side of inscribed cube.

Area of its base $\times$ by $\frac{1}{3}$ of its altitude = Solidity of a cone or pyramid, whether round, square or triangular.

Area of one of its sides $\times$ 6 = the surface of a cube.

Altitude of trapezoid $\times$ $\frac{1}{2}$ the sum of it parallel sides = Area.

EQUIVALENT VALUES OF CENTIGRADE AND FAHRENHEIT SCALES

Temperature		Temperature	
Centigrade	Fahrenheit	Centigrade	Fahrenheit
0	32	80	176
5	41	85	185
10	50	90	194
15	59	95	203
20	68	100	212
25	77	105	221
30	86	110	230
35	95	115	239
38	100.4	120	248
40	104	125	257
42	107.6	130	266
45	113	135	275
50	122	140	284
55	131	145	293
60	140	150	302
65	149	155	311
70	158	160	320
75	167	165	329

INDEX